ANGELS
IN THE ER
& Angels on Call

Robert D. Lesslie, MD

Guideposts

New York

Foreword

It may take a while, but most of us husbands eventually learn that we need to listen to our wives. For some like me, it takes longer than others.

I've always been a storyteller, so it only seemed natural for me to put some true tales from my years in busy ER's on paper. When finished, I thought they were pretty good. So did my friends and family, and even an agent in New York. After more than five years of trying to get it published, it didn't happen. The stack of orphaned pages went on a cabinet shelf and the door was shut. For more than ten years, that was their home.

A few years ago, I was moved to give writing one more shot. The cabinet was opened and out came my rejected manuscript. Maybe *this* time... That's where my wife came in.

"Your stories are great, Robert. But something's just not right. You've left out the best part of who you are, and that's your faith. Don't write another word until you've prayed about this, and until you have a clear direction."

As much as it grieves me to admit it, she was right

We both prayed, and then we waited. There was no lightening bolt, no burning bush. But then in time there was a hushed voice and a gentle prodding.

My approach to this had been all wrong. I had thought it was enough to just tell interesting and funny stories, but the Lord had a different idea altogether.

During the years my manuscript sat patiently on its shelf, He was not interested in refining my writing. He was refining me. I was now a different person, with a different heart and a different understanding. Suddenly, these stories were no longer just stories. It was all about the people in them, and they were all part of the refining.

As I looked back over my decades in the ER, I realized that the Lord had placed a lot of special and unique people in my path. Some were friends, some coworkers, and some complete strangers. Each of them had a story to tell, and they taught me valuable lessons. Many inspired me with their deep faith and perseverance in the face of overwhelming trials. *These* were the stories I needed to tell. *These* were the people who had changed my life, opened my eyes, and softened my heart. And I realized these were not *my* stories, but *His*. I was only the story teller.

Once I understood this, the book seemed to write itself. I found an amazing agent in the person of Les Stobbe, who in turn put me together with the wonderful people of Harvest House Publishing. And contrary to what they say, the rest is *not* history. It's still evolving, and the refining continues. No longer working in the ER, I spend my professional time in our urgent care center in Rock Hill, SC. It's not as wild and crazy as the emergency department, but each day I continue to meet people who have a story to tell and something to teach.

In these pages, it will be my pleasure to introduce you to some of the amazing people who have touched and forever changed my life. My prayer is that their stories will touch your life as well, and that the Lord will continue to refine each of us.

Angels in the ER

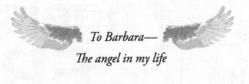 *To Barbara—*
The angel in my life

Contents

Introduction for *Angels in the ER*

"Daddy, I never knew this is what you did."

The words were from my older son, who was then thirty. And he made them after reading my first book, "Angels in the ER." It was either the best compliment I had yet received, or the worst criticism.

I thought about it for a while, and came to the correct conclusion that it had been a compliment. For all of his life, he had known I was an ER doctor, and he had some general idea of what went on behind those ambulance doors. But I had made it a point not to bring my experiences home with me, and not to burden my wife or children with the day's tragedies or even triumphs.

Now for the first time, he had been able to read about those things. But more than that, he had learned about the people and experiences that had shaped my life and changed me in ways that took me almost thirty years to fully understand.

As I began putting these stories together, I knew with certainty these "crossings" were not random or coincidental. The Lord had placed them in my path in order to teach me more about Him, and more about myself.

That hadn't always been obvious to me, having been accused on more than a few occasions of being hard-headed. But after a couple of decades, I got it. These stories needed to be told.

Since the book has been released, I have been asked which of the stories or chapters is my favorite. That's a tough one for me, almost like asking which of our four children is my favorite. But I always come back to chapter 14 — "On Crossing the Bar."

The story deals with a son who has just lost his father. During my interaction with the young man, I am able to share some of my own late father's words and advice, and some personal experiences that transcend our less than perfect understanding of what is real and tangible. And I was able to share a moment when I knew without a doubt that God's hand was on my shoulder.

To my own son's comment, I replied, "It's time you knew what I've been doing all these years."

Angels in Our Midst

Twenty-five years in the ER have taught me a lot of things. I know without a doubt that life is fragile. I have come to understand that humility may be the greatest virtue. And I am convinced we need to take the time to say the things we deeply feel to the people we deeply care about.

I have also come to believe that there are angels in our midst. They may take the form of a friend, a nurse, or a complete stranger. And on occasion, they remain unseen, a subtle yet real presence that instructs, comforts, and protects us.

The ER is a difficult and challenging place to be, both for patients and for those of us who care for them. Yet the same pressures and stresses that make this place so challenging also provide an opportunity to experience some of life's greatest wonders and mysteries. It is with a sincere appreciation of these mysteries and a profound sense of privilege that I offer some of my thoughts and experiences in these pages.

—Robert Lesslie, MD
March 2008

The **Nature** of the **Beast**

*Even though I walk through the valley of the shadow
of death, I will fear no evil, for you are with me.*

—Psalm 23:4

Everyone in the department turned to the ambulance entrance. We had all heard the screaming and shouting, especially the piercing wail of a young woman. Suddenly the automatic doors burst open, and a crowd of fifteen or twenty people, all teenagers or maybe a little older, spilled into the ER. In their midst they carried a young man. His arms and legs dangled wildly, and his head rolled from side to side. His T-shirt was soaked with blood.

"Somebody, help!" The cry came from someone near the front of the pack. "Jimmie's been shot!"

We all moved in the direction of the door. Jeff Ryan, the charge nurse this night, was the first to reach the wounded man. "Follow me," he instructed the people carrying Jimmie. "And don't drop him."

He led the group toward the trauma room, and called over his shoulder to the unit secretary, "Get Security!"

At the doorway, Jeff turned and took the bleeding boy into his arms and then carried him to the middle of the room. As he was carefully placing the young man on the stretcher, a few members of the crowd tentatively stepped into the trauma room.

"Nope." One word from Jeff stopped them in their tracks. "You guys will need to wait outside."

Few people questioned Jeff Ryan's authority. He was in his early thirties, stood six feet tall, and weighed about two-twenty-five. He had been in the ER when I first came to Rock Hill, and I soon came to appreciate the fact he was one of the finest nurses I would ever work with. He looked like a big teddy bear, but something in his eyes let you know that beneath that gentle exterior lurked a rugged strength and potentially explosive temper. I've seen it explode a few times…and woe to the person in its path. We referred to Jeff as our "enforcer."

Within a few minutes, Jimmie was completely undressed, lying on his back. He had an IV line in each arm, each rapidly infusing normal saline. A catheter had been inserted into his bladder and oxygen was being administered through nasal prongs held in place by an elastic strap encircling his head.

I examined his abdomen for the second time. One bullet hole, just above his belly button. This was an obvious entrance wound, and there was no exit. He had been awake and talking since we placed him on the stretcher. His vital signs had been fair at the outset, with only a mildly depressed blood pressure. This had quickly improved with the IV fluids, and now things appeared to be stabilized. The lab techs had come down and they were now cross-matching blood for transfusion. We would give it as soon as it was available. The on-call surgeon, Sam Wright, had been notified. Fortunately he was still in the hospital—in the operating room finishing up a case.

A few minutes later he was on the phone.

"Sam, this is Robert," I spoke into the receiver. "I've got a nineteen-year-old male here in the ER with a single gunshot wound to the abdomen. He's alert and his vital signs are stable, but there's no exit wound. The X-ray looks like the bullet's lodged somewhere near his right kidney. And it looks like something small, maybe a .22." I was making a guess about the caliber but in reality, it didn't make much of a difference.

"Get him ready for the OR," Sam replied through the speaker-phone. "Looks like we'll have to open him up and see what's going on. I'm closing up the appendectomy you gave me earlier, so I'll just meet him here in the operating room."

"Okay, we'll do that. He should have gotten about a unit of blood before you see him."

"Fine." Then he was gone.

Jeff was making some notes on our patient's clipboard.

"Dr. Wright ready to see him in the OR?" he asked me.

"Yeah, as soon as everything's in order," I answered.

He picked up the board, stepped over to the side of the stretcher, and checked to be sure both IV lines were flowing. Then he headed for the door.

"I'll get some help and we'll get him going," he told me as the door was closing.

I looked down at Jimmie and asked, "Are you sure there's nobody we need to call? Family? Relatives?"

He had already been asked this several times and each time had told us that no one needed to be bothered. The "friends" who had brought him to the ER were of no help either. Once Jimmie had been deposited in our trauma room they had disappeared. Maybe they had heard Jeff request Security, or maybe they knew that a police squad would soon be on its way. Whatever the reason, they were gone.

We were alone in the room, and I was waiting for the transport team to come.

"Doc, I'm not gonna make it," he stated matter-of-factly.

This blunt pronouncement surprised me. I glanced down at him, checking his color, and then over at the cardiac monitor to be sure I wasn't missing something. He seemed stable enough.

"Jimmie, you're going to be fine. I know this is no fun for you, but it's a straightforward wound, and Dr. Wright will get you fixed up. You may have nicked some intestine or something like that, but he'll patch things up, and you'll be going home in a few days." I didn't have to try to sound confident, because I was. This would be a basic surgical procedure. Unfortunately, we saw too many cases just like this. He would be fine. He was young and healthy.

Now peaceful and calm, he continued to stare straight up at the ceiling. His arms rested at his sides, and a sheet was drawn up to his waist. He had a lot of tubes connected to him, but he was stable and looked good.

"No, man," he said, quietly resigned and still staring at the ceiling. "I'm not gonna make it out of that operating room." His tone and words bothered me. He needed to be encouraged.

"Jimmie—"

Before I could finish, the door opened and the two men of the transport team came into the room. They made the necessary preparations and began pushing the stretcher toward the door. I stood out of the way.

Jimmie was halfway through the door when he twisted his head around and looked directly at me.

"Not gonna make it, Doc."

"Everything's going to be fine, Jimmie," I told him once more, and then he was gone.

Of course I was right. And I would be able to tell him so in a few hours. I looked at the clock on the wall. 12:30 a.m.

At 1:00 a.m., a nineteen-year-old girl hobbled into the department and was led to room 2 by our triage nurse. She had stepped in a hole (which happened to be just outside one of our town's drinking establishments) and sprained her right ankle. It was pretty swollen, and we would need an X-ray to make sure it wasn't broken.

We had no sooner sent her down the hall in a wheelchair to X-ray than the ambulance doors swung open. EMS brought a twenty-five-year-old woman directly to the cardiac room. She had a long-standing history of kidney disease and extremely high blood pressure. Tonight she had apparently suffered a stroke. She was breathing, but was not responding to pain or verbal stimulation. We would need a CT scan of her head, and quickly.

Within a few minutes, her stretcher was heading down the hall toward Radiology.

I stood at the nurses' station, writing on the charts of these two patients. A busy evening was turning into a busy night.

Suddenly, an unfamiliar voice bellowed behind me, almost in my ear.

"Where's my baby? Where she be?"

Startled, I turned around and found myself nose-to-nose with a middle-aged woman. She was dressed in a blue-and-white-striped bathrobe, barely held closed with two large safety pins. A black silk nightgown could be seen extending below the bottom edge of the robe, almost sweeping the floor. And on her feet she wore bright-red bedroom slippers, fashioned after some fuzzy, unidentifiable animal.

But my eyes were drawn to her head. Her hair was in curlers, huge pink ones, held in place by something I couldn't quite make out. I looked a little closer, and I recognized it—it was a large pair of women's panties.

"Where is Naomi?" she asked no one in particular. "Her friend-girl said she was over here!"

She began to look around the department, searching frantically for her daughter. She stepped toward one of the exam rooms and was about to pull the curtain aside when I was able to stop her.

"Ma'am, I'm Dr. Lesslie. Come with me, and we'll help you find your daughter."

She stopped and looked at me, about to speak. Then she turned her head slightly to one side and looked over my shoulder. Her eyes widened hugely.

"My baby!" she screamed, pointing down the hallway. "What have you done to my baby?"

She swept me aside with one large arm and ran down the hall, bumping me into the counter.

"My baby! What have you done to her?" she screamed.

Our young stroke victim was returning from CT. She lay flat on the stretcher, still unresponsive, and was being rolled up the hall to her room.

"Look at her! You killed her!" She was screaming even louder now. She barreled through the radiology techs, brushing one aside as she grabbed the girl's face in her hands.

"She dead! You killed her!"

There was an instant of silence. Her eyes rolled back in her head, and her face turned to heaven.

And then a piercing wail, "Do Jesus! Help me, Lawd!"

Jeff was moving toward the woman. He would try to calm her and then lead her to a private room. This type of outburst was not unusual in the department, and though disconcerting, we had all grown accustomed to it. But this was all new to our other patients, and a few inquisitive heads peered from behind curtains, trying to get a glimpse of the scene. They didn't want to get too close, though. This woman was on fire.

"Who did this? Who killed my baby?"

Jeff walked to her side and quietly said, "Ma'am, she's not dead. We're taking good care of her." He patted her gently on her shoulder.

She would have none of this and jerked away from his hand.

"I want to know who did this!" Her voice was becoming menacing. Then she looked directly at me and took a step in my direction. She pointed a threatening finger at me and said, "I'm gonna sue you! I'm gonna own this hospital! And you're gonna be sorry." There followed some choice descriptives of my heritage, and then she turned again to the young woman, patting her on the forehead. Once more she lovingly took the girl's head in her hands.

"Baby, what they done to you? What they done to you? I'm gonna—"

She stopped in mid-sentence and froze where she stood. Then her head tilted from side to side as she studied the face of the girl lying before her. A puzzled look began to spread across her face, and her eyes began to widen in surprise. Suddenly, she was distracted by a movement further up the hallway and looked up. It was our ankle-injury patient. She was returning to the ER in a wheelchair, her X-rays in her lap.

Our distraught mother stood straight up, dropping the young woman's head back on the stretcher.

"*There's* my baby!" She ran up the hallway, smiling in relief, her arms extended before her. The safety pins that had been barely holding her bathrobe together had finally given up and the robe flew open, flapping wildly at her sides as she ran. When she got to the wheelchair, she knelt and embraced her daughter. She hugged her tightly, rocking her back and forth.

"You all right, honey baby? You okay?"

There was nothing to say or do. We just stood there.

It was 4:30 a.m., and I was beginning to flag a little. One more cup of coffee and I might live to see the sunrise.

I was turning to walk towards the lounge when I saw Sam Wright coming up the hallway. He still wore his surgical cap and scrubs. They were soaked with perspiration, and I noticed splashes of blood from his knees down to his shoe covers.

He collapsed into one of the chairs behind the nurses' station, pulled off his scrub cap, and tossed it into a nearby trashcan.

"Man, that was tough," he said, shaking his head.

I walked over and sat down beside him. He was talking about Jimmie. "What did you find, Sam?" I asked.

"We got him to the OR and onto the table. As soon as we put him to sleep, his pressure started to fall. Not much at first, but then it really crashed. When I opened him up, there was blood everywhere. I tried to cross-clamp the aorta to even begin to see what was going on. The bleeding was coming from a place I couldn't get to, and I never got complete control of it."

He paused and looked up at me, shaking his head.

Then he continued. "That bullet nicked the side of the aorta and then lodged just below the kidney. It didn't hit anything else. Amazing. The nick must have immediately clotted off, and he didn't do much bleeding. Not until he got to the OR. The clot came off, and everthing broke loose. Eight units of blood. As fast as we got the blood into him, it was on the floor. We tried everything. We worked..." he paused, looking at his wristwatch. "We worked on him for three-and-a-half hours."

He stopped, and his shoulders slumped forward. He stared unseeing at the floor.

"This is a tough one, Robert. I don't know what else I could have done."

We sat there, silent. Jeff came up the hall with two cups of black coffee and set the steaming Styrofoam cups on the counter. Neither of us moved.

"And you were right." Sam spoke again. "It was a small-caliber bullet—.22, I think."

The ER and Rock Hill and the rest of the world moved on around us. And I thought of the last words Jimmie had spoken to me.

The ER. It all happens here. This is an amazing place to observe and study the human condition. We see and experience every feeling and emotion, and do so in an intense and highly charged environment. Gone are the trappings of proper decorum and behavior. Gone are the concerns about what others may be thinking about us. Where else would you see a fifty-year-old banker walking down the hallway in a hospital gown, uncaring that his derriere was exposed to a bunch of strangers?

But we are all undressed in the ER, all of us. Our strengths and weaknesses are openly and sometimes uncomfortably exposed. This is true for patients and physicians alike. As caregivers, whether nurse or doctor, orderly or secretary, we quickly learn the limits of our willingness and ability to empathize, to sacrifice, and to step outside of ourselves. It is possible to remain aloof, distant, and shielded…but it comes with a price.

Ultimately, the ER is a place where the faith of each one of us will be tested. Our beliefs will be tempered and refined, or exposed and discarded as worthless. Here we can learn who we are and on what ground we stand. And sometimes, it is a place where our faith can be found.

These pages tell the stories of people who have traveled into this dark valley. Through their experiences and struggles, we can search our own hearts for answers to finding grace and peace in the darkness.

2

The **Least** of **These**

*I was hungry and you gave me something to eat, I was thirsty and
you gave me something to drink, I was a stranger and you invited
me in, I needed clothes and you clothed me, I was sick and you
looked after me, I was in prison and you came to visit me.*

—MATTHEW 25:35-36

The ER is a lot of things to a lot of people, but one of its most important functions is to serve as a safety net for those who have nowhere else to go. These are the people with no money, no insurance, no family, no friends. The ER offers the best and last chance they have for medical care. Sometimes it's the only place they have for care of any kind.

It may be difficult to imagine someone would consider the ER a place for comfort and companionship, but a good example of this occurs every Christmas. Most people would want to be at home, or with family and friends, you'd think, and a trip to the ER would be an unpleasant necessity only because of dire illness or injury. But that's not the case for a large and largely invisible part of our society. Mid to late morning will see a steadily growing stream of people who should be elsewhere.

They have no one else to spend Christmas Day with than whatever staff happens to have the misfortune of being on duty in the department. They have no other place to find a holiday meal, bland and unexciting though it may be. And when you take that closer look, and you try to imagine what life must be like for this man or woman, and especially what word you should speak or action you should take, it can get pretty uncomfortable.

It was two in the afternoon on a cold and clear Tuesday in February.

"General, this is Medic 1, over."

I recognized Denton's voice and picked up the ambulance telephone. Denton Roberts was one of the lead paramedics for the hospital's EMS. He was in his mid-thirties, bright, aggressive, and his assessments in the field could always be trusted. He had attended Clemson for a couple of years and given some thought to applying to medical school. Once he started working as a paramedic, though, he knew he had found his niche.

"Medic 1, this is Dr. Lesslie, go ahead," I responded.

The receiver crackled briefly. "Dr. L, we're bringing in a 65-year-old man with abdominal pain." There was a momentary pause. "It's Slim."

That was all he needed to say. I looked around the department to see which bed was available. "Bring him to room 2, Denton. What's your ETA?"

"About five," he said. "Room 2 it is."

I placed the phone back in its cradle.

Slim Brantley was one of our "regulars." He had been a regular since I began working at Rock Hill General. Depending on the time of year, we might see him once or twice a week. When the weather was good, he might go a month or so before calling an ambulance and coming to visit. We were in the midst of a cold snap, and this would be his third visit in the past nine days.

Lori walked up to the nurses' station with a clipboard in her hand.

"We've got a friend coming in," I told her.

"Slim?" she guessed, placing the board in its rack.

"Yep," I answered. "Again."

"Well, it's been two days, so I guess it's about time. Abdominal pain?" she queried, knowing the answer.

"Bingo."

Lori Davidson had been working in the ER for seven or eight years. She was the mother of three young children, a boy and two girls. She had a quiet, unassuming demeanor, and yet she displayed a confidence and compassion that immediately put our patients at ease. I was always glad when she was on duty.

"I'll get Slim's room ready," she told me.

It requires a significant effort to reach the exalted status of "ER regular." Not just anyone achieves this lofty appellation. At any given time, we probably have only ten or twelve people in that circle. Just the fact that you come to the ER on a frequent basis does not necessarily make you a regular. We have drug seekers who do just that, but we don't consider them regulars. That's a whole different set of problems. Our regulars come to the ER over and over again with generally the same complaint. It might be abdominal pain, as in Slim's case, or alcohol-related issues, or back pain, or seizures. It can be any of a number of things. But each of our regulars has developed their own unique handle.

For years, one of our favorite and most persistent regulars was a woman named Sarah May. She was in her sixties and lived with her older sister. At some point, she had become convinced that a root doctor practicing in Rock Hill (I'm not sure if he was board-certified in that specialty) had put a snake in her. I think it was a black snake. But she was absolutely positive a snake was crawling around in her belly. She would writhe on the stretcher, rub her abdomen, and plead with us to get the snake out of her. What do you do with that? Invariably, she came to the ER by ambulance, usually a little after midnight. EMS would call in with "We have a woman here, in no apparent distress. We're at 100 Pine Street." That was all we needed: her address.

"It's Sarah May again," would be the universal response. And in about fifteen minutes, she would be rolling into the ER.

Over the years, things changed with Sarah. On several occasions, I had her committed to a psychiatric hospital in Columbia for an evaluation. After a week or two, she would end up back home. She didn't like this experience, and didn't like being committed to a mental hospital. Apparently they had as much luck getting that snake out of her as we did. Eventually she developed the practice of calling the ER before she called EMS.

"Is that Dr. Lesslie on duty tonight?" she would ask our secretary. When the answer was in the affirmative, there would be a pause, a faint sigh, and then "Oh, well..." followed by a click. And no visit that night. But there were plenty of other visits for her, and her ticket to the ER was always that snake.

Slim Brantley, for whatever reason, had chosen abdominal pain as his handle. Or maybe it had chosen him. Though he had been worked up on numerous occasions, no pathology had ever turned up. He did have some real disease, though. Too much alcohol and three packs of cigarettes a day had taken their toll. He had very little lung reserve and had become very susceptible to pneumonia. And his heart had been giving him problems lately, as shown by recurrent episodes of a rapid heartbeat and dizziness. Those things were real. But his abdominal pain was not. It was his free pass to the ER, and it got him in the door and into a bed. And in short order, it usually got him a warm meal. After an hour or two, his pain would be gone, he would feel better, and he'd be ready to go home.

I have often wondered where someone like Slim lives. One evening, Denton Roberts and I were sitting behind the nurses' station. For whatever reason, the conversation turned to Slim, and Denton told me about the time he had picked him up under a bridge. It had been midsummer, and Slim had constructed a lean-to of cardboard boxes. Apparently, based on the litter surrounding this impromptu abode, canned beans and Ripple wine had been his sustenance for several days. On another occasion, he had been picked up in someone's garage, where he was sleeping on a ratty cot between two broken-down lawn mowers. The owner of the house had provided this shelter in exchange for the few odd jobs Slim was still able to perform.

I had no idea what he did when it was really cold. Apparently he had some friends who would provide a place to stay until he made them mad or started a fire in the basement, and then they'd kick him out.

We tried everything with Slim: social services, charity organizations, and on many occasions, detox. We even had him committed to a mental hospital once. But nothing worked. It was never very long before he ended up back in the ER.

And here he was on his way in again tonight. We were busy, but it shouldn't take too long to evaluate Slim and get him squared away. Now this is where I had to be careful. When medical students or first-year residents rotate through the ER, I have to constantly remind them that even our "regulars" get sick, and you have to be vigilant in your assessment of them, as with every patient. Maybe more so. I have to remind myself of that as well. The temptation, of course, is to blow them off as "just the usual" and move on to the people who *really* need your help. Sometimes that approach can be disastrous. It had proved disastrous for another of our ER regulars, Faye Givens.

Faye was a middle-aged woman who had visited our ER on a frequent basis for years. Her complaint was always "nerves," and by the end of her visit, she would invariably ask for "a sleeping pill." Sometimes a simple Tylenol tablet would suffice, and she would happily go on her way. At other times, she would become adamant about receiving a shot for her condition, becoming quite loud and disruptive. To my knowledge, she had never been diagnosed in our ER with any serious condition.

One evening she came in by ambulance, complaining of her usual "nerves." This time, however, she added the complaint of a severe headache, pointing to her forehead. Dr. Canty, one of my younger partners, was on duty, and like the rest of us, he knew Faye very well. His cursory exam did not elicit any bothersome findings, and he was prepared to try giving her a Tylenol and send her home.

He instructed Lori, on duty that particular evening, to do just that. She went to Faye's room but immediately came back to the nurses' station, her medicine cup still containing the small white tablet.

"I'm just not sure about Faye tonight," she told him. "Something's just not right about her. Maybe you'd better take another look at her."

Dr. Canty stopped what he was doing and looked at her. A part of him responded to Lori's concern, trusting her proven judgment. A small cloud passed over his previously clear decision, causing him to second-guess himself momentarily. But this quickly passed, and he blew off this interruption. He had seen Faye on many occasions and it was always the same—no emergency, no serious medical problem. It was always just a disposition dilemma—how to get her out of the department with as little trouble as possible.

Yet he respected Lori. Partly to placate her and partly to dispel any remains of that bothersome cloud, he walked over to where Faye was sitting on the edge of her stretcher. Her head was hanging, lolling slightly from side to side. Even this posture was part of her usual behavior.

"Faye, how is that headache?" he asked her.

"Doc, it's killin' me. Like somethin' is stickin' in the middle of my head. Can't you give me somethin' for it?" she pleaded.

He reached out and took her head in his hands, once more making sure her neck was completely supple. It was. And then he looked again at her eyes. Amazing! They were crossed, and she was able to hold them that way! That took a real effort. Her look was comical, and he tried desperately to suppress a chuckle.

An Academy Award–winning performance, he thought to himself.

"I'll be right back," he told her, walking out of the room and over to Lori.

"She's fine," he said, a tone of finality in his voice. "Go ahead and give her the Tylenol and let her go."

Reluctantly, Lori did as instructed, and Faye was soon on her way home.

Two days later, she returned to the ER, dead. Her autopsy revealed she had a large tumor pressing on the ocular structures in the front of her brain. That was what had caused her eyes to be crossed, and was what killed her.

I was behind the closed curtain of room 5 when I heard the clicks and wheezes as the automatic ambulance doors opened. Then I heard Denton as he confirmed his destination with Lori. "Room 2?" he asked her.

"Yes," she answered. "That's fine."

"Ooooooooo!"

It was a moan I would recognize anywhere. Slim.

"Oooooooo! My belly!"

I finished giving instructions to the patient in room 5, pulled the curtain aside, and stepped out. Turning back to the middle-aged man on the stretcher, I said, "Go ahead and get dressed. A nurse will be right with you." I pulled the curtain closed behind me.

Denton had deposited Slim on the bed in room 2, and Lori was taking his temperature. My eyes caught Slim's and he furtively looked away.

"BP's 110 over 70," Denton informed me. "And his pulse is about 90, but a little irregular. He looks okay to me," he added, holding the EMS clipboard in his hand while I signed the bottom of the transport sheet.

"Okay, Denton. Thanks."

He pushed the stretcher out of the cubicle and moved toward the nurses' station while I stepped into Slim's room. Lori had replaced the blood-pressure cuff in its holder on the wall and was attaching two electrodes to his chest, connecting him to the cardiac monitor.

"114 over 72," she told me, turning on the monitor and then making a note on a paper towel that had been hastily placed on the countertop. "No fever. 98.4."

"Ooooooooo! Doc, do somethin'! It's killin' me!"

The monitor came to life, and its *beep-beep-beep* drew my eyes to the screen mounted on the wall over his head.

I thought immediately of Rita Flowers.

Rita was a recently graduated RN, rotating through the ER as part of her hospital orientation. She was a bright young woman, but the jury was still out as to whether she had the judgment to be a good critical-care nurse. At this point in her career, she was of course quite green, and very naïve.

On one particular day, she had the good fortune to take care of Slim. He had come in by ambulance with his usual complaint of abdominal pain. She was quite concerned by his writhing, vociferous demonstrations, and she hurriedly checked his vital signs and connected him to his monitor. Her obvious concern was not lost upon him.

She had hastily stepped across to the nurses' station and grabbed the nearest available physician.

"Doctor, you need to come and see this man!" she pleaded. "Now!"

The ER doctor had looked over her shoulder and readily identified her patient.

Turning back to the chart on the counter, he said, "It's okay, Rita. I'll be there in a few minutes."

She stood there, not knowing what to do. She looked around for help, but everyone seemed busy. Racing back to his cubicle, she glanced at the cardiac monitor. It was now nice and regular. That was good.

Slim continued to moan, his eyes closed, his hands clutching his belly. Slowly one eyelid crept up, and he waited for his opportunity.

Rita turned to the countertop by the side of the stretcher and began making some notes. Slim slowly reached up to his chest and grasped one of the monitor electrodes attached there. He jiggled it forcefully and cried out in agony.

"Ooooooo!" he yelled, rolling from side to side.

Rita looked at him, and then instinctively at the monitor on the wall. All kinds of wavy lines were crossing the screen! She had never seen anything like it before. What was she supposed to do? Call a code? And then suddenly there was a nice, quiet, regular rhythm. Slim's moaning stopped. Rita breathed a sigh of relief.

"Please get me somethin' for this pain," he pleaded.

Rita glanced at the nurses' station, and then back at Slim.

"I'll see what I can do, Mr. Brantley."

She turned again to her charting. Slim waited a moment, and then again jiggled the electrode.

"Ooooooo!" Louder this time.

Rita looked at the monitor and there were those same strange, undulating waves. His heart was going in and out of some peculiar, chaotic, and obviously dangerous rhythm. Something terrible was going to happen if she didn't do something. And then he was quiet, and the monitor resumed its steady *beep-beep-beep*.

That was enough.

"I'll be right back," she told him, stepping toward the entrance of the cubicle, on her way to get some help.

She was met by Virginia Granger, head nurse of the department.

Virginia, our most seasoned veteran, held up her hand, stopping Rita in her tracks. She nodded at Rita and then indicated that she needed to follow her back to Slim's bedside. She had been observing the whole affair.

Virginia indeed presented an imposing figure. She had turned sixty a few weeks earlier, and to her chagrin she had unsuccessfully kept her age a secret from the ER staff. Ramrod straight and always wearing a blindingly white and overstarched blouse and skirt, there was no mistaking her military background. She had worked in various army hospitals for more than twenty years and had brought that bearing and organizational experience to our ER. And she had brought the same pointed, black-trimmed nurse's cap she had worn constantly since graduating from nursing school.

Virginia stood over Slim, hands on hips, lips pursed, and brow furrowed. She was a menacing sight.

"Slim Brantley," she said, drawing out his name for effect.

His eyes slowly opened, and his chin sank to his chest. A schoolboy caught in the act of thumping the head of the girl sitting in front of him.

She waited a moment, then took his hand away from the electrode on his chest and placed it by his side.

"Slim, I don't want you to ever do that again," she admonished him. "Ever."

Slim, still the little boy, said, "I won't, I promise."

Virginia nodded solemnly, winked at Rita, and then stepped out of the room.

Rita just stood there, staring down at Slim for a moment, perplexed and confused. When she finally realized what had been happening here, she turned to follow Virginia back to the nurses' station.

"Ma'am," a small voice behind her whispered. "Could I get somethin' to eat?"

I had taken care of Slim for the past fifteen years, and amazingly he never seemed to change. He was six-foot-four, maybe six-five. You couldn't really tell. Even when he was "well," he slumped over, his long arms dangling by his side. And he was really skinny. He had probably never weighed more than 170 pounds on any occasion I had seen him. His face was wrinkled, craggy, and his eyes had the smoky appearance of too much booze over too many years. His teeth, those few left in his head, were yellowish brown and in sad repair. His hands were quite remarkable. His fingers were extremely long, as were his ridged and filthy fingernails. The index and middle fingers of his right hand were stained a deep and dirty yellow, attesting to a steadfast relationship with his Marlboros.

Today Slim seemed especially unkempt. His clothes were layered for the cold weather. He had on two pairs of trousers, the outermost a stained and torn green plaid. His black boots were well worn and, surprisingly, they matched. More surprisingly, the soles were intact. He had no socks. He wore two light-blue sweaters, the outer one at least two sizes smaller than the inner. Under this was what appeared to be an umpire's jersey.

"Doc, can you give me somethin' for this pain? It's worse than ever! Ooooooo!"

I examined Slim, asking him where he had been staying, when the pain had begun, and whether there were any associated symptoms.

The usual things I needed to know. All the while, I perfunctorily confirmed that his exam was normal, or at least as normal as it could be for Slim.

Convinced nothing serious was going on, I picked up the clipboard for room 2 and began writing. "Slim," I said. "Your belly checks out okay. Doesn't seem to be anything bad going on. Do you think if you had something to eat, you would feel better?" Somehow, I knew the answer to this question.

Slim began to rub the hollow that was his stomach. "Well, Doc, ya know, that would probably do me a lot of good. The pain seems to have eased a little. What do you think they're servin' in the kitchen?" He looked hopeful and a lot more comfortable.

"I don't know, Slim, but I'll try to find out."

Walking over to the nurses' station, I pulled his curtain closed behind me.

"Amy, would you call down to the cafeteria and see if they could send up a tray for Slim?" I asked her.

"Already on its way," she replied. "A double."

Like me, Amy had helped take care of Slim for a lot of years. She was thirty-two years old and one of the best unit secretaries who had ever sat behind the nurses' station in the ER. And that was saying a lot. It took a lot of savvy, patience, and gumption to handle the almost constant barrage of telephone calls and frantic orders being thrown at her. In addition to possessing all of those important traits, she was also our resident NASCAR enthusiast. In quieter moments she would sometimes remind us of the time she shook the hand of Junior Johnson.

Thirty minutes later Slim was eating, quiet and content. The department had gotten busier. A cardiac arrest was on its way in, and we had two patients with carbon-monoxide poisoning who had been fortunate enough to make it to the ER to be treated. They should recover without any problems.

As I came out of room 3, I walked past Slim's curtain. I was stopped in my tracks by an offensive odor. I looked around and then glanced at the nurses' station. Amy was staring at me. She was shaking her head, pinching her nose with one hand and pointing accusingly at room 2 with the other.

"Not again!" I said to her, exasperated.

She simply nodded in response.

One of Slim's major problems over the past few years was the development of an untimely loss of bowel control. Untimely in that it usually occurred in our department, right after he had eaten. To his credit, he was always apologetic.

My opportunity to reflect upon this unwanted circumstance was cut short by the bursting open of the ambulance entrance doors. Two paramedics hurried a stretcher toward the cardiac room. It was our heart attack.

The patient was a ninety-two-year-old man with extensive cancer and advanced Alzheimer's disease. There was nothing we could or should do for this elderly gentleman. I instructed the paramedic to stop chest compressions, and we studied the monitor. Flat line. We watched for a few minutes but nothing changed. He was gone. He had no family members, and no one would be coming over from the nursing home.

Thanking the EMS crew, I started writing up his record and walked back to the nurses' station.

As I passed room 2, I happened to glance over and was able to see through the partially parted curtain. I stopped and watched.

Lori was in the room with Slim. Gloved, she was cleaning him up from his gastrointestinal mishap. And she was smiling at him.

"Ma'am, I'm awful sorry about this," he said to her, his eyes lowered, looking away. It's hard for a man to maintain his dignity when he's sitting in the middle of a public place with his pants down.

"Slim, it's alright," Lori said, still smiling. "Accidents happen. And I'm just glad you're feeling better."

She continued to clean him. The odor was still terribly strong.

Then she was finished, and she peeled off her gloves and tossed them in the contaminated waste container. She washed her hands in the sink and was stepping toward the entrance of the room when she paused, stopping by the head of his bed. She put her hand on his shoulder, patting it gently.

"Slim," she said softly. "You need to take better care of yourself. You need to stop your drinking."

"I know, Ma'am, I know. It's just hard," he responded. "But I'll try."

"Good, Slim. That's all we want you to do. Just try."

Lori had been down this road many times with Slim. And yet she was still offering her support, again demonstrating that somebody cared about him.

She turned from the stretcher and took her hand away from his shoulder. As she did so, Slim reached up and gently grabbed her wrist. Lori stopped and looked down at him.

"Lori." It was the first time he had ever used her name. "Thanks."

That was all. "Thanks." Lori looked at Slim for a moment and then just nodded. He let go of her wrist, and she walked out of the room. She came up to where I stood and stopped, realizing I had been watching. A little color came to her face. No words were needed, though, and she just smiled, nodded, and walked away.

That was one of the last times I saw Slim. He died a few years ago. Yet I remember this particular ER visit well, and Lori's unflinching care for the man. This had been more than just doing her job. It was a manifestation of her spirit and her selflessness. I've tried to respond more like Lori when I find myself in similar circumstances. Sometimes I succeed. Sometimes I don't. But when I don't succeed, when I back away from an unpleasant circumstance or a patient who is less than attractive, I at least realize my shortcoming. Maybe that's the first step.

The King will reply, "I tell you the truth, whatever you did for one of the least of these brothers of mine, you did for me."

—MATTHEW 25:40

3

A **Turn** in the **Road**

*For a little while you may have had to suffer grief
in all kinds of trials. These have come so that your
faith—of greater worth than gold, which perishes even
though refined by fire—may be proved genuine.*

—1 Peter 1:6-7

It seemed like a simple thing. Frank and Katie Giles were on their way from Cleveland to Myrtle Beach, South Carolina, traveling southbound on I-77 when it happened. They had driven this road many times in the past—in fact, each year for the past fifteen. Two of their best friends had moved to the beach years earlier, and the annual trek had become a tradition. Also, it was a chance for the Giles to take a vacation as winter was reluctantly beginning to lose its grip on the Ohio Valley. Frank had just turned sixty-six and had retired a few months ago, so this would be the first time they would be able to spend two full weeks at the beach with their friends.

It had seemed innocent enough, a trivial thing. They were still in North Carolina, negotiating the last remnants of morning rush-hour traffic in Charlotte, and Katie had asked Frank if he wanted her to drive for a while.

When he didn't respond, she looked up from the magazine she was reading and repeated her question. "Frank, you've been driving for almost two hours. Do you want me to take over?"

His hands gripped the wheel perhaps a little too tightly, and he stared straight ahead. She studied his face for a moment. His eyes were tracking the busy and unpredictable traffic surrounding them, and he was handling the van without any problem. And yet there was something wrong. His eyebrows were raised anxiously, something unusual for him, and his lips were trembling, as if trying to form a word or a sound.

"Frank?" Katie said, now worried. She reached over and touched his arm.

And then it was over. Just like that. It had been only half a minute, maybe a little less.

"Wha..." he stammered, shaking his head as if to clear it. "What did you say, Katie? Do I want you to drive? No, no, I'm fine," he answered, now more relaxed.

She continued to search his face, relieved by what he had just said. But she was still concerned, and the uneasy feeling was only slowly beginning to fade.

"Whew, Frank. You had me worried there. You must have been daydreaming." She put her magazine in the passenger-door pocket.

He straightened his arms out, pressing himself back in the seat.

"That was really weird," he began. "I could hear you talking plain as day, and I could see everything going on around us. But I couldn't say anything. I knew what I wanted to say but I couldn't make myself say it. My mouth wouldn't work. Darnedest thing that's ever happened to me."

"Frank, are you alright now?" Katie asked, her anxiety returning.

"I'm fine now," he responded, realizing he needed to calm his wife. "I just couldn't talk, just for a second. No headache, no nothing. I'm fine. Honest." He patted his wife's knee as they sped down the highway.

She looked intently at her husband of forty years. He seemed all right. He was his normal self now, making sense, and he seemed in control of his faculties. Yet something like that shouldn't happen. She just knew it.

She was silent for a few miles and then said, "Frank, we need to stop and see a doctor."

He jerked his head to look at her. "What? I'm fine, Katie. Honest. We don't need to stop anywhere, and I don't need to see a doctor."

"No, we're going to stop. It's still several hours to Myrtle Beach and I won't feel right unless we have you checked out."

She was sitting bolt upright, her arms folded across her chest. He was very familiar with this posture and knew her mind was made up. They passed a mileage sign, and she said, "Look, Rock Hill is just ten miles away. We'll stop there. That's a good-sized town, and they'll have a hospital. We'll just follow the signs."

And then she was silent. Frank knew this silence, and knew that it would do no good to try to dissuade her. They would stop in Rock Hill and find a hospital.

The process begins. Someone punches your ticket, hands it back to you, and then you're on the train. There's no stopping. And just as when you've boarded a train, you have no control over where the process is heading. It's almost as if it has a mind of its own.

It's often a simple thing—an innocent-appearing symptom, a seemingly meaningless change in the way you feel, an unexpected finding in a routine examination. You go to your doctor or to the ER to have this "new thing" checked out. One examination, one test leads to another. Something else turns up. "We need to look into this further." Or the unwelcome words, "We're going to need to have you see a specialist."

When the pretense of self-determination and control is stripped away, when the flimsy, artificial layers we construct for our protection are gone, it is our mortality that stares us in the face. Almost daily, one of the staff members in the ER will utter the phrase, "I don't know how they can stand that. What will they do?" It is posed as a rhetorical question, and goes unanswered. But the dark thought hangs in the air. It sobers us for a moment, strikes a chord that is both familiar and uncomfortable. *There but for fortune...* And then we move on.

Not so for the person holding the ticket.

Frank was sitting up in room 2. He was in a hospital gown and seemed embarrassed as he struggled with the tie strings behind him. Katie was trying to help. She clucked as she shook her head. "Why do they always make these things so short?"

"They do, don't they?" I said, entering the room and pulling the curtain closed behind me. "Hi, I'm Dr. Lesslie. What can we do for you this morning?"

They both looked up. Katie had managed to knot the strings and secure Frank's gown.

"Hello, Doctor," Frank began. "I'm not sure I even need to be here, but my wife—"

Katie quickly interrupted. "His wife is concerned about him and wants him evaluated. We're on vacation, and Frank had an unusual episode a little while ago while we were driving on the interstate. I just want him to be checked out."

She went on to explain the brief problem her husband had experienced. Frank sat leaning forward on the stretcher, his arms folded and his head down.

When she had finished, I asked Frank how he felt now and what he remembered of the incident.

"Doc, I feel fine now, completely normal," he responded. "And about what happened on the road, it was just really unusual. I could hear Katie, and I knew what I wanted to say, but I couldn't make my mouth work. It was strange. And then it passed and was gone."

He seemed fine now, but the story was bothersome. He might have had a small stroke, or he might have an aneurysm that was beginning to leak. His heart could be throwing out tiny clots. This could represent a number of potentially serious things, or it could be just a passing problem, one that would never recur.

His physical examination was completely normal. His vital signs were also within normal limits, his neurological status was fine, and his cardiac exam was okay. But something just didn't seem right, and the fact they were on the road, headed away from home, bothered me.

"Well, everything looks good now, but I think we should just check things out a little more. What I would recommend is that we get a

CT scan of your head and make sure there are no problems there," I explained.

"Dr. Lesslie, I—" Frank began.

But Katie interrupted him again, patting him on the arm. "Dr. Lesslie, you go ahead and do what you think needs to be done. I want to be sure everything is alright before we head on to Myrtle Beach."

Frank looked up at her, and an expression of mild consternation gave way to one of resignation.

I looked at him, seeking his approval.

"Well...okay, Doc. If that's what you think is best."

"I do, Mr. Giles. It should only take an hour or so, and when we get the results we should be able to send you on your way. I'll just feel better about things if I know the scan is normal."

"We'll feel better too, Doctor. And thank you," Katie responded, smiling.

The Radiology Department was adjacent to the ER, just around the corner. Fortunately the CT machines were not too busy this morning. They were able to get Mr. Giles in right away, and in thirty minutes to an hour or so I would get a faxed report from the radiologist. As I stood at the nurses' station writing on his record, I didn't anticipate a bad outcome. I knew I was being cautious, maybe overly so. But with people from out of town who are just passing through, you tended to be a little extra careful. Most of our patients are from Rock Hill, or from within the county. And most have family physicians they can see in the next day or two for follow-up if needed. And if they get worse, they can always come back to the ER. But for those who are traveling, you want to be sure you aren't sending them down the road with a problem that has not been identified or resolved.

The department had gotten busier while I had been in room 2 with the Gileses. I had taken care of a sore throat, started the workup of an elderly man with abdominal pain, and taken a quick look at a lacerated finger, when I saw Frank Giles being wheeled back into the department by two X-ray techs, his wife walking by his side. They were smiling at me as they were taken to his room.

I was talking to Amy, requesting some lab studies for the gentleman with abdominal pain. "We'll need a CBC, electrolytes, amylase, lipase, and an obstructive series for room 3, if you can get that going. Oh, and see if you can find a family member. He's not able to tell me too much."

"Sure thing," Amy responded. She'd anticipated this and had already notified the X-ray techs.

Frank Giles's chart was on the counter, and I noticed there was no faxed report attached to it. Usually the report would beat the patient back to the department. I glanced at the fax machine that sat at Amy's elbow. Nothing.

Then the phone rang.

Amy picked up the receiver while continuing to fill out the lab requests for the patient in room 3.

"ER," she answered. "Ms. Conners speaking."

There was a brief pause, and then, "Sure, he's standin' right here, Dr. Stringer. Let me give him the phone."

"It's for you," she said, handing me the receiver without looking up from her paperwork. "Dr. Stringer in Radiology."

Matt Stringer had joined the Radiology staff a little over two years ago. He had extensive training in neuroradiology and, just as important, he was easy to work with. He seemed to understand the pressures we were under in the ER, and he never tried to second-guess us when we ordered studies, especially requests made in the middle of the night. He would frequently walk over to our department with films he thought were especially noteworthy, and together we would go over them. He had taught me a lot about the rapidly changing technologies of scanning and the newer forms of imaging.

"Hey, Matt," I spoke into the phone. "What's going on?"

"Robert, this Mr. Giles you sent over for a CT scan, what can you tell me about him?" The tone of Matt's voice was all business, something unusual for him.

"Well, what do you mean? From a neurological standpoint he's fine. He had a brief episode earlier this morning of expressive aphasia, but that resolved and he's been fine since. Why, what do you see on his scan?" I asked, becoming concerned. This should have been straightforward, a normal and perfunctory report. Apparently it was not.

"You mean he hasn't had any problems before today?" Matt questioned. "No headaches, imbalance, change in behavior?"

"No. Not that he or his wife told me about. Why?"

Matt paused and then said, "You'd better come over to the department and take a look at this scan with me."

"I'll be right there."

I told Amy where I would be and glanced briefly at room 2, where the curtain was pulled open. The Gileses were quietly talking to each other and didn't look in my direction. I turned and walked down the hall toward the back of the ER and then to Radiology.

Matt Stringer was in one of the viewing rooms, sitting in a black leather chair. He was studying a row of films attached to a light box. He pressed a button and with a soft mechanical groan, the row moved upward and an entirely new set of films came into view.

"Hey, Matt," I greeted him, stepping into the dimly lighted cubicle. "What do you have?"

I stepped behind him, leaned over his right shoulder, and looked at the view box. He was reaching out his hand and pointing to one of the X-rays, but my eyes had already found his intended target. I was stunned.

"Take a look at that, Robert," he said, gently tapping the film. In front of us was a CT scan, a cross section of Frank Giles's skull and brain. And in the middle of what should have been normal brain matter was something that shouldn't have been there. The size of a tennis ball, it was clearly demarcated, being a different shade of gray from the surrounding tissue. The ominous-appearing mass had extended its tentacles into Frank's defenseless cerebrum.

I knew at once what it was, but I asked Matt anyway, hoping I was wrong. "What do you think that is?"

"It has to be a glioblastoma. And pretty aggressive, from the looks of it," he answered. "And you say this guy hasn't been having any symptoms? Look at the size of this thing. That would be hard to believe."

I continued to stare at the X-ray, and my mind raced. *A brain tumor.* How was I going to break this to the Gileses? What was I going to tell them?

"No, Matt. I asked both of them repeatedly, and he has been doing great. No headaches, no visual changes, no weight loss, no gait disturbance. Nothing. Just that brief episode this morning," I told him. It didn't seem logical to me, either. This was a huge tumor and it occupied a lot of space. You would think from its size and location it would have announced itself by now.

"Hmm," Matt mused. "Well, it doesn't really matter, does it? This thing is going to kill him. It's too big and too invasive to do anything with. It's in a terrible location and it must be growing pretty fast. Does this guy live here in town?"

I told Matt of the circumstances in which the Gileses found themselves. He rubbed his chin and looked up at me. "Good luck, Robert. I don't envy you having to tell them about this."

I wasn't feeling so good about it myself. "Well, thanks, Matt. I guess I'd better get back to the ER and sit down with these folks."

"Okay, I'll see you later. Let me know if I can do anything." He turned back to his work and pressed the button on the desktop. With the same quiet mechanical groan, the films from Frank Giles's CT scan disappeared from view, and the X-rays of someone else's life took their place.

The walk back to the ER was long but not long enough. The fact that I didn't know these people wouldn't make this any easier. They were good folks, and they would immediately understand the implications of what I had to tell them.

Virginia Granger was standing at the nurses' station as I approached. She looked up from the legal pad she had in her hand and took off her glasses. Tapping the pad with them, she said, "Dr. Lesslie, there are a couple of things we need to go over before we have our staff meeting in the morning. Do you have a few minutes now, or would another time be better?"

I picked up Frank Giles's chart from the countertop. "How about later, Virginia? I need to take care of a few things right now."

She put her glasses back on and studied my face, her head canted to one side. "Are you alright? Is there a problem?"

Glancing in the direction of the Gileses' room, I noted that the curtain was pulled closed. "I've got some bad news for the people in room 2, and it will take a few minutes." I briefly told her what I had just learned.

Virginia pursed her lips, nodded her head slightly, and said, "Why don't I go in there with you? Maybe I can help."

I looked up from Frank's chart and into her eyes. They were a steely gray. What most people found cold and intimidating, I found compassionate and incisive. Her years in the military and in the ER had tempered this compassion with an edge of reserve, but had not defeated it. And I knew she had delivered equally devastating news to too many people like Frank and Katie Giles.

I appreciated her offer, and for a moment considered taking her up on it. "No—but thanks, Virginia," I told her. "I'd better just do this myself."

Katie stood at the head of the stretcher, her hand resting on her husband's shoulder. They looked up as I came into the room. I pulled the curtain closed behind me and sat down on the stool that stood against the wall. There was an expectant look on their faces, and the traces of a smile on Katie's. Frank sat stiffly, the fingers of his hands interlocked and resting in his lap.

What should I say? How was I going to begin this? And then Katie helped me. "Well, what have you found, Doctor? Is everything all right? Can we resume our trip?"

I held Frank's chart against my chest and leaned forward.

"Frank, Katie, I'm afraid I have some bad news."

She tensed, and her hand, which had been gently resting on his shoulder, now gripped it tightly. Her eyes widened.

"The CT scan was not normal. There's a problem."

"What kind of problem?" Katie asked, insistently. "What's the matter?"

Frank was silent.

"Frank, I'm afraid you have a brain tumor."

Katie gasped, and her hand went to her mouth.

The color drained from Frank's face. "A brain tumor?" he echoed. There was a brief pause. "How bad is it, Dr. Lesslie?"

This was something I could handle, a clinical question. This was familiar and more comfortable turf.

"First, I'm not a neurosurgeon," I explained. "But this thing is pretty large. It's in a bad location and it looks aggressive."

"What does that mean?" he asked.

"The radiologist that looked at your scan thinks it is most likely a certain type of tumor that grows quickly. One that's not going to do well."

There was silence for a moment, and then Katie spoke. "And what does that mean?"

"Again, Mrs. Giles, I'm not a neurosurgeon. But this is a bad problem. And it's something that needs to be taken care of, as soon as possible."

"No, what I want to know is—" she persisted, but her husband patted her on her arm and interrupted her.

"Doctor, what do you think we should do? What should we do right now? Do you think it's safe to go on to Myrtle Beach, or should we just head back home?" he asked me.

I had already thought about this, and I told him what I would do in this circumstance. "My advice would be to cancel your trip and head back home. You're going to need to see your personal physician, and together you can decide how you want to proceed with this. The episode this morning was something small, but I'm afraid something worse could happen at any time. I think it will be safe for you to travel—but Mrs. Giles, I would advise that you do the driving."

Katie had tears in her eyes, and she nodded her head.

"But what about our friends at the beach?" he asked, looking up at her. "They'll be expecting us this afternoon."

Katie was silent.

I stood up. "Why don't the two of you talk this over for a few minutes? If you decide to go on to Myrtle Beach, I will call down there and see if I can arrange for some help if you should need it. Whatever you decide, you'll need to take a copy of your CT scan with you, and I'll arrange for that. I'll be back in a couple of minutes."

Pulling the curtain closed behind me, I walked over and sat down beside Amy. I was drained.

The couple of minutes turned into half an hour as the elderly gentleman with abdominal pain demanded my attention. His X-rays revealed that he had perforated his large intestine and would need the services of a surgeon. When this had been arranged, I stepped back into room 2 to check on the Gileses.

The atmosphere of the room had been dark and oppressive when I left. Now it had completely changed. He was dressed, and they were both standing by the bed, their arms around each other's waists. And they were smiling.

Frank was the first to speak. "We've decided to take your advice and we're going to head back home. We'll need to make a few phone calls and then we can be on our way."

It was Katie's turn. "And we want to thank you for your help, Dr. Lesslie," she told me. "This has certainly been a surprise, and not what we ever wanted to hear. But it is what it is, and we needed to know about it."

I just stood there and listened.

"Katie's right, Doctor. And we'll handle this. We'll be all right with whatever comes our way."

There was a pause, and I was just about to turn from the room when Frank continued. "We are spiritual people, doctor. Not religious, necessarily. There's a difference, you know."

A movement from Katie drew my attention. It was then that I noticed the small silver cross that hung by a chain from her neck. Her hand had gone to the cross, and she clutched it gently.

"I'm not an old man, by any means. Or at least I don't feel old," Frank chuckled. "But I've had a lot of good years and we've done a lot of good things. If this thing, this tumor, is a bad one and it can't be fixed—well, then, so be it. And if I thought this life, these few years we have on this earth, were all that are given us—well, I suppose I would have something to be upset about. But that's not what we believe. This is just the first part, the first step. And I'm okay with this thing. We're okay."

Katie looked up at her husband and smiled, then pressed herself closer to him.

Standing at the nurses' station, I was finishing the work on Frank Giles's chart as Virginia Granger led him and his wife out through triage. His eye caught mine and he gave me a nod of his head, and then, amazingly, a wink. Then the couple disappeared behind the closing door. They were beginning a new and unexpected journey.

Frank's ticket had been punched. He was on his train, and Katie was with him. Wherever that train was headed, they would be on it together. And I sensed that wherever the journey ended, they would be okay.

I have set the LORD always before me. Because he
is at my right hand, I will not be shaken.

—PSALM 16:8

All **God's Children**

*Every man naturally desires knowledge; but what good
is knowledge without fear of God? Indeed a humble
rustic who serves God is better than a proud intellectual
who neglects his soul to study the course of the stars.*

—Thomas à Kempis

O ne universal truth is that the ER is the great leveler of person-
ages. We reach a common ground and find ourselves dealing
with the same problems as everyone else around us: pain and suffering,
health and disease, and sometimes life and death. At that point, our
addresses make no difference, nor do our titles and degrees, nor do
the quality and purchase price of the clothes we wear.

Another infallible truth of life in the emergency room is that just as
soon as you believe you are good at what you do, that you are capable
of handling anything thrown at you, at that moment or in the not-
too-distant future, you will be brought low. We have to learn not to
take ourselves too seriously and to get our egos out of the way so we
can be useful to others. This is the case not only for those of us who
work in the ER. As it turns out, this is a challenge just as much for
the patients, no matter what their walk in life.

2:15 p.m. It was a Tuesday afternoon, mid-May, and the weather outside was beautiful. It had been a manageable day thus far, and the staff
was in good spirits. Lori Davidson was working triage. She opened

the door out of that area and brought Mrs. Betty Booth out into the department, leading her toward the observation room.

As they passed the nurses' station, Amy Conners looked up from behind the counter.

"Good afternoon, Mrs. Booth," she said, smiling at the elderly woman.

"Good afternoon, Amy," Mrs. Booth responded, nodding her head but not returning the smile. "I hope my room is clean and ready," she added.

It wasn't exactly *her* room, but maybe it should have been. She had been coming to the ER each afternoon for three weeks to receive special medication for a bone-marrow condition. Her doctor had ordered that it be given intravenously, and the process took about two hours. During that time she would be our guest in one of the observation-room beds. At this time of day, these beds were seldom used, and she usually had a moderate degree of privacy.

"I'm sure everything is ready for you," Amy responded, rolling her eyes for my benefit once Lori and our guest had passed by.

Mrs. Betty Booth was a pillar of the community, as had been her family for several generations. Her lineage was dotted with a few mayors, city councilmen, and even a state senator. She was a widow now, with no children, and she represented the last vestiges of "old Rock Hill." This appellation was important to her and she wanted to be sure that those who attended her understood it. She was very demanding about her care and surroundings. She brooked neither inattentiveness nor any avoidable disruption of her established routine. We had suggested she come to the ER in the early afternoons, as this was usually our quietest time. Still, it was an ER. We couldn't guarantee peace and tranquility, even in the observation room.

On this particular day, she would be alone in OBS. The room was clean, quiet, and she would be able to choose her own stretcher.

"I'd like to be over in that bed," she instructed Lori, pointing to the back right corner of the room—bed C. "And make sure that the curtains are drawn."

Lori dutifully helped Mrs. Booth onto the stretcher, raised the head to a comfortable level, and gave her a blanket straight from the warmer.

"Your nurse will be with you in a moment to start your IV," she told her. "I'll need to go back out to triage now."

"That will be fine, Lori. And make sure you tell her not to dawdle."

Lori walked out of the room and over to the nurses' station.

"Who's got OBS today?" she asked, glancing at the assignment board.

Virginia Granger was sitting at the nurses' station, working on one of her administrative reports. "Becka's got it, Lori, but she's on break right now. Give me the chart and I'll get things started. I know Mrs. Booth."

Amy handed her the chart and headed back to triage.

Becka Hemby was twenty-two years old and a recent graduate from the local nursing program. She had been in the ER for only about a month. Though she had the potential to be a good ER nurse, she was still learning the ropes.

Within a few minutes, Virginia had Betty's IV started and had ordered her medication from the pharmacy. It would be delivered shortly. Mrs. Booth was reclining comfortably, reading her *Southern Living* magazine behind her closed curtains. Everything seemed to be on schedule.

And then things turned south. It seems to happen that way, doesn't it? Just when everything seems under control, rolling along smoothly, there's a sudden bump in the road—and then a pothole.

The bump in the road came in the form of our young nurse, Miss Hemby. She had come back from her break and gone out to relieve Lori in triage. All routine. Lori would be back in fifteen minutes and Becka would resume her regular assignment, which included the observation room. It was those fifteen minutes that would prove to be crucial. That's when the pothole arrived, in the person of Jasper Little.

Jasper was one of our regulars. He had a predilection for MD 20/20 and would frequently consume it to the point of oblivion. This was an unusual time of day for him to appear in the department. His blood alcohol level usually didn't reach the customary .40 range until later in the evening. But someone had given him ten dollars to help with an odd job and he had headed straight to his favorite store.

Becka greeted Mr. Little and took him into triage. There she obtained his vital signs and tried to make some sense out of what he was saying. He could barely walk, and he seemed to be speaking something other than English. She made a wise decision to place him in a wheelchair and rolled him into the department. She rightly assumed Jasper would need some fluids and medications, and she glanced at the board at the nurses' station to determine the most appropriate room. In her brief time with us, she had helped take care of him during one of his bouts with the DTs.

Hmm, she thought. *OBS has only one patient, Jasper'll probably be with us for a while, so I'll take him there.*

She rolled Jasper into OBS and over to the stretcher of bed B, in the back left corner of the room. Mrs. Booth was contentedly reading behind her curtain, unaware of her new roommate.

Just then, Lori came back from her break. She stuck her head in OBS and told Becka she was headed out to triage, and she took Jasper's wheelchair with her. She didn't look up to see the identity of the new patient.

Becka busied herself with Mr. Little. It was no small task to get him up on the stretcher and secure him behind the raised rails. She knew department policy and got him undressed to his underwear and into a hospital gown.

"You stay right here, Mr. Little," she instructed him. "I'll be right back."

He mumbled a response that was completely unintelligible and then lay back on the bed and closed his eyes.

I happened to be the one who picked up Jasper's chart when it hit the counter. I assumed that this would be a routine visit: IV fluids, multivitamins and thiamine through his IV line, and observation for several hours. We would get a blood alcohol on him and put together a pool to see who could come the closest without going over. Briefly, the thought crossed my mind that he probably shouldn't be in OBS with Mrs. Booth. She considered it her private domain, and she certainly didn't travel in the same circles as Jasper Little. Nevertheless, he was already bedded down, and what was the worst that could happen?

We found out in about an hour. Becka had checked on Mrs. Booth and made sure she was comfortable. Her medication was infusing smoothly and she should be ready to go home in thirty minutes or so. Becka then stepped across to Jasper's stretcher.

"Mr. Little," she said, gently shaking his shoulder. "How are you doing?"

He raised his head off the pillow and half opened his eyes. "Gotta pee," he declared.

"Excuse me?" Becka asked.

"Gotta pee," he repeated. His head fell back on the pillow and his eyes again closed.

She looked at his IV line. It was running wide open and he had already received almost two liters of fluids. *He probably does have to urinate,* she thought.

She glanced at the counter behind the stretcher and didn't see a urinal or bedpan. She was concerned that Jasper was still too unsteady on his feet to get him up and walk him to the bathroom.

"I understand, Mr. Little," she told him. "I'm going to step out for just a second and get a urinal for you. I'll be right back."

"Gotta pee," he mumbled.

I was at the nurses' station when Becka came out of OBS and headed for the supply closet. She was in there for several minutes before sticking her head out and asking, "Does anyone know where the urinals are kept?"

Before anyone could respond, there came a loud shriek from OBS. It was Mrs. Booth. "Oh, good Lord! Somebody help me!"

Becka bolted out of the supply closet and headed for OBS. I put down the chart I was holding and followed her.

"Somebody help! Do something!"

When I reached the doorway, Becka was pulling aside Mrs. Booth's curtain and asking, "Mrs. Booth, what's the…"

She stopped in mid-sentence and just stared.

Betty Booth sat bolt upright in her bed, her hands covering her mouth and her eyes wide as saucers. Then with one hand she pointed to the foot of her bed.

There in all his glory stood Jasper Little. He had somehow gotten out of his stretcher and walked across the room, IV pole in tow. Becka had put his gown on backward, so the opening was in the front. He stood at the foot of Mrs. Booth's bed with his hands on his hips, eyes closed, and pelvis thrust forward. He was relieving himself on the end of her stretcher, and he was doing so with unrestrained enthusiasm.

"Gotta pee," he mumbled, smiling and nodding his head.

Becka quickly pulled the curtain closed and led Jasper back to his bed. Mrs. Booth remained speechless, shaken to the core. The next day, her physician arranged for another facility to administer her medication. We haven't seen her since.

10:15 p.m. Two police officers escorted a middle-aged man into the department.

"Good evenin', Doc," one of them greeted me as they approached the nurses' station. "Got some business for you."

I glanced up and nodded hello, barely noticing the man between them. He was handcuffed, his hair tousled and his shirt partway out of his pants. I glanced down at his feet and noticed he wore only one shoe. Then I looked at his face again and realized he looked familiar. My index finger went to my chin and my head cocked to one side as I struggled for his name.

Then it came to me. The look of recognition on my face must have been obvious, because the officer who had spoken nodded his head and said, "Yep, got a VIP for you here."

The shackled visitor didn't seem to hear this. I'm not sure he was hearing much of anything. He reeked of alcohol, and his slouching posture and lolling head indicated he had passed way beyond being "under the influence."

Jeff Ryan had walked up to the counter. "Go ahead and take him back to ortho," he instructed the officers. "There's no one in there and he should be out of the way."

"Sure thing," they responded and headed down the hallway. They knew their way around the department as well as we did.

When they were a safe distance away, Jeff said, "Now isn't that somethin'?"

"Isn't that Joe Sightler?" I asked. "The mayor of Hazelton?" This was a small town about twenty minutes outside of Rock Hill. He was a high-profile local politician, frequently in the news, and never one to shy away from controversial issues.

"That's Joe alright," Jeff answered. "Looks like he's in a bit of a pickle tonight."

"Or at least pickled," Amy punned from behind the desk. "He can barely stand."

This should be interesting, I thought. I had some other work to do, and it would take a while for his chart to make its way to the counter. Still, it was going to be interesting.

Every emergency department has had its share of VIP patients. We've had movie actors, professional football players, politicians, and professional wrestlers. Even famous biblical characters—I once took care of a man who claimed to be John the Baptist. They all get treated the same and are shown no favoritism, nor do they receive any special perks. (We did keep a close eye on John, though. He was a little different.) The fact is, we all put our pants on one leg at a time. We all have the same weaknesses and maladies, the same needs and the same quandaries. Joe Sightler might be a well-known politician, but in this ER on this night, he was just a man in need of medical attention. I wasn't exactly sure what that attention was going to be, but it didn't look like it would be anything serious. He would be in line just like everyone else.

I picked up his chart from the countertop just as one of his police officers walked up.

"Mr. Sightler was involved in a fender bender," he told me. "Actually, I'm not sure it even qualifies as a fender bender. He was at a local restaurant this evening and had a few too many to drink. We were stopped at a red light right beside the restaurant when he came out and got in his car. We sat through the next green light and just watched, 'cause we couldn't believe what we were seeing. He barely made it across the parking lot without falling. We thought, *No way is this guy gonna try to drive!*"

The officer stopped and shook his head, still unable to believe what had happened. Then he continued. "We pulled into the lot and tried to stop him, but before we could, he gunned the motor and backed right into a light post. I guess he couldn't see the post, 'cause he kept rammin' into it. Hit it a couple of times. I had to reach in and cut off the motor."

When he paused this time, I glanced down at Joe's chart and searched for "chief complaint." The business office had typed in, "Auto accident. No complaints. Police request blood alcohol."

"Let me go check him out," I told the officer. "And we'll get you guys out of here as quickly as we can."

"No hurry, Doc. Our shift's almost over. We'll take Joe down to the station, and it looks like he'll be spending at least tonight with us. I guess we'll be in the paper in the morning."

"Probably so," I agreed.

After checking Joe out and determining he had no significant physical injury, we awaited his blood alcohol. He had agreed to have it drawn, having slurred, "I don't have anything to hide."

My guess was it was going to be north of .40.

This wasn't the first time, unfortunately, we had taken care of the mayor in an inebriated condition. You'd think he would have practiced some discretion with his use of alcohol, but he seemed oblivious to the potential repercussions. Or maybe he assumed he was above any public reprimand or ballyhoo.

As I walked back up the hall, a momentary lull in our overhead music caught my attention. Our automatic CD changer was located in the doctor's office and we were able to select the music in the ER. Within a few seconds, sounds from Motown drifted through the department. I recognized the voices of the Temptations as they began "My Girl."

Standing at the nurses' station, I was handed a lab slip from the fax. It revealed Joe Sightler's blood alcohol: .465, more than four times the legal limit.

"That should about do it," the officer remarked, looking over my shoulder.

"I guess he's all yours," I told him. "We'll have him ready to go in just a few minutes."

It was then that the universally familiar rhythm at the beginning of "I Heard It Through the Grapevine" wafted through the department.

"Good tune," the officer remarked, his head rocking in time to the song.

Mr. Sightler must have heard the music as well. An unexpected movement down the hallway caught my attention and I looked in the direction of the doorway of the ortho room. Joe was out of the room and walking up the hallway. You couldn't exactly call it walking. He was still in his hospital gown, barefooted. His hands were raised shoulder-high, palms facing forward, and he was doing a kind of shimmy motion. His eyes were closed and his head rocked from side to side.

"Ooooo, ooooo, I bet you're wonderin' how I knew…" he crooned. Actually, his pitch was pretty good.

Two radiology techs turned the corner behind him. They were pushing a wheelchair with an elderly woman in it. She had injured her ankle and we had sent her around for an X-ray. The three were met by the stately mayoral vision as he meandered up the hall. Only their view was a little different from ours. Joe's gown was open in the back and untied. His underwear was hanging on a hook somewhere. And his behind was gloriously exposed to the whole world.

The woman in the wheelchair seemed to appreciate it. Though we heard a faint yelp and saw her cover her eyes, she continued to peek between her spread fingers. The radiology techs just smiled. They had seen quite a few hineys before. Heads began popping out from behind curtains and people got to see one of their elected officials up close and personal.

"Mm-hmm," the officer murmured. "Would you look at that."

I supposed the mayor would have kept on dancing right out of the department if we'd let him. But maybe not. When he neared the nurses' station he stopped, opened one eye, looked in my direction, and winked.

The officers led him back down the hall and helped him get dressed. One leg at a time.

When pride comes, then comes disgrace, but
with humility comes wisdom.

—Proverbs 11:2

5

The **Experience** of **Grief**

Although the world is full of suffering, it is
also full of the overcoming of it.

—HELEN KELLER (1880–1968)

Grief. We are told that as humans our handling of grief or loss can be logically and predictably chronicled through four distinct phases. First there is shock, followed by denial, then anger, and finally resolution.

All griefs and losses, major and minor, work the same way. We travel through the phases, backing up, retracing our steps, making progress again, relapsing, and on it goes. The ability to reach resolution and stay there is a gift, a thing for which we ought to be grateful.

For most of us, this final resolution is a rare occurrence. Our natural inclination is to travel in circles, not in a straight line. And these circles can be destructive. Shock, denial, anger. Shock, denial, anger. Never reaching resolution.

Every day in the ER we see people faced with small griefs, and many times with overwhelming losses. We watch as they come to grips with their emotions and deal with sudden and unexpected life-changing events. Sometimes we can help. Often, we can't. I have found that you can frequently predict how people will respond in crisis. Over the years you gain a sense of who seems grounded and in control of their emotions. And who is not. You can usually identify that person who is only one word, one whisper, one sideways glance away from totally losing it. Many times you will be correct, but not always. Sometimes the actions and reactions of people will take you completely by surprise.

I had been working in the ER of Rock Hill General for a few years. On this particular Sunday morning about twenty years ago, one of my partners, Bill Blanchard, had been on duty in the department. It was a beautiful morning—springtime, quiet, nonthreatening. The ER was peaceful. At 9:30, Bill was having his second cup of coffee and was reading the local newspaper. There were only a handful of nonemergent patients remaining from a brief rush at sunrise and Virginia Granger, the charge nurse that day, was discharging one of them. She passed through the nurses' station where Bill sat with his paper in one hand and his cup of coffee in the other. His feet were casually occupying the countertop.

As Virginia passed by she paused, looked over the top of her glasses at his shoes, and simply said, "Dr. Blanchard."

He didn't need a second warning.

"Oh, excuse me," he responded, coming to an upright position in his chair with his feet firmly located on the floor. He kept his head in the newspaper, not looking up as he ceded this turf to Virginia. It was an act born out of respect more than out of intimidation, though Virginia had quite a menacing reputation in the hospital, especially among new physicians. She brooked no tomfoolery in her department.

But Bill was no intern, having completed his training in emergency medicine in a large urban medical center eight years earlier. He had been in this particular hospital for more than six years and was a seasoned ER doc. He was one of the favorites of the occasional medical student or intern who rotated through the department because he was always accessible for their many elementary questions. "What's the dose of amoxicillin for a two-year-old?" "Does 'TID' mean twice a day or three times a day?" "I think this guy in room 5 has pink eye. What should I treat him with?"

I never saw him demonstrate any impatience, even when one befuddled intern confronted him with, "Dr. Blanchard, I've got a guy here I think has appendicitis. Now, I know the appendix is on the right side, but is it *his* right or *my* right, and does it depend on which way I'm facing him?"

"Hmm," Bill had calmly responded, with an air of appropriate but feigned seriousness so as not to embarrass this fledgling physician. "I suppose that would be *his* right, wouldn't it?"

He was a steadying influence for each of us and shared freely of his practical and varied experience.

Yet he was about to teach all of us one of his most important lessons, though not by intent or design. And it was certainly not of his own choosing.

This particular morning Bill was the only physician in the ER. He moved on to the sports section of the paper, taking advantage of the rare respite.

Virginia had noted his reposturing, with both of his feet now firmly on the floor. She acknowledged her approval with a slight nod and proceeded toward her patient's room. She was interrupted by the high-pitched squawk of the EMS radio.

"ER, this is Medic 1. Do you read me?"

Bill casually looked up from his paper as Virginia put down her chart and walked over to the radio. Having done this thousands of times, she matter-of-factly took out her pen, picked up the phone, and prepared to make notes on the pad of paper beside the radio.

"This is the General ER, Medic 1. Go ahead."

There was silence and then a brief burst of static.

"ER, we're out on the interstate with a 10-50 (auto accident). Two PIs (personal injuries), one dead at the scene. The other looks okay. Twenty-five-year-old male. We're bringing him in on a backboard, full spinal protocol. Ten minutes away."

"10-4, Medic 1. Minor trauma 3 on arrival," Virginia instructed the paramedic. She finished her notations and picked up her chart, once more trying to discharge her patient.

Bill spoke over his newspaper to her. "Sounds like a bad accident. A little unusual for a Sunday morning."

"Yeah," Virginia answered. "But you never know. People do strange things."

Ten minutes later, the ambulance entrance doors opened to admit a stretcher being pushed by one of the hospital's paramedics. His partner EMT steadied the side of the gurney. Their patient was strapped securely to a backboard, head held firmly to it by Velcro straps.

From the nurses' station Bill could get enough of a glimpse of the young man to determine he was in no immediate danger. The patient's eyes darted to and fro and he kept asking, "Where is my wife? How is she?"

The EMT pushed the stretcher into minor trauma and the paramedic walked over to the nurses' station, clipboard in hand. He approached Bill, leaned over, and quietly spoke. "Dr. Blanchard, this is really a tough one." He tilted his head down the hallway toward this newest patient.

"Young couple, got married yesterday somewhere in Tennessee. Spent the night just north of town and were on their way to the beach for their honeymoon. An eighteen-wheeler changed lanes in front of them, and this guy swerved and lost control. Flipped over twice. The girl didn't have a seat belt on and was thrown out of the car and down an embankment. Pretty bad head injury. Looked like she died on impact. He hardly has a scratch on him."

The paramedic stood up straight, put his hands on the small of his back, and stretched.

"Does he have any idea what happened to his wife?" Bill asked him.

"No, not a clue. We didn't say anything. And the highway patrolman wouldn't tell him. I guess you get to," he added sheepishly.

"Yeah, well, I guess so," Bill conceded. He had been in this position too many times before.

Virginia worked efficiently, and within half an hour Bill had cleared the young man, Mr. Jones, of any significant injury. In fact, he had no complaints and had only noticed a few scratches on his left hand. He continued to ask about his wife, and Bill deftly avoided any specific response. He was awaiting the arrival of the highway patrolman to confirm the story given him by the paramedic.

Bill walked past the young man's room and noticed he was up and off the stretcher, standing by the gurney. His hands were in his pockets and he was quietly staring at the doorway. Virginia had just told him that as soon as they had definite news about his wife they would share that information with him.

When Bill reached the nurses' station he said, "Virginia, why don't you take him to the family room. Try to keep him calm, and I'll be in there in a few minutes."

"Okay, I'll try," she answered. Bill knew that Mr. Jones would be in good hands with Virginia.

While he stood at the nurses' station documenting the record of this young man, a highway patrol officer walked into the department and approached him.

"Dr. Blanchard," he began. "I guess you know what happened out there this morning."

Bill recognized the officer, Tim Reed, and was relieved he was the one working the accident. He knew Tim from many other tough encounters such as this, and always found him professional and thoughtful.

"Yeah, Tim. EMS told me about it. But I'd like to hear it from you too. What happened?"

Tim recited the same bleak story given to Bill by the paramedic. He did add that the trucker had sped away but had been stopped several miles down the road. He had been charged with driving with an expired DOT card. Other charges would be pending.

"Thanks, Tim," Bill told him. "That's what I need to know. I guess I'll go back and talk with Mr. Jones." Without thinking, he picked up the clipboard of the young man waiting in the family room.

"Sorry about that, Dr. Blanchard. You know it's against our policy to inform relatives about deceased loved ones. Wish you didn't have to do this."

"I wish no one had to do this. Thanks."

He walked toward the family room, trying to compose a few words that would somehow lessen the pain for this young man, and for himself. Nothing came to mind. It never did.

The family room was located in the back of the department. It was small, ten by ten, containing a small sofa, two chairs, a table and lamp, and a telephone. The bare essentials.

Bill opened the door and found Virginia and Mr. Jones sitting in the chairs. They both looked up as he entered, and they got to their feet. Virginia stepped around Bill and into the doorway.

"I'll be at the nurses' station if you need me," she told him.

From the distraught but puzzled look on Mr. Jones's face, Bill figured that Virginia had not told him anything about his wife's condition. He heard the door close behind him and the two were alone.

He also figured that Mr. Jones knew something terrible had happened and that Dr. Blanchard would not have anything good to tell him.

"Have a seat, Mr. Jones," Bill said, motioning with the clipboard to one of the chairs.

"No thanks, I'll just stand," he responded. "What can you tell me about my wife? How is she? When can I see her?"

He was a large, athletically built young man, six-one or six-two, and he must have weighed two hundred and fifty, easily outweighing Bill Blanchard by more than seventy-five pounds.

Bill was still struggling with how to begin the conversation and how to convey the awful news. Should he be direct, blunt, to the point? Should he gradually ease into the fact that this man's wife was dead, killed instantly in the wreck?

He was turning these thoughts over in his mind as he stepped farther into the room and sat down in one of the chairs. As he did so, he forgot that he was positioning himself dangerously far from the door. Rule Number One: In such a situation, always—always—stand between the family member and the door.

Mr. Jones, in his nervous, purposeless pacing, happened to end up directly in front of the doorway, blocking any rapid exit. Unfortunately, this new circumstance was completely lost on Bill. Momentarily oblivious to the situation, he began what he thought would be the gentlest way to let Mr. Jones know about his wife.

He began by describing the accident, of which the young man had little memory. He explained about the truck driver and his careless high-speed maneuvering. Then he told him about his wife.

"The truck apparently caused you to swerve to avoid a collision, and you lost control of your vehicle. The car flipped several times and your wife was thrown out." He purposefully didn't mention that Mr. Jones had been seat-belted and his wife had not. There would be enough time for self-recrimination in the months and years ahead.

"I'm afraid that when she fell out of the car, she struck her head on the ground. With the speed of the vehicle and the force of the impact, she suffered a significant head injury. I'm sorry I have to tell you this…but she didn't make it. She's gone. But it's certain—"

He was about to tell him she hadn't suffered, that her death had been immediate, but he didn't have the chance. It was then he realized his mistake. The young man in front of him was about to explode, and Bill was in the worst possible position.

Mr. Jones was looking at the floor, trembling, with clenched fists. Bill slowly stood up from his chair, hoping to correct his unthinking mistake.

Too late. Mr. Jones erupted. He grabbed Bill by the throat and effortlessly slung him through the air, then turned and slammed him into the door.

"You son of a b——!" he screamed. "You killed her! You killed my wife!"

There was little Bill could do. He struggled to free himself, but his assailant was too big and too strong. The clipboard fell and clattered on the tiled floor as Mr. Jones repeatedly slammed Bill against the door. And then he began to punch him in the face with a fierceness born of his frustration and grief.

Virginia heard the commotion and immediately ran to help. She tried to open the family-room door. There was no lock on it, but Dr. Blanchard's body was jamming it shut. She pushed as hard as she could but to no avail. She ran back to the nurses' station and called Security.

Two officers arrived within minutes and as they approached, there was an ominous quiet within the room. The door now opened without resistance. They saw Mr. Jones standing in the corner, his back to the door. His head was hanging down and his forehead was pressed against the wall. He was breathing heavily, but he was calm.

Lying motionless on the floor was the body of Bill Blanchard. Blood was dripping from his mouth and there was a small, dark-red pool forming on the cold tile under his face. His glasses were lying beside his head, the lenses shattered and the frames mangled.

He would survive, though it would be weeks before he would be able to return to work in the ER. Three missing teeth, a fractured jaw and eye socket, two broken ribs.

Rule Number One…

7:45 a.m. It was raining. A tropical storm had dealt the coast a glancing blow and we were receiving the remnants of its flanking layers of clouds and the moisture that came with them. The streets were slick, and the visibility was poor.

"We're going to be busy this morning," Amy Conners pronounced to no one in particular. She was straightening out the disorganized paperwork of a busy night, left by her third-shift counterpart. "Always is when it rains like this. You'd think people would learn to drive in bad weather. Slow down, or somethin'. Or stay at home."

She would be right, of course. This rain would result in a lot of fender benders, and potentially a few serious accidents. We would probably see them all.

As if on cue, the EMS radio pierced the fragile calm of our early morning.

"ER, this is Medic 2."

Lori had been checking the medication log. She put the leather-bound notebook on the counter and walked over to the radio.

Picking up the phone she responded. "Medic 2, this is the ER. Go ahead."

"ER, we've got an eighty-two-year-old lady here, auto accident. Full cardiac arrest. She's intubated, no response to any medications. CPR in progress. Should be there in five. Any further orders?"

Lori looked over to me for a response. I shook my head.

"No, Medic 2. Continue CPR. Trauma room on arrival."

"10-4." The radio fell silent.

Lori and I walked across the hallway to the trauma room to make the usual preparations.

"See, I told ya," Amy intoned prophetically. "I'll call the lab and X-ray."

"Thanks," I said. This didn't sound too promising. The chances of survival for this unfortunate woman were very small. Her age, the lack of response to rescue efforts, and the probability this trauma had come from an auto accident all portended a fatal outcome.

It turned out the circumstances surrounding this elderly patient were not what we had assumed. She had been driving her husband to see his cardiologist for his monthly visit. He had a heart attack six months earlier and was doing well. She was enjoying good health and had no significant medical problems. They lived out in the country, on a farm that had been in their family for several generations.

They had been driving into town this morning and she had started to rub her chest. Then she complained of indigestion, which she put down to a hastily prepared and consumed breakfast. Her husband didn't think much of it until he noticed the car was beginning to veer a little toward the curb. He had glanced over at his wife and saw that her head was lolling from side to side. Before he could say or do any-thing, she had slumped over the steering wheel. The car had swerved completely off the road, slowing and gently coming to rest against a street lamp.

A witness had called EMS, and within a few minutes we had received our call from Medic 2.

She had apparently suffered a massive heart attack and was flat-line when she arrived in the ER. Despite our efforts, there was nothing we could do to change that. She was pronounced dead twenty minutes later.

"Mr. Reid is in the family room, Dr. Lesslie," Lori informed me. "He's there by himself, but I think some family members have been called."

I was finishing my notes on his wife's chart. "Thanks, Lori. I'll be one more minute."

She didn't move, but remained standing by my side. "Do you want me to go back there with you?" she asked.

"No. Thanks, but I'll be okay. Just send his family back when they get here."

I had Mrs. Reid's clipboard in my hand as I stepped into the small family room. Mr. Reid was sitting on the sofa, his hands folded, his gaze fixed on the floor. He was a tall man, of medium build, with a face and neck wrinkled and weathered by many decades in the sun. He looked up as I entered.

Fleetingly, the thought occurred that I needed to position myself between this man and the door. It was a protective reflex, Bill Blanchard's lesson having been indelibly etched into my memory. But this was an eighty-year-old man, hardly a threat.

I stepped across the small space and sat down beside him on the sofa. I shook his hand, and he somehow managed a faint attempt at a smile.

"Mr. Reid," I began. "I need to tell you about your wife."

He nodded slightly, his eyes telling me he already knew what I was going to say. He had known from the moment he had seen her slump over in the car.

We talked for several minutes and then fell silent. He had sobbed for a moment, and then collected himself. He was calm and somehow at peace.

His eyes glistened as he said, "You know, she's had a good life. A good family. Grandchildren that love her. But it hasn't always been easy, workin' a farm all these years. But that's what she wanted. Wouldn't ever consider leavin'."

And then he expressed his concern for his sons and grandchildren. "They're really gonna miss her. They're farmers too, and live on the family land. They see her every day. I don't know what to—"

His last thought was interrupted by the opening of the door. I looked up to see two middle-aged men and a teenage boy stepping into the room. These were big guys. And they all wore well-used, dirt-stained overalls, the badge of men who made their living with their hands. The door closed and the older men sat down in the two chairs. The teenager stood against the door. Their eyes were fixed on Mr. Reid, and then they moved to me.

Bill Blanchard. Suddenly his swollen and bruised face flashed across my mind. I gripped the clipboard in my hands, flimsy protection should I need it.

I was about to say something when Mr. Reid spoke.

"Boys, I hate to tell you this, but Mama's gone." It was a simple statement, but all that needed to be said.

The two men immediately got up from their chairs, and the boy straightened up, bolt-upright in front of the door. Their gaze went from Mr. Reid to me, and back to Mr. Reid.

"Daddy," one of the sons uttered. The single word contained volumes of grief and loss and love. And then they began coming across the room.

Mr. Reid was slowly getting to his feet, seeming much older and weaker than he had a few moments earlier. He seemed unsteady now. I also stood up, and glanced in the direction of the door. The teenager stood motionless, his arms dangling by his side as he stared intently at his grandfather.

One of the men reached out and brushed my shoulder as he hurriedly stepped forward. In an instant, the two sons held their father in their arms, sobbing.

I stood watching, and it was only then I realized how tightly I had been gripping the clipboard in my hands. I felt small and out of place.

One of Mr. Reid's sons turned to me and said, "Doc, I know one of the paramedics that brought Mama in. I saw him in the parking lot a minute ago and he told me she was in bad shape when they picked her up. He told me you had done everything you could to try and save her. Moss and I here want to thank you for that," he said, motioning with his head to his brother.

He held out his hand to me and I shook it, not knowing what to say.

I stepped out into the hallway and closed the door behind me. I was alone, and I stood there for a few minutes. I looked down at the clipboard in my hand and felt a little foolish. What good would this flimsy piece of glued-together material have done me had these two big men and the teenager turned violent? And then I felt small again, remembering their response to the news of their mother and grandmother. These men, this family, were firmly grounded, and though their loss was sudden and awful, they had somehow maintained their composure. They had supported each other with a tangible love and a quiet dignity.

Yet you never know. You can never really predict how people will respond in these circumstances. You have to be watchful.

Always remember Rule Number One.

I walked back down the hall to the nurses' station.

6

The **Generations Pass**

*All men are like grass, and all their glory
is like the flowers of the field.*

—Isaiah 40:6

It was a Saturday night around 9:30, and we had been really busy. Most of our rooms were full and the stack of charts for unseen patients kept getting higher.

I picked up the chart from the top of the pile, noted the room location, and headed off in that direction. I glanced briefly at the information at the top of the clipboard:

> Minor trauma—C
> William Purvis
> 35 yr old WM
> Laceration of chest

"That's a pretty bad one," the triage nurse commented, nodding at the chart in my hand as she passed by.

Great. A complex laceration could take a while to repair, and all during that time the ER would be backing up. Well, we'd just have to see what it looked like.

William Purvis was lying on the stretcher of bed C. It was in the back right corner of minor trauma. Each bed in this room was encircled by ceiling-mounted curtains that could be drawn aside to create more open space or pulled around for privacy. Since he was alone in the room, the curtains had been pulled back and the room was open.

I walked over to his stretcher and pulled out the curtain that separated his bed from the one beside him. Should someone else come into minor trauma, I presumed Mr. Purvis would want some privacy.

"Mr. Purvis, I'm Dr. Lesslie," I announced. "What happened to you this evening?"

He was lying comfortably, propped up by a pillow, and was holding a large gauze bandage across his chest. Blood had oozed through the cotton mesh in a few places.

"This!" he said, removing the gauze and revealing a twelve-inch gash that extended from his left nipple to the pit of his stomach. It was clearly down to muscle, but at the moment there was no bleeding. The pressure he had applied must have helped. He was obviously exasperated, and he dropped the bandage back on his chest.

It was then I noticed he was wearing black leotards and bright-red wrestling shoes. I studied his face for a moment, trying to place his name. He looked familiar, and then…it dawned on me.

"You're one of the Bruiser Brothers, aren't you?" I asked him.

He nodded without looking up at me. "Yeah, I'm Max."

The Bruiser Brothers, Max and Irv, were two of my kids' favorite wrestlers. They were some of the leading "bad guys," and for some inexplicable reason my children identified with them. Hmm. In fact, I had seen them only a few weeks ago when they had come to town. I had been the "event physician" for a big wrestling extravaganza, performing a couple of required licensing examinations before the show. I was then required to be on hand lest something go wrong. It seldom did. These were well-trained athletes and usually things were well-planned and well-choreographed.

"Max, or William, I'm a big fan of yours." I lied a little here. "Tell me more about what happened tonight."

This half of the Bruiser Brothers was enormous. He must have been at least six-foot-five, and the chart said he weighed in excess of three hundred pounds. From what I could see, most of that weight was muscle.

He shifted slightly on the stretcher, wincing from the pain.

"We were wrestling over at the Civic Center this evening," he began. "We'd just finished our bout and I was climbing out of the ring ahead of Irv. Just got down the steps when this old coot sitting on the front row jumps up with a knife and slices me. I got a glimpse of the blade—looked like a big hawkbill—but everything seemed to happen in slow motion. I couldn't get out of the way quick enough—and then this," he pointed to his chest again. "Irv jumped down the steps and coldcocked the guy."

"Wow!" I remarked. "You'd think they'd have better security."

"You'd think," he agreed. "But this guy must have been in his seventies. I'd be more worried about some of the ladies sitting around him. They really get wound up."

"What happened then?" I asked.

"I got out of there as fast as I could, that's what happened," he exclaimed. "That guy was crazy and I wasn't hangin' around. People were screamin' and Irv was yellin' and pushin' me down the aisle. And here I am."

It must have been mayhem. Those wrestling spots were always packed, and the crowd must have really reacted. And I was betting it would be on TV on the coming Saturday.

I had to check myself. Max was a patient now and not a celebrity. I needed to shift back into physician mode. Still, it was kind of interesting having him here. He wasn't a movie star or the vice president, but he was famous, at least in this part of the country. Or maybe infamous.

"Okay, let me take a look at that cut," I said, carefully removing the gauze. As I examined the wound I asked, "Has anything like this ever happened before?"

"You mean gettin' attacked after a bout? No. Not to me. I've never been cut before. Matter of fact, I've never even had stitches. But as far as the wrestlin', no, I've never been hurt. Sure, we get spit on and cussed at. That just goes with the territory. And one time, a lady hit Irv in the head with her pocketbook. But we've never really been hurt."

He paused and shook his head, then glanced down at his exposed chest.

"How bad is it?' he asked.

"Not too bad," I answered. "It'll be fine. You're going to need a few stitches—actually quite a few—but it'll do fine."

Lori came into the room and began setting up a suture tray. I put on my surgical gloves and began the process of anesthetizing the edges of the wound. It took me about forty-five minutes to clean and close the laceration, but it came together nicely and would do well.

During that forty-five minutes, Max and I chatted about the vagaries of being a professional wrestler. It sounded like a difficult lifestyle, certainly not as glamorous as you might imagine. There was a lot of work and a lot of training. And then there was the issue of being a "bad guy." Still, this was fascinating stuff.

As I was putting the finishing touches on my handiwork, I heard Lori come into the room and direct another patient to have a seat on the stretcher beside Max. Her voice came through the drawn cloth curtain.

"Sir," she told the patient, "just make yourself comfortable here and the doctor will be with you as soon as he can."

"Okay," was the muffled reply.

"Looks like you're gonna be busy tonight, Doc," Max whispered, tilting his head in the direction of the adjacent bed.

"Yeah, but it's Saturday night," I answered. "What do you expect? Especially with a bunch of wrestlers in town."

He chuckled, relaxing a little now that we were finished.

"Okay Max, we'll need to take these stitches out in about ten days," I instructed him. "Just keep this clean and dry. I'll give you something for pain in case you need it and some cream to apply a couple times a day. As far as taking out the stitches, you can have your family doctor do it, or if you're in the neighborhood, just come by here."

"Thanks, Doc. Thanks a lot. Maybe I'll see you the next time we come to town," he replied.

"Yeah, maybe so. After I tell my kids about this, I'm sure they'll insist we all go to see you and Irv wrestle. Maybe they'll get to shake your hand."

"That'd be good," he answered. "You just never know."

A nice guy, I thought. Not the scowling, brooding eye-gouger presented on TV.

I stood and stretched, taking my gloves off and tossing them into the trashcan at the foot of the stretcher.

"One of the nurses will be back in just a minute and put a bandage on that," I added in parting.

Stepping toward the door, I glanced at our newest patient. I stopped just out of Max's line of vision and stared. There on the stretcher of bed D sat an elderly man, his hair disheveled and his shirt partially pulled out of his pants. He was looking down at the floor, holding his jaw with both hands. I could see that the left side of his face was swollen and bruised. A small trickle of blood made its way down his chin from the corner of his mouth.

A movement behind me drew my attention from the old man. Max had stood up and was getting his clothes together. He was supposed to wait for the nurse, but he might be getting impatient. I glanced back at this new patient. Was this a bizarre coincidence, or was this Max's assailant? I couldn't take a chance.

Without wasting another second, I stepped into the cubicle of bed D and pulled the curtain on around to completely enclose the area. The old fella looked up at me but didn't say anything. I just stood there and smiled.

Lori walked into the room, asked Max to sit back down, and then dressed his wound.

After a few minutes she said, "There you go, Mr. Purvis, all done. Here's a prescription for something for pain and some directions for taking care of this wound. The stitches come out in ten days. Any questions?"

"No, I think that about does it, ma'am," he said. And then louder, through the curtain, "Thanks again, Doc."

"Sure thing, Max," I answered. The old man kept staring at me, silent and puzzled. I just stood there and continued to smile at him goofily. When I was sure Lori and Max were well out of the room, I relaxed and breathed a sigh of relief.

Whew! I collected myself and then addressed the patient. "I'm Dr. Lesslie. What can we do for you tonight?"

He looked up at me and slowly shook his head. As I looked closely at him, I thought he must be at least eighty. But it was a worn-out eighty, and in his wake were too many cigarettes and too much alcohol.

For a moment he didn't say anything. Maybe he had been drinking and had fallen down, or been in an auto accident and struck his face on the steering wheel.

And then, there it was.

"Doc, I was at the wrasslin' matches tonight." His words came painfully through his injured jaw. "One of them Bruiser Brothers was tusslin' with Jumbo Mullins, and Jumbo was givin' him what for. Then Max, I think it was, started gougin' Jumbo in the eyes and he got him pinned. That ain't fair, especially after the way Jumbo lost his belt to Big Al Gargantua last month. Anyway, I've been pullin' for Jumbo Mullins for about ten years and this just weren't right. Gougin' him in the eyes and all."

He paused here and rubbed his swollen jaw.

"Anyway, I was a hollerin' at the ref, but it didn't do no good. When the bout was over, they came out of the ring and I was just standin' there, mindin' my own business, and one of them boys walked by and punched me! Just outta nowhere! You can ask my nephew, Skeeter. Busted my jaw, looks like."

Funny he didn't mention anything about wielding a hawkbill knife. I knew better than to raise that point.

"Let's take a look there," I said, stepping closer and gingerly examining his bruised and puffy face. There was an obvious step-off in the mandible and I could feel it grinding when he tried to talk.

"I think you're right about your jaw," I told him. "Looks like it's probably broken. But we'll need to get some X-rays to be sure. I'll have one of the nurses bring you an ice pack for that. Just stay put here and we'll get you around to Radiology in a few minutes."

"Dang-nab that boy!" he blurted out. "If he'd a' come straight at me, I think I coulda took him. But no, he had to sucker punch me! Came outta nowhere. That ain't right."

"Well, don't worry about that now." I tried to calm him. "We need to get you taken care of. Just hold on right here."

I pulled the curtain open and stepped toward the doorway.

"That just ain't right!" he muttered again.

I glanced back and caught a glimpse of our would-be pugilist jabbing the air with a clenched fist. The sudden movement jarred his jaw and he flinched, moaned, and again grabbed his face.

I walked up the hall and reflected on what had just transpired. Here was Max Bruiser, a well-known and admired professional wrestler, felled by a wizened, anonymous old fellow, old enough to be his grandfather. I was reminded of a scene from the movie *Patton* as rendered by George C. Scott portraying George W. Patton at the end of his career. The general was telling the story of Roman conquerors who returned triumphantly from battle and proudly rode in their chariot through the city. A slave was instructed to stand behind them and repeatedly whisper a reminder of their fallibility: "All glory is fleeting."

That hasn't lost its meaning.

In further confirmation of this, I realized our elderly brawler's bright and shining moment of glory was quickly coming to an end. Two police officers had just entered the department and were heading toward minor trauma.

It was 2:00 p.m. on a Wednesday.

"Dr. Lesslie, you might want to go see the guy in room 5," Nancy remarked as we passed in the hallway. She had recently transferred to the department from the pediatric floor and was in triage today. She seemed to be a little perplexed.

Stopping, I looked at her and asked, "What's the problem?"

She turned and faced me, shaking her head. "It's an old man with chest pain. And boy, is he cantankerous. Had some left-sided chest pain for a couple of days and is just now getting it checked out. Blood pressure and pulse are okay, but he wouldn't let me check his temperature. Said he had fever and he knew it and I could just write that down."

"Did you check it anyway?" I asked, assuming that she had not given in to this patient's request. Obtaining accurate vital signs on each patient was important, in addition to being our policy. Once you clearly explained this, most people usually settled down and let you do your work.

"Nope, I didn't. And when you meet this guy, you'll understand why." She turned and walked to the back of the department. "I'm taking a break," she called over her shoulder.

When I reached the nurses' station, the clipboard of room 5 was on the top of the stack of patients to be seen. Curious, I picked it up.

> 89-year-old M with chest pain.
> BP 148/82. Pulse 92.
> Respirations 24.
> Temp ?

I was glancing over to the closed curtain of room 5 when Virginia Granger walked up.

"Know who that is?" she asked, nodding her head in the direction I was looking.

"The man in room 5?" I responded, looking once again at the clipboard.

John Abernathy. The name was familiar, but I couldn't quite place him. His address didn't help. He lived on a street in one of the older, nice neighborhoods in the middle of town.

"That's Dr. Abernathy," she explained. "I watched him come in with Nancy. Hasn't changed a bit since I last saw him. Ten years ago, maybe."

Dr. Abernathy. Now I remembered. He had been a family physician here for forty-some years and had retired a few months before my wife and I had moved to town. That was almost nineteen years ago. Shortly after that, we had crossed paths several times at social functions, and then nothing. Like Virginia, I probably hadn't seen him in ten years, maybe fifteen. And I hadn't heard much of anything about him. Every once in a while someone would tell me that Dr. Abernathy used to be their family doctor. But those people were fewer and farther between all the time.

"Did you ever know him?" Virginia asked me.

"Not really," I answered. "He had retired before I came to the ER. I've met him a few times, but I don't really know him."

"Well, you're in for a treat," she said, grinning. I didn't like the look or sound of that.

"What do you mean, 'a treat'?" I questioned.

"Let's just say that John Abernathy is set in his ways, and can be kind of ornery. Or at least he used to be. Maybe he's mellowed these past few years. But I doubt it. Why don't you go on over there and find out," she prodded, again tilting her head in the direction of room 5.

From what Nancy had said, the chances he had mellowed were slim.

"Hmm," I sighed. "I guess I'll just do that."

I picked up the clipboard and was turning in that direction when Virginia added, "Oh, and I think I remember hearing his wife died about two years ago. Don't think he has any family in the area, so he might be all alone. Thought you might need to know that."

"Thanks, Virginia," I told her. "That might be helpful."

Pulling aside the curtain of his room, I found Dr. John Abernathy sitting bolt upright on the stretcher. His arms were folded across his chest and there was an unpleasant scowl on his face.

"Do I know you?" he asked, more accusing than questioning.

I pulled the curtain closed behind me and sat down on the stool beside his gurney.

"Dr. Abernathy, I'm Dr. Lesslie," I said, introducing myself. "I think we've met a few times in the past."

He studied my face. "Hmm, you do look a little familiar," he conceded, a little less harsh now. "You work here in the ER?"

John Abernathy appeared younger than his eighty-nine years. He still had a full head of wavy gray hair, and his eyes were clear, blue, and piercing. He was a slender man and appeared fit. He had donned a hospital gown but had kept his T-shirt on, making a quiet but unambiguous statement of defiance and autonomy.

"Yes, I'm an ER physician here at the hospital. This is where I work," I explained.

"Don't have a private practice in town?" he pursued. It occurred to me that John might not be familiar with the practice of emergency medicine and with the staffing of emergency departments with full-time physicians. It had been twenty years since he had been in practice, and things were different now.

"No, I don't have a practice in town. This is where I hang out. After medical school I trained in emergency medicine. It's a specialty now, just like family practice or surgery. You were a family doctor, weren't you?" I asked him, becoming more comfortable now that we seemed to be finding some common ground.

"Yeah, yeah," he answered, stroking his chin and staring up at the ceiling light. "I was a family doctor for forty-three years." Then he looked straight at me again. "Worked right here in this hospital, ya know. Delivered babies, had patients in the ICU with heart attacks, strokes, all of that. Changed some since then," he added, glancing around the room. "Probably couldn't find my way to the cafeteria, much less the ICU."

I began to remember more about John Abernathy, or at least what I had heard about him from other physicians and friends in town. He had been one of the first GPs in the area and had developed the largest practice in the county. By all accounts he was a good physician and people trusted him. They didn't necessarily like him, though. He had a reputation of being blunt and unyielding. And he made it clear that he was the physician and the one in charge. There apparently was little negotiation when it came to treatment decisions or alternatives.

Outside of his office and the hospital, he was still "the doctor." That was his accepted and expected persona. Should some unsuspecting waitress or clerk address him as "Mr. Abernathy," he was quick to inform them he was a physician. "That would be Dr. Abernathy, young man."

"Yeah, come to think of it, I've heard something about you ER doctors. TV show, or something. Tell you what, though. When I was in practice, we took care of our own. Didn't have a doctor spending all of his time in the emergency room. If someone came to the hospital, the nurse in the ER would call us, and if it was something she could handle, she'd just send 'em home or to the office. Something more serious, we'd just stop what we were doing and come on in. Didn't matter whether it was day or night."

He paused, nodding. Then he added, "Yep, we took care of our own."

I thought better of informing him that we were now seeing more than 150 people a day in the ER, as opposed to the 10 or 12 per day who had come through twenty-five years ago. Things *had* changed.

"You know," he went on, "one of the medical wings upstairs is named after me." He studied my face for an acknowledging response.

I struggled momentarily and then suddenly remembered.

Nodding my head and smiling, I said, "Yes, the Abernathy Wing. It's up on the fourth floor. It's a postsurgical area now, but it's still the Abernathy Wing."

A look of satisfaction appeared on his face and he said, "Yep. Named after me. Been a while since I've been up there."

That was a good thing. Though I was glad I had been able to retrieve this information from my remote memory banks, he didn't need to see the plaque bearing his name. It was scratched, tarnished, and mostly hidden by a plastic plant placed in front of it. Its existence had stuck in my mind because of my curiosity about its origin. Now I knew.

"Yep, the Abernathy Wing," he repeated.

Standing up, I placed his clipboard on the counter behind me and asked, "Dr. Abernathy, tell me about this chest pain you've been having."

He looked up and pointed to the left side of his chest, about a handbreadth below his armpit. "Hurts right here when I take a deep breath or lie down. I've had some cough for a couple of days and now a fever. Don't know how high, but I'd guess about 102. I think it's probably pneumonia."

That would be my hunch as well.

"We'll need to get an accurate temperature here, don't you think?" I asked, as benignly as possible.

He looked askance at me and then nodded his head. "I suppose so," he conceded.

Lori had pulled the room curtain aside and stuck her head through the opening. "Everything okay here?" she asked, looking at me. "Do you need anything, Mr. Abernathy?"

He rolled his eyes and was about to speak. I cut him off with, "Lori, we're fine. But would you tell the secretary we'll need some blood work, blood cultures, and a chest X-ray? Thanks."

She left the room. "Does sound like pneumonia, doesn't it?" I remarked. "We'll see what your chest X-ray looks like and if it is, you need to plan on staying in the hospital."

"Thought I might," he answered, frowning and gesturing to a small overnight bag on the floor. "Brought a few things with me, just in case."

Twenty minutes later, we had our answer. Dr. John Abernathy's chest X-ray was hanging on the view box just outside the observation room. He had a large pneumonia in his left lung, explaining the fever, the cough, and the chest pain. At his age this was a serious problem, but with antibiotics and fluids he should be better in a few days.

Virginia Granger walked over and stood beside me. "Pneumonia?" she asked, pointing to the irregular whited-out area in his left chest.

"Yeah, and a pretty good one," I answered.

She looked at me over the top of her bifocals. "I guess you found out he's an interesting bird," she said. "He's been through a lot, I understand. I have a friend who lives on the same street and she tells me that after his wife died a few years ago, he mainly stays in the house. Doesn't get out much at all. And no family here in town." She paused and then, "Pretty lonely, I suppose. And if he has to be admitted to the hospital, he's not going to like it."

Not many people liked the idea of having to go into a hospital, but I was curious about her comment. "Why do you say that?"

"Well, Dr. Lesslie, you may think I'm 'old school,'" she said while adjusting the starched nursing cap seated squarely on the top of her head, "but John Abernathy is *really* 'old school.' He comes from an era when the family doctor was one of the pillars of the community. Everybody knew him and respected him. He couldn't go anywhere without people coming up and shaking his hand and saying they'd never forget how he'd helped their mother, or wife, or son. That's just the way it was. And now…" she sighed, shaking her head. "Well, now…you didn't even recognize him, did you?"

"No, I—"

"And that's okay," she interrupted. "He's been out of the mainstream for a lot of years. I was thinking a minute ago that I'm the only one here in the department who knows who he is. Maybe one of only a handful in the whole hospital. Sorta sad, don't you think?"

It was a rhetorical question, and I waited as she mused. Then she continued, "Sad because he built his whole life around that idea, of his being the town doctor. And now, what does all that matter? Who cares anymore, except maybe him? He's just kind of lost out there, drifting."

She was right, of course. Treating John's pneumonia would be the most straightforward part of his care.

I needed to inform Dr. Abernathy of his diagnosis and that we would be admitting him to the hospital. I was just stepping into room 5 when I overhead Frank, one of our lab techs. "Okay, buddy, this might stick just a little." He was preparing to draw blood from

Dr. Abernathy's left arm. John had winced when Frank said this, but it was not from the anticipated poke of the needle. It was from being addressed as "buddy." That had stung, and I wasn't sure how he was going to respond.

To my surprise, the wince faded to a look of resignation, and he remained silent. His shoulders slumped, and for the first time, he looked like an old man.

My next shift was two days later. Mid-morning, I had the chance to go upstairs and check on some of the patients we had admitted when I had last worked. I especially wanted to check on John Abernathy.

"302," the unit secretary told me. "You'll be his first visitor."

Room 302 was near the nursing station and I only had a short walk. Pushing the door open, I tapped on it lightly. "Dr. Abernathy?"

Hearing no response, I stepped into the room. John was sitting in bed, reclining at 45 degrees, with his head supported by a pillow. The wall-mounted television had not been turned on, and he was staring out the window.

He turned as I entered. "Hello, Dr. Lesslie," he said. "Came by to make sure I hadn't gone AWOL?"

"Yes, as a matter of fact," I responded, smiling. "And to see if you needed anything."

"Well, thanks," he said. "Actually, I think I'm doing pretty well. No more fever and the chest pain is much better. That young whippersnapper of an internist tells me I might be able to go home in a day or two. Still wet behind the ears, but he seems to know what he's doing," he conceded.

"But the food here is terrible," he continued. "Used to be better. Or at least I think it did." He paused then, a perplexed look on his face. "But you know, maybe it's always been terrible. How would I know? I've never been a patient before this."

We talked for a few minutes and then it was time for me to head back to the department.

"Dr. Abernathy, take care of yourself and get better," I told him. "You're in good hands, so just do what they ask you to do, okay?"

"You must have been talking to Virginia Granger," he replied sardonically. "Always had to keep an eye on that one."

I laughed. "Yeah, Virginia has told me a thing or two about you. And yes, you do have to keep an eye on her."

I was pulling the door open to leave when John Abernathy spoke quietly behind me. "Dr. Lesslie...Robert. If you get the chance tomorrow, and I'm still here...would you come by again and we'll chat? But only if you get the chance."

"I'll make the chance, John. If you're still here and not at home," I told him.

"Thanks."

The door closed behind me, and I stood in the hallway for a moment, thinking.

"Excuse us," an orderly spoke from behind me. "Comin' through."

He was pushing a wheelchair occupied by a teenager. The boy was dressed in his street clothes and was probably being discharged. As they rolled by, the door across the hall opened. Two nurses walked out of the room, looked over at me, nodded, and continued their conversation.

"I can't believe she can get away with that," one of the nurses said. Then their conversation faded and became unintelligible as they walked off toward the nursing station.

The overhead intercom crackled. "Dr. Smith, report to Radiology *stat*. Dr. Smith to Radiology."

On it went—life, time, people. For another minute I just watched and listened.

7

Demon Rum

Wine is a mocker and beer a brawler; who-
ever is led astray by them is not wise.

—Proverbs 20:1

U nder the influence of alcohol, people do and say things they
would never dream of when sober. We see this demonstrated
every day in the ER. Sadly, these actions cannot be undone, nor can
these words ever be unsaid. Wine is indeed a mocker.

The voices behind the curtain of room 2 had been quiet enough at the
beginning. The mother and father of our fifteen-year-old patient had
arrived in the department and had just entered the cubicle. They were
checking on their son, asking how he was, making sure he was okay.

EMS had brought Johnny to the ER after he had been involved in
a minor auto accident. He had recently received his learner's permit,
and it seems he and a couple of friends had clandestinely taken one
of the family cars out for a spin. One of the older boys had managed
to procure two six-packs of beer, and off they went.

It was three o'clock on a warm May afternoon, and it wasn't long
before the beer was consumed. The group decided to tour several
neighborhoods near Johnny's home, with him woozily at the wheel.
He failed to negotiate a sharp turn in Forest Hills Estates and went
on to carve a new driveway through an azalea bed. Then he smashed

a large, concrete birdbath before finally wedging the sedan between two pine trees.

Johnny had banged his forehead on the steering wheel. It was nothing serious, just a few bruises and a small laceration that would need to be repaired. When he tried to exit the car, he found the driver's door firmly jammed by one of the trees. Looking around, he realized his friends were nowhere to be found. They had managed to climb through one of the back windows and had taken off.

Through the fog of his five beers, the young man was beginning to understand his plight. He shuddered as he looked up through the shattered windshield of his father's car. There, on the front steps, stood the lady of the house. She was in her mid-sixties, wearing a floral housedress and a navy-blue apron. She stood stone still, staring at the wreckage of her yard, her fists angrily planted on her hips.

Johnny just shook his head, slumped in the seat, and waited. Within minutes, the police and EMS had arrived.

The voices behind the curtain were becoming a little louder, a little more agitated. It seemed to mainly be the father, but occasionally we could hear the son as well.

"What…! Who were…No, you just hold on…!" A few words and phrases carried across the department. Outbursts and unintelligible pieces of sentences, but clearly the temperature in room 2 was rising.

Amy Conners looked up from her logbook. "You might need to go check on things in there," she said to me, tilting her head in the direction of the voices. "Think I should call Security?"

"No, we won't need that," I assured her. "They'll calm down in a minute. But I'll go over and have a few words with them."

I was reasonably confident in my assessment of the situation. I had briefly spoken to Johnny's parents when they arrived in the ER. They seemed calm enough, though obviously concerned. His father was a professional of some description and was dressed in a business suit. His mother was tall, slender, and very quiet, letting her husband ask the questions for the two of them.

As I made my way to room 2, the sounds coming from behind the curtain took an ominous turn. The distance was only a matter of a few steps. But in the moments it took to cross that brief space, I clearly heard the father yelling at Johnny and Johnny responding with slurred expletives. Then came the sounds of scuffling, of the stretcher being pushed against the wall, and the grunts of two men struggling with each other. Then a woman's scream. And silence.

"Hold on here!" I demanded, pulling the curtain aside and stepping into the room.

I will never forget the bizarre and troubling scene played out before me. Johnny's father stood nearest me, his fists clenched by his side, his hair tousled and his tie flipped over his shoulder. He stood glaring at his son. Johnny was standing only a foot or so from his father. His head was hanging down, and his T-shirt was rumpled and pulled out of his jeans. A thread of blood trickled down his forehead from the still-open laceration. His arms hung limply by his side and he stared at the floor. He swayed a little from side to side, still quite drunk.

Then I noticed his mother. She stood cowering in the back corner of the room, pressing herself against the end of the stretcher and the countertop. She held her face with both hands, her eyes staring. She was looking from her son to her husband, and back to her son again. Tears streamed down her cheeks. The only sound in the room was her muffled sobbing.

Her jaw had been shattered by Johnny's punch.

An operation would repair the fractured bone, but that blow could never be taken back. It would be a part of this family, of this relationship, forever.

Later, at the nurses' station, I looked up from the clipboard of room 2 and put down my pen. I stared at the closed curtain across from me. I had just remembered something. Next Sunday would be Mother's Day.

It was 10:30 on a Friday evening. Sometime between six o'clock and midnight usually marks the official beginning of the weekend. Our volume will pick up, and the nature of our patient encounters begins to change. It's not a coincidence that this time of the week marks the beginning of an increase in alcohol consumption. More wrecks, more falls, more fistfights. Everybody seems to be having a big time.

This particular overnight shift had thus far proven to be typical. We had already had a knifing and a moped accident. The knifing was a superficial laceration of a young man's buttocks, inflicted as he attempted to escape the grasp of an acquaintance he had just whacked over the head with a beer bottle. The moped accident was more interesting. Three large individuals had attempted to ride this small conveyance at the same time, convinced they would be able to jump a low rock wall on the edge of a field. Gravity had reared its ugly head, and I would have a few of theirs to suture. Nothing serious.

Jeff and I were standing at the nurses' station talking about this daredevil trio, when the automatic ambulance doors hissed open, announcing the arrival of new business. We both looked up to see one of our EMS units wheeling two stretchers into the department.

Denton Roberts was guiding the first gurney into the ER, and he stopped adjacent to where we stood. On the stretcher was a thirty-year-old woman, awake and looking around. Her face was pale, her expression anxious, and there were a number of abrasions on her forehead. Pieces of glass were scattered through her long blonde hair.

"What happened here?" I asked Denton, reflexively taking her wrist and checking her pulse. It was a little fast, but strong and regular. An IV had been inserted into the back of her other hand and was connected to a bag of saline that hung from a pole at the head of the stretcher. I could see it was flowing wide open.

"Auto accident out on Highway 5," he answered. He nodded behind him at the following stretcher. "The guy there was driving. Both of them have had a little too much to drink. Actually, he's pretty soused and he went off the road, into a ditch. She's complaining of belly pain and he has some back pain. Both of their vital signs are okay.

No loss of consciousness. She was still seat-belted in the car. When we got there, he was walking around in the middle of the road. Put 'em both in full spinal protocol and started IVs. He looks all right, but you're gonna have fun," he finished, with a wry smile.

"What do you mean?" I looked in the direction of our second victim.

"Well, let's just say he's not a happy camper," Denton added, nodding.

If I had any doubt as to his meaning, I was quickly enlightened. "Full spinal protocol" meant that a person would be strapped down on a rigid backboard, arms by their sides, legs straight out, and head and neck strapped in place, allowing no movement. This was necessary to protect someone with obvious or potential spinal injuries. But it was also very uncomfortable.

"Get me off this thing!"

Sandy Green, Denton's partner, was struggling with our next guest. Sandy was trying to guide the stretcher into the department with one hand and attempting to keep the patient from falling off with the other.

"And get this thing out of my arm!" He was referring to the IV that had been placed in his right elbow, which he was clumsily attempting to grasp. Sandy needed another hand, maybe two.

"Jimmy, you be still and let them help you." The calm and plaintive admonition came from the young woman in front of me.

"I don' need no help! I need to get outta here!"

Jeff had already moved toward the second stretcher and was trying to help Sandy maintain order.

"Hold on a minute, Jimmy," he instructed him. "Let us just get you to a bed and check you over, and then you can get out of here, okay?"

"I don' need to be checked over! Just lemme get up from here!" was the response.

I looked up at Denton. "Take them back to minor trauma. A and B. I don't think there's anyone in there right now."

"Okay, Doc," he answered, and he started down the hall with his patient.

As Sandy came by the nurses' station, I patted him on the shoulder. He was a large man, and he was sweating profusely. "Just follow Denton," I told him.

He nodded without saying a word.

I glanced down at his patient. He was probably in his early thirties, dressed in blue jeans and a T-shirt, and he had on running shoes. His long jet-black hair looked dyed and was unkempt. On his right forearm was a large tattoo. The name "Amanda" was emblazoned in black ink over a large red heart. Other than this tattoo, I didn't see a mark on him—no scratch, no blood. Nothing.

"Sheryl!" he called out. "Where they takin' you?"

Sheryl? I glanced again at the tattoo. Hmm. Love is a fickle thing.

"Just relax, Jimmy." Sandy tried to calm him. "We're going with her. Just hold on."

They moved off down the hallway, with Jimmy eloquently expressing his displeasure with the current circumstances.

"I told you to get me off this thing!"

While I finished up with two other patients, Jeff made an assessment of our auto accident victims. He walked up to the counter with their charts in his hands.

"Finally got Jimmy calmed down," he told me. "I don't know how long he'll stay that way, though. He's pretty drunk. And pretty obnoxious. He's on bed A. Looks okay, just complainin' of low back pain. But he's movin' around pretty good."

I finished up the chart I was working on and put it into the "Discharge" basket. "Good. And what about her?"

"I don't know. I think she's got somethin' goin' on," Jeff said. "Heart rate's about 110, and her belly is tender. Blood pressure is 110 over 70. Everything else seems okay. I upped her IV."

"Good," I responded. "I'll go take a look."

I had worked with Jeff long enough to know that when he thought something was going on, it usually was. He didn't overreact, and he'd seen a bunch.

Tammy, one of our evening nurse techs, was in minor trauma with our two patients. They were on adjacent beds with a curtain separating them. Jimmy was lying quietly for the moment, his eyes closed. I walked over to bed B.

"How are you feeling, Sheryl?" I asked.

She looked up at me. "Not too good, Doc. What's wrong with me?"

"We're going to find out," I told her, as I gently began to palpate her abdomen. Jeff was right. It was tender and was becoming distended.

"Does this hurt over here?" I asked, pushing down on her left upper belly, just below the rib cage. The spleen lives here, and I was suspicious it might have been injured in the accident. If it was ruptured and bleeding, that might account for the distension.

"Ooh! Yes! That hurts!" she cried out, but still remained calm.

I stopped pressing and took my hands off.

"Okay, we won't do that again," I told her. "But it looks like you might have injured something in your abdomen, maybe your spleen, so we're going to get a CT scan as fast as we can. I'm also going to have one of our surgeons take a look at you."

"Is it bad, Doctor?" she asked.

"Well, it depends on what we find," I answered. "But we'll get it fixed, whatever it is. Okay?"

"Okay," she sighed, and closed her eyes.

Before I turned to leave I asked, "Oh, and one other thing. Have you had anything to drink tonight?"

I could smell alcohol on her breath, but she didn't appear to be intoxicated.

She didn't hesitate with her answer. "Just one beer. That's all."

I made a note on the chart, believing her. The usual response in the ER to this question is "Two beers, Doc." It doesn't matter how smashed a person appears, it's always "two beers." I suppose the honesty switch gets turned off when your blood alcohol reaches a certain level.

Moving to bed A, I made a quick assessment of her partner. He was snoring now, and he barely opened his eyes as I examined him. His vital signs were completely normal and I could find no evidence of any significant injury.

I did manage to rouse him enough to ask a question. "How much have you had to drink tonight, Jimmy?"

"Two beers," was the slurred response. I didn't write that down.

At the nurses' station I asked the unit secretary to see if Tom Daniels was in the hospital. He was the surgeon on call tonight, and if he was around, I wanted to catch him before he went home.

A few minutes later she picked up the phone, then covered the mouthpiece and said, "Dr. Daniels is in the OR, finishing up a case. Do you need to talk with him? It's the OR supervisor."

"No," I told her. "Just ask him to stop by the ER when he's finished. Tell him I might have a spleen for him."

She relayed the message and hung up. "He should be here in about ten minutes," she told me.

They were ready for Sheryl in CT, but ten more minutes wouldn't make much difference. We could wait.

"Jeff, Jimmy in minor trauma will need a urine," I instructed him. "Just check for blood. We'll make sure he didn't injure his kidneys and then he should be able to go."

"Sure," he answered. "But he'll have to use a urinal. I don't think he can walk."

"You're right," I said. "Good luck with that. You may not even be able to wake him up."

Jeff went into the supply room and came out with one of our stainless steel urinals. He walked down the hall toward minor trauma, and I was a few steps behind him.

I was about to turn into the four-bed room when I caught sight of Tom Daniels coming around the corner in the back of the department. He still had on his surgical scrubs and cap.

"Long night?" I asked him.

"Long day," was his response. "It's been nonstop. The OR said you might have something for me. A possible spleen?"

"Yeah, she's right in here."

I led him into minor trauma and noticed Jeff trying to rouse our somnolent patient in bed A. We moved past that bed and behind the curtain separating him from bed B.

"Sheryl, this is Dr. Daniels," I said to her. "He's the surgeon on call tonight, and I wanted him to take a look at you."

Tom walked over to the side of the stretcher. "Sheryl, is it? I'm Tom Daniels. Dr. Lesslie tells me you've been having a pretty rough night."

He proceeded to examine her, asking questions as he proceeded. As he palpated her abdomen she moaned and shifted herself on the bed. He looked up at me and nodded.

"Sheryl, I agree with Dr. Lesslie. Something's going on inside your belly and we're probably going to need to go to the operating room to find out what that is. We'll get the CT scan first, and then decide on a plan. Okay?"

"Okay, Doctor," she answered. "I just want to stop hurting."

As she was saying these last words, I heard some grunting from behind me on the other side of the curtain. I had been aware of some unusual noises behind us, but this was louder and more ominous. Then, "Ooh! Enough!"

Then more grunting and the sounds of a struggle. Suddenly, the urinal flew across the room, clanging loudly against the ceiling light over bed C, then the IV pole in the corner, and finally the floor. It spun around a few times and came to a stop.

Jeff had been trying to get a urine specimen from Jimmy, and Jimmy was not being compliant. When he had first been roused from his alcoholic slumber, he had struck out with a fist, catching Jeff cleanly on the left ear. Then he'd kicked him twice, once in the stomach and once on his thigh. The final straw came when he grabbed Jeff's forearm and drew blood with his fingernails.

Tom Daniels looked at me. I turned, pulling back the curtain.

The grunting was coming from Jimmy, and for good reason. For a moment I watched, mesmerized. Jimmy was still flat on his back on the bed. But Jeff was straddling him, his big left hand pressing down on his chest. Every minute or so, Jimmy would squirm and struggle and try to kick him.

"Aaaaah! Get off me!"

Then he tried to spit into Jeff's face. Jeff was too quick and managed to dodge the liquid projectile. But Jimmy's action led to an unexpected and unwanted result. Jeff's right hand had been poised just above Jimmy's face, and now he quickly thumped him across the bridge of his nose. It was not a forceful blow, not enough to break the skin or any bones. But it was enough to get his attention. It smarted and Jimmy let out a yelp.

"Ooh, get off me!"

The cycle repeated itself. For a few seconds, Jimmy would be still. Then he would start squirming again, trying to kick Jeff. And once again he tried to spit on him. Then a quick pop to the face.

"Ooh! Somebody get him off me!"

It was then I noticed Jeff's eyes. I had seen him angry before, but fortunately not very often. It usually took a lot to provoke him. His face would turn red, he would get very quiet, and then it would blow over. But this time it was different. Jimmy must have found the right buttons tonight. Jeff's eyes were mere slits and his pupils were pinpoints. I shuddered.

Here was one of our best nurses, a hulk of a man. And he was strong. Yet I had seen these huge hands gently hold a two-month-old and deftly start an IV in its tiny hand. And I had watched as he almost tenderly lifted a ninety-year-old woman from her wheelchair onto an examining bed. But I never dared say that to him.

Tonight he was a different person—someone I hadn't expected to see, and someone who scared me a little.

"Doc!" Jimmy had noticed me standing beside the stretcher. "Get him off me!"

Jeff still straddled Jimmy's body, his right hand poised just above his face.

I glanced at Jeff but he was staring intently at his patient.

I looked again at the pleading man on the bed. "Jimmy, if you'll behave yourself, I'll try to get him off you. But you'll have to behave. No more kicking and no more spitting."

"Okay! Okay! Just get him off me!" he replied.

Jeff was not moving. He seemed not to be impressed with Jimmy's sincerity or newfound contrition. I wasn't so sure myself.

"Jimmy, I'll try to do that, but you'll have to promise to calm down. Do you hear me?" I asked him. "No more kicking."

Tom Daniels had walked over and now stood at my shoulder. He surveyed the scene while stroking his chin, an amused look on his face. "Make him cross his heart and pinky swear," he whispered in my ear.

I looked at him and frowned. "Tom, I'm trying to save this man's life," I chided.

"Please, Doc, get him off!" Jimmy was wearing down, and I thought it would be safe to rescue him.

"Jeff, it's time to let him up. Come on, hop off that bed," I tried to persuade him.

Without a word and with an unexpected agility, Jeff sprang to the floor. He walked over to the corner of the room to pick up the urinal, pressing the wrinkles out of his scrubs with the palms of his hands.

Jimmy wasted no time and certainly not this opportunity. He sat up on the bed and dangled his feet over the edge, trying to locate the floor.

"I've had enough! You guys are crazy! I'm outta here!"

"Jimmy, just calm down," I told him. "We'll be glad to check you out, but you're going to have to behave. Just keep your seat."

It was to no avail. Jimmy was determined to get himself out of our department.

"I said I'm outta here and I am!" He got to his feet and with better balance than I had anticipated, he walked to the doorway. He stumbled once and turned in the direction of Jeff. "You're one crazy #$%#&!" And then he was gone.

Tom Daniels looked in Jeff's direction. "Jeff, you okay?" he asked.

"Mm-hmm," was the response. He was okay. He was not back to himself yet, but he was okay. He walked over to bed B. "She need anything else right now?" he asked us, his face still red from his recent activity.

"No," Tom replied. "Just keep her IV going wide open and let's get that CT as fast as we can."

Sheryl had her CT scan: a ruptured spleen and probable torn intestine. Thirty minutes later, she was in the OR and had just been put to sleep.

I was alone, sitting behind the nurses' station. The door to triage opened and an elderly man came into the ER. He walked over to the counter and slapped both hands down in front of him.

"Are you the doctor?" he asked me.

"Yes, I'm Dr. Lesslie," I answered. "What can I do for you?"

"I'm Stanley Wells, Jimmy's daddy," he answered. I sat up a little straighter in my chair. "And I wanted to have a word with you."

I studied him for a moment. I guessed he was fifty-five, maybe sixty years old, though he looked much older. His face was worn and wrinkled and he stood hunched over. Too many hard days and harder nights. And too many years with Jimmy.

"Yes, what about Jimmy?" Several thoughts came to my mind. He had collapsed in the waiting room. He had gone home to get a gun. He was calling the police. But it was none of the above.

"I just want to apologize. I know he's a handful. Obnoxious young buck, especially when he's been drinkin'. And he's pretty drunk tonight," he told me. "I understand he caused quite a ruckus back here."

"Well, he did get a little rowdy, Mr. Wells," I said, taken a little off guard but definitely relieved. "I guess you know he was involved in a pretty serious auto accident?"

"Yeah, I've already talked to the police about it," he answered. "How is that woman, Sheryl? I think he met her at the bingo parlor last week. Seems like a nice girl. She gonna be okay?"

"Well, she's in the operating room right now. She has some internal damage and bleeding, but she's in good hands and I think she'll be alright," I answered.

"Doggone that boy! I told him a hundert times to stop drinkin', and 'specially not to drive when he has been. But he don't listen. Never has, and I guess he never will. Three DUIs, and now this. I don't know what I'm gonna do with him."

He paused and studied the backs of his gnarly hands.

"Anyway, Doc, I just wanted to come back here and apologize for the way my boy acted. I hope he didn't hurt no one."

"No, he didn't. But we were trying to check him over for any injuries when he took off. I think he's going to be okay, but if he wants to be looked at, just bring him back here."

"Thanks, Doc, but I doubt if he wants to come back in here. He's sittin' out in the waiting room with the police and I think he's gonna be leavin' with them. He's in some trouble this time. He ain't got no driver's license, and he's already smarted off to the cops a coupla times."

He paused and shook his head. "I think he's okay though. He ain't complainin' of any pain or anything. But if he changes his mind, I'll bring him straight back."

"You do that, Mr. Wells," I told him. "If you have any questions about Jimmy, just bring him back or give us a call."

He stood straight up now, and put his hands in his pockets.

"Okay, and thanks. But like I said, I'm real sorry for the way he acted out."

"Don't worry," I said. "And I hope you have a better night."

I watched as he walked back out through triage.

Twenty minutes later, Jeff stood with me at the nurses' station. He was at my left elbow and was writing Sheryl's chart, making sure all we had done was duly noted. Moments earlier, Tom Daniels had relayed a message to us through the OR scrub nurse. Sheryl was fine. Her spleen had indeed been ruptured and had needed to be removed. Everything had gone well and he was now closing up. Maybe Sheryl would learn something tonight. Not necessarily about meeting guys at a bingo parlor, but maybe about not riding with someone who had been drinking. It would be a costly lesson.

I heard footsteps behind me, coming from the triage entrance.

"Doc." The voice sounded familiar, but the tone was different. I turned around to see Mr. Wells once again, now standing before me.

"Yes, Mr. Wells. What can I help you with?" I asked him. "Does Jimmy want to be seen now?"

Jeff kept writing on the chart in front of him, never looking up.

"Not exactly, Doc," Mr. Wells announced, a perceptible edge to his voice. "I want to talk with you a minute."

"Sure," I replied. "What's the problem?"

"Well, I just went out and was talkin' with Jimmy. The police have taken him down to the station, but before he left, he told me somethin' that was pretty disturbin'."

"And what was that?" I was afraid I might already know the answer.

"Jimmy told me that when he was back here the doctor jumped on him and beat him up. Held him down and kept hittin' him in the nose."

He paused and stepped closer to me, his face only inches from mine. And he was angry.

"Now I know that Jimmy can get obnoxious when he's been drinkin', but that ain't no call for you to beat up my son, Doc. What with him bein' under the influence and unable to protect hisself and all. That just ain't right and I'm here to complain about it."

He stood with his hands on his hips, indignant.

Jeff never looked up from his work. He just kept writing.

"Mr. Wells, let me say a couple of things," I began. "First of all, I am the only doctor on duty tonight. And secondly, I did not hold your son down and I certainly did not hit him in the nose."

"Well, somebody did!" he exclaimed. "I can see the red marks on his nose, and Jimmy said a doctor done it, and he don't lie to me. Well…not usually."

"Let me say it again, Mr. Wells, and I know you're upset, but I'm the only doctor back here, and I did not beat up your son."

I tried to be as convincing as possible, but he was not yielding.

"Now listen to me, Doc—" he started again.

But I interrupted with, "Mr. Wells, let me tell you what happened back here. We were trying to evaluate your son, to check him out and make sure everything was okay. But he became obnoxious, as you said earlier. And he started cursing and spitting and kicking. And finally, one of the nurses had to sit on him and make him behave."

I peeked at Jeff out of the corner of my eye. He had stopped writing, but he didn't move. He just looked down at the chart on the countertop.

Mr. Wells backed away. He was obviously trying to digest this new information. Then he held his hands outstretched in front of him, palms up.

"You mean to tell me that a nurse beat up my boy?" he asked, incredulous.

"That's right, Mr. Wells," I told him. "A nurse had to make him behave."

Jeff didn't move.

"You mean a nurse…" he muttered, visibly slumping.

"Yes, Mr. Wells, a nurse had to make your son behave," I confirmed.

He stood staring at the floor, silent for a moment.

"A nurse beat up my boy. Well, I'll be doggoned."

He never once looked in Jeff's direction.

Then Mr. Wells straightened himself, held out his hand to me, and said, "Well, Doc, I want to thank you for trying to help my boy. And I apologize again for his behavior. I know ya'll did all you could for him."

I shook his hand. "No problem, Mr. Wells. I hope that everything goes alright for you and your boy."

He nodded, turned, and shuffled toward the triage door.

"I can't believe it," he muttered. "A dang nurse beat up my boy."

He stepped through the door and was gone.

"Quick! Get me a number 4 airway tube!"

We were going to lose the eight-month-old if we couldn't secure his airway.

"And get respiratory down here, *stat!*" I added.

Less then a minute earlier, EMS had burst through the ambulance entrance doors, carrying this young child. "Head injury," Denton, one of the paramedics, had called out, heading straight to major trauma. "Barely breathing and not much of a pulse!"

Lori and I had hurried into the room and quickly assessed the infant. Denton had laid him on the stretcher and then taken a step back. He was breathing hard and was obviously upset. The baby had no muscle tone and only a faint, slow heart rate. There was no immediately obvious injury, but I quickly noticed that his pupils were markedly dilated and deviated to the right. That was not a good sign.

Within minutes, he had been intubated and a respiratory therapist was carefully forcing air into his lungs with an ambu bag. Lori had an IV going and was making sure he was not too chilled. His oxygen saturation had improved with the ventilation of his lungs, as had his heart rate and cardiac output.

With a sigh of relief, I stood up straight and looked around the room for the delivering paramedic. Things were stable for the moment and I needed a better idea of what was going on here.

I located him at the foot of the stretcher and I asked, "Denton, what's this about a head injury? Do you have any idea what happened?"

Denton was making notes on the EMS clipboard. He looked up and said, "We got a call to Jones Avenue, about a child having trouble breathing. When we got there, well, it was absolute chaos. There must have been ten or twelve people in the house and they were all screamin' and hollerin'. Someone said he fell and hit his head. Couldn't get any sense out of any of them. I think they were all drunk. Anyway, his parents were behind us in a truck and should be here any minute."

He stopped and resumed writing up his report. Looking up again he added, "Oh, and Doc, the parents are drunk too."

We would need a CT scan of the child's head, and Lori was going to the nurses' station to get it ordered. As she opened the door, three people bowled their way into the room, pushing her back against the counter.

"Where's my baby? Where's JJ?" This came from one of the two women. Denton was right. She was clearly intoxicated. She staggered as she made her way to the side of the stretcher.

"How is my baby?" she asked, struggling to focus her blurred vision on the small body lying before her. She was barefooted, as were her two companions. Like them, she wore cut-off blue jeans and a dirty T-shirt. "Is he gonna be alright?"

Lori had called for the CT scan from the open doorway and now came back to the stretcher. She was trying to calm these visitors and restore order. I tried to explain the situation in terms they would understand, and tell them what our immediate plans were.

The mother's name was Maylees, and it turned out the other woman, Jenny, was Maylees's sister and JJ's aunt. The man was in his mid-twenties. His name was Bubba, and he was Maylees's common-law husband. We assumed he was also the father of the baby.

Jenny had walked over and wrapped her arms around her sister, though this didn't provide much support. They listed to one side and had to take a quick step to right themselves. Bubba stood back from the stretcher, leaning against the wall. His eyelids were half closed and his head was bobbing. He was also obviously drunk. I wondered who had driven the truck.

"Maylees, can you tell me what happened to your son?" I asked.

She glanced in Bubba's direction and then said, "Yeah, we had some friends over this afternoon, and JJ was in the kitchen and must have tripped and fell and hit his head."

"Yeah, that's right," Jenny slurred in agreement.

I was distracted by a movement in the corner of the room and looked over to Bubba. In spite of his alcohol content, he was really quick. A cigarette was dangling from the corner of his mouth and before I could say anything, he had taken his lighter from his pants pocket and was clicking it. A small flame appeared at the tip of the lighter, and he was leaning forward, his hands cupping the cigarette.

"Hold on there, Bubba," I called out. "You can't smoke that thing in here. Put that lighter out."

Responding to his name, he looked up. "Huh? Oh, okay," he said sluggishly. He extinguished the lighter, took the cigarette out of his mouth, and carefully placed it behind his right ear.

Now, what had Maylees just told me? She had been telling me how JJ had hurt his head.

"He tripped and fell in the kitchen?" I asked, resuming my questioning.

Lori looked over at me, a doubtful expression on her face. Why that look? Wait a minute…JJ was seven-and-a-half months of age, still an infant. Unless he was a prodigy, he probably wasn't walking. This answer didn't make sense. Something else was going on here. I nodded to Lori.

Before I could ask another question, two radiology techs came into the room.

"We're ready for him in CT," one of them reported.

"You can all wait in here if you want," I told the three. "This should not take long, and as soon as we know something, I'll let you know."

Maylees and Jenny backed away from the stretcher, making room for the techs. "You take care of him, now," Maylees told them.

"Yeah, take care of him," Jenny echoed.

Forty minutes later we had our answer. I had walked around to the Radiology Department and was reviewing the child's head scan with the radiologist.

"Here is a skull fracture," he pointed, indicating a starburst pattern on the back of JJ's skull. That indicated a significant and direct blow. "And here's a good bit of blood in his head. See how everything's shifted over?"

The findings were obvious. "Yeah, but that should be able to be drained, don't you think?"

"Should be, but that's not the real problem," he continued. "Look right here."

He pointed to the base of the skull where it sat upon the atlas, the first cervical vertebra. The atlas was displaced a good two and a half centimeters posteriorly. His spinal cord had been severed.

"This kid's dead, or soon will be," he said matter-of-factly.

He was right, of course. There was nothing anyone could do for JJ. I just stood there a few minutes, looking at the films.

As I walked back to the department, I considered my options in dealing with this child's parents. They would need to know the full extent of his injuries and the inevitable outcome. First though, I needed to know what really happened to JJ.

When I reached the nurses' station, I asked Lori to come with me to major trauma. JJ would be following us in a few minutes.

I opened the door, and we found Maylees and Jenny sitting on the stretcher, their legs hanging over the edge. Bubba was sitting on the floor in the corner of the room. His legs were splayed in front of him and his head drooped on his chest.

"How's JJ?" Jenny asked.

"He's about the same," I answered. "And they should be on their way back here with him now. But there's something on his scan that doesn't make sense," I told them.

Maylees and Jenny looked at each other and then at me.

"You told us he tripped and fell in the kitchen," I continued. "But what doesn't make sense is that his head injury is mainly on the back. When kids trip, they usually fall forward."

I paused and studied their faces, waiting for a response. They looked at each other again and then back at me. Bubba just stared at the floor.

"So, tell me. Does JJ really walk? And if he doesn't, then tell us what really happened."

They were silent for a moment and then Jenny spoke up. "No, JJ doesn't walk. And he didn't trip, or anything. Bubba…" she said, nodding at the slumping figure in the corner, "Bubba had him out on the concrete patio and was throwin' him up in the air and catchin' him. JJ was screaming, scared to death. And everyone was laughin'. So Bubba just kept throwin' him up, and then…then…he dropped him. And his head hit the concrete. And he was just layin' there. That's how it happened."

Maylees was nodding her head in agreement.

Lori had closed her eyes upon hearing this. My knees became weak for an instant as I thought of my own children. And then I became angry.

The opening of the door drew my attention, and I watched as Lori walked out toward the nurses' station. She would be calling the police.

Wine is indeed a mocker. And too often a murderer.

8

It **Must** Have Been a **Miracle**

You are the God who performs miracles; you dis-
play your power among the peoples.

—Psalm 77:14

Yeah, Doc. I had this spot on my lungs a year or so ago and now
it's gone. A miracle, don't you think?"

A miracle. I have never personally witnessed anything I would call
a miracle of healing, nor have any of my colleagues—at least that they
have told me about. And I have never read of any such occurrence
documented in the medical literature.

This is not to say that wondrous things don't happen every day in
the medical field. I think it's pretty amazing that a broken wrist, if
properly immobilized and left alone, will heal in three or four weeks.
Or that a lacerated forehead, with appropriate attention, will heal itself
in a matter of days. What cardiac surgeons are able to do borders on
the miraculous: stop a beating heart, reroute and restore a compromised blood supply, and start the heart beating again.

But even though I have no personal testimony concerning a verified
miracle of healing, I continue to be impressed by everyday encounters
that come close.

For instance, an impressive clinical encounter is the handling of
a diabetic who has taken too much insulin. Your blood sugar starts
to drop, and at dangerously low levels, you lose consciousness. Most
diabetics recognize the symptoms leading up to this and know to get
some sugar into their systems. A new diabetic, or one who takes poor
care of himself, will come to the ER unconscious or comatose. The

history will usually give us the correct diagnosis. A quickly given load of IV glucose will rapidly resolve this condition. The comatose patient sits up and asks, "What's going on?" It's like turning on a light. Not exactly a miracle, to be certain, but surely something special.

And so, while miracles are not necessary or essential to my faith, I continue to be open to the miraculous. In fact, a few years ago I thought I had happened upon just such a case.

Christmas Eve. I was unlucky enough to have drawn the short straw and was working the night shift. You would think the ER wouldn't be busy on this pre-holiday night. To the contrary, most holidays are among our busiest times. All of the doctor's offices in town are closed, there is usually a liberal amount of alcohol flowing, and people just seem to get lonely.

It was 9:30 p.m. and I was standing at the nurses' station, talking with our ward secretary, Marcella James.

"Any big plans for tomorrow?" I asked her. She was a young woman, early twenties, and I knew she had two small children.

"Nope, gonna be workin' here," she answered. "The hospital's paying a big bonus and I couldn't pass it up. I do get a chance to be home in the morning with the children, though. That'll be good."

The triage nurse placed the chart of a new patient in the "To Be Seen" basket. I turned around and watched as she led a teenage girl and her mother down the hall. She directed the two into our Gyn room and then closed the door behind them.

"Hmm, wonder what that is?" I mused.

"Tonight, could be anything," Marcella opined.

I picked up the new chart and began to read.

Samantha Towers.
15-year-old female.
Chief complaint: abdominal pain and nausea.

I looked down to her vital signs. Blood pressure and pulse were recorded as normal. No fever. All that was good.

"Well, I guess I'll go find out."

After tapping lightly on the exam room door, I pushed it opened and stepped in.

"Samantha Towers? Hello, I'm Dr. Lesslie," I said, looking at the young girl who was now sitting on the exam table. Her knees were drawn up to her chin, and she had covered herself with a hospital sheet. Her toes were peeking out and I noticed her nails had recently been painted bright red. Closing the door behind me, I addressed the older woman who was sitting on a stool in the corner. "And you're…?" I paused, leaving room for a response.

"I'm Samantha's mother, Sarah Stroud," she stated.

Two different last names. I glanced at the medical chart and quickly noted that the "single" box in the marital status section had been checked.

Ms. Stroud was very perceptive. She had noticed my furtive glance at the clipboard. "I got divorced when Sam—Samantha—was ten. She wanted to keep her last name." She shrugged. "All the same to me."

"Okay, good," I remarked, pulling over the other stool in the room and sitting down. I put the chart in my lap and both hands on my knees. Leaning forward a little, I asked, "Samantha? Would you rather be called Sam, or Samantha?"

"Sam would be fine," she whispered.

"Speak up, Sam," her mother directed. "He's got to be able to hear you."

"Sam is fine," she repeated, louder this time, followed by a sideways glance at her mother.

"Okay, Sam. What's the problem tonight? What brings you to the ER?"

She looked at her mother.

"Go ahead and tell him, Sam," Mrs. Stroud said. "Tell him why we're here."

Sam looked back at me. "It's my stomach," she said. "It's been hurtin'."

"Alright," I coaxed. "And when did this start?"

This was going to take a while. I almost looked down at my wrist-watch, but then I remembered Mrs. Stroud. She would probably catch me. I shifted my weight on the stool.

It turned out that Sam had been experiencing some vague lower abdominal pain for about three weeks. It had gotten a little worse over the past few days, but now the main problem was nausea. Every morning she awoke with severe nausea, and by noon she had vomited half a dozen times. There had been no fever, no bleeding, and no trauma. She had no history of any significant medical problems.

Hmm. A young woman with abdominal cramping and morning sickness. This was starting to sound a little familiar.

"Sam, when was your last period?" I asked her.

She immediately looked at her mother.

Sarah Stroud quickly spoke up. "She's never missed a period. Regular as a clock. The last one was…when? Two weeks ago?" she asked her daughter.

"Yeah, that's right," Sam answered, nodding vigorously. "It was two weeks ago today."

"Okay," I responded, placing a question mark in the box entitled "last menstrual period." Something didn't seem right here.

"Now, Sam. I need to ask you a few personal questions." I glanced over at her mother who was staring at me with pursed lips, waiting.

Looking back at Samantha, "Have you ever been sexually active? Ever had sex with anyone?" I asked as delicately as I could.

"Good Lord, no!" her mother answered for her. "This child is a virgin! Why, of course not. You tell him so, Sam."

I had kept my eyes on Sam during this exchange. She had been watching her mother and had not blinked an eye. She remained completely impassive.

She looked at me then and coolly said, "No, Doctor. I have never had sex."

"Are you—" I tried to pursue the issue.

"There. See? She's never had sex," her mother interrupted. "Now, can you please tell us what you think is the matter with Sam? What is causing her pain and vomiting?"

I shifted my feet and studied the medical chart, weighing my options. It appeared obvious that any further direct questioning would not be fruitful. In fact, it would probably end with these two women walking out of the ER.

Standing up, I said, "Well, let's just check your tummy and see where your pain is located."

I walked over to the side of the table.

"Samantha, could you just lie back on the bed for me? Just get comfortable."

As I said this, her mother stood up from her stool and walked over behind me. She stood at my shoulder, watching.

Samantha dutifully followed my instructions and lay down on her back. Her hands were folded behind her head and she gazed at the ceiling, seeming quite relaxed.

"Okay," I said, lowering the sheet just enough to expose her abdomen. "Can you point to where it hurts the most?"

She was a slender girl and I immediately noticed a rounded protuberance just below her belly button. I glanced over my shoulder at Mrs. Stroud. If she had noticed anything her expression certainly didn't betray it.

Looking back at Sam I said, "Just show me where it hurts."

She used the index finger of her right hand to make large, circular motions over her entire lower abdomen. Not very helpful.

"Alright," I said, placing my left hand on her mid-abdomen with my right hand on top of it. "Tell me if this hurts."

Her abdominal exam did not reveal any significant tenderness, and she was unable to localize any point of maximum discomfort. I had been studying her face throughout, and she had remained passive and seemingly quite comfortable.

What I *had* found was a firm, nontender mass located just below her umbilicus and extending down into her pelvis. About twenty weeks along, I guessed.

After listening to her heart and lungs and completing my exam, I pulled the sheet back up, covering her. She grabbed the edge and again pulled it up to her chin.

"Well, Sam, I need to ask you one more time. Are you sure your periods have been regular and you've never been sexually active?"

"I thought we covered this, Doctor," her mother answered, obviously agitated. "If you're going to keep badgering her about this, we will leave right this minute. You heard what she said. She's never had sex with a man."

Sam continued to stare at the ceiling.

"Alright." I backed off. "Let's, uh, let's just check a few things. We'll get a CBC and a urine specimen. Then I'll be back with you."

Mrs. Stroud had stepped over to the side of the table and was patting her daughter's arm.

"And how long will all that take?" she asked impatiently.

"Not long," I answered. "Twenty, thirty minutes. And then we'll talk."

I walked up the hallway, considering my options here. We would get a pregnancy test, and I knew it would be positive. But how was I going to break that news to Samantha and her mother? They seemed convinced she was a virgin.

Stopping at the nurses' station, I put the chart on the counter and began writing. After jotting down a few notes, I looked over at our secretary.

"Marcella, could you get a CBC and a urinalysis in Gyn?" I asked her. "And a pregnancy test too."

"Sure, Doctor." She immediately reached out for the appropriate lab slips.

Jeff had been standing nearby and he walked over.

"What's goin' on? You seem a little bothered," he observed.

I told him Sam's story, and my dilemma.

"Well, you never know. Maybe they're telling the truth. Maybe she *is* a virgin, and maybe she's pregnant," he said, smiling. "Happened once before."

I looked at him over the top of my glasses. "Now wouldn't that be something?" I remarked, not amused.

It took forty minutes, but we had our answer. Samantha's CBC was completely normal, as was her urinalysis. And her pregnancy test *was* positive. The lab tech had walked the results around to the ER and as she handed them to me she said, "Turned positive almost before the drop of urine hit the card."

"Hmm," I muttered. "Thanks."

I picked up her chart, attached the lab results, and headed down the hall to the Gyn room. This was going to be interesting.

Jeff was pushing a wheelchair up the hall. The eighteen-year-old patient in it had sprained his ankle playing basketball and was on his way back from X-ray. As our paths crossed, Jeff asked, "Got your miracle?"

I returned his Cheshire-cat smile with a disapproving frown.

Mrs. Stroud didn't move from Samantha's side as I closed the door of the exam room behind me. She looked at me questioningly, while Sam just stared up at the ceiling.

"Sam, Mrs. Stroud," I began. "I think we have our answer." I held her chart in my left hand. Then I placed my right palm on top of it, staking my claim to the forthcoming diagnosis.

"And what is that, Doctor?" Mrs. Stroud asked.

"We've got our lab results back and they..." I started but then stopped, deciding on a different approach. "Sam, are you sure your periods have been—"

"Dr. Lesslie, that is just about enough!" Mrs. Stroud interrupted, with a subtle but unmistakable arching back of her shoulders.

I gave up. "Okay, okay. Let's just go over her lab studies."

Edging closer to Mrs. Stroud and the exam table, I opened the chart and began to review the lab-report slips attached to the top sheet of paper.

"Alright, this is her CBC, and it checks for any evidence of infection or anemia. And it's fine. And this," pointing to another slip, "is her urinalysis. No problem here—no blood, no infection. All that is good."

I took a deep breath before pointing to the next lab slip. "And this one, this is a pregnancy test. We checked, just to be sure. And as you can see, it is positive."

There, I had said it.

"What?" the mother exclaimed, grabbing the chart from my hands. "That's impossible!"

"Well, you can see for yourself," I explained, pointing to the appropriate box on the slip and the large "+" sign. "The lab doesn't make mistakes about this kind of thing."

"I don't care about the lab!" she shouted. "This has to be wrong. It must be someone else's report." She said this while looking down at her daughter. Sam continued to stare at the ceiling. It might just have been the exam room lighting, but she seemed a little pale now.

I stepped between Mrs. Stroud and Samantha and I patted the young girl on her belly and said, "Mrs. Stroud, I want you to feel something."

Slipping the sheet down far enough to expose Samantha's lower abdomen, I guided Mrs. Stroud's reluctant hand to the now-diagnosed gravid uterus.

"Can you feel this?" I asked, helping her fingers outline the grapefruit-sized growth. "This is her uterus, her womb. I would guess she is about twenty weeks pregnant."

Mrs. Stroud felt the firm, curved mass, and then pulled her hand away.

"Must be a mistake," she stated, shaking her head resolutely. "Sam is a virgin, and there must be a mistake somewhere."

Samantha continued to stare at the ceiling, and she again pulled the hospital sheet up to her chin.

"Doctor, this is impossible, and I, we—" Mrs. Stroud stammered.

She was struggling, and I interrupted, trying to help her. "Tell you what. Why don't the two of you talk for a few minutes. I've got a couple of things to do and then I'll be back. Okay?"

There was no immediate response, and I exited the room in silence.

At the nurses' station, Jeff stood waiting.

"What's the verdict?" he asked, with a smile.

"Well, Jeff," I answered. "I'd say the odds are getting slimmer. But there's still an outside chance we could have our Christmas miracle."

"Yeah, sure. I'd say those odds are between slim and none," he teased.

Twenty minutes later I handed the chart of an elderly gentleman in room 3 to our secretary. "We need some blood work and a chest X-ray," I told her. Fever, cough, shortness of breath—it would probably be pneumonia.

Just then, the triage nurse put another chart on the countertop, making a total now of at least eight new patients who needed to be seen.

That was enough. It was time to go and talk with Mrs. Stroud and her daughter. Doggone it, I needed to find out if I had my miracle or not.

As I closed the Gyn room door behind me, it was as if I had stepped into another universe. The atmosphere had radically changed, and instead of being met by a belligerent mother and an indifferent daughter, I saw the two standing before me side-by-side. They were smiling and had their arms around each other. Samantha was now dressed, and Mrs. Stroud had her pocketbook slung over her shoulder.

The door latch clicked behind me, and I waited for one of them to speak. It was Mrs. Stroud.

"Dr. Lesslie, I think we know what's going on now. And we think you are right. Sam *is* pregnant," she told me, smiling. I stood before them, tense, my head tilted to one side, waiting. "And," she continued, almost triumphantly, "she's not a virgin."

I slumped a little in my disappointment, but was careful not to lose my balance and fall over.

"So she's not?" I repeated, placing her chart on the exam table and thrusting my hands deep into my lab-coat pockets. I was struggling to find my comfort zone.

"No, and we figured out what happened," she went on. For the first time Sam was looking at me, as she listened to what her mother was saying. And there was the hint of a smile on her face.

"Yes," Mrs. Stroud went on matter-of-factly. "Back in the fall, maybe even late August, we had a family reunion out on our family homestead. About an hour or so from here, I'd guess, out in the middle of nowhere. Well, there were eighty, maybe ninety of us, with a whole bunch of youngsters. Teenagers too. Mainly we sat around talking and eating and the kids were swimming and fishing in the old pond."

She paused here and looked down at Sam. "It seems that Sam here and a bunch of her cousins went down behind the pond dam with some wine one of them had sneaked along with him. Before long, they were pretty soused. Right, Sam?"

Samantha only nodded and continued to look at me.

"Well, Sam says that was when Uncle Freddy came down and… well, he got her all alone and he had his way with her."

I was stunned. Not so much by what she was saying…I had heard much worse. But I was astonished by the manner in which she was saying it. Here was a woman who only a short time ago had been angrily confronting me for asking about the chastity of her daughter, and who now was calmly and coolly relating a tale of incest.

"That Freddy," she continued, "he's no good. He's part of that Tennessee side of the family. But not my family! He's on my husband's side. Or ex-husband, I should say. Anyway, he's no good, and it doesn't surprise me, not one bit. I'll have a word with him, you can be sure of that." She said these last words while patting Samantha on the shoulder.

I picked up the clipboard for the sole purpose of just doing something, anything. I didn't know what to say.

Mrs. Stroud came to my rescue. She took her arm from around her daughter, stood up straight, and asked, "So, Doctor, what do we do now? You think Sam's four to five months pregnant?"

We talked for a few minutes and I told them they would be given the name and phone number of an obstetrician in town. "You can follow up with him next week."

They both thanked me and walked out of the ER. I stood in the hallway for a moment, watching them leave. Poor Sam, and poor Uncle Freddy.

And what about my miracle? I guess I would have to wait.

As it turned out, that wait would be short-lived—only about six months.

"Dr. Lesslie, we need you in here *stat*." Jeff's voice was calm, but I recognized the tone. He meant business, and I immediately headed into the cardiac room. I had been walking up the hallway, talking with one of our surgeons about a young boy with appendicitis in room 5.

"What's the problem?" I asked, entering. My eyes were immediately drawn to the elderly man on the stretcher. I was not yet aware of the arrival of this patient and didn't know anything about him.

He was pale and obviously afraid. He looked from side to side, all the while tightly clasping the hand of a woman I assumed was his wife.

"Seventy-eight-year-old, history of heart disease," Jeff told me while starting an IV. "Came in from one of the doctors' offices in town. POV (privately owned vehicle). Blood pressure is 60 over zip."

Stepping closer to the stretcher, I reached out and put my hand on his uncovered shoulder. His skin was cool and damp to the touch. I glanced at the cardiac monitor and could see the telltale changes that suggested an acute heart attack. His rhythm was regular, about seventy a minute, and then...

"Jeff, get the defibrillator over here!" I turned to the woman standing at the side of the stretcher. "Ma'am, would you step back for a minute?"

She immediately released her husband's grasp and put her hand to her mouth, shrinking back against the equipment carts lining one of the walls.

Jeff was reacting quickly. He'd seen the same thing I had. The regular rhythm on the monitor had suddenly deteriorated into the spiked, choppy pattern of v-tach (ventricular tachycardia), an unstable and life-threatening electrical pattern. As confirmation of this change, our patient had turned dusky and was staring up at the ceiling, his facial muscles now lax. His low blood pressure must have dropped even lower. Then, just as quickly, we watched as the v-tach deteriorated even further. The tracing on the monitor screen told us he was now in ventricular fibrillation. His heart had lost all electrical organization and was simply quivering in his chest, a failing, purposeless "bag of worms." He was dying.

It was his good fortune this had happened in the ER, in front of us, and with the necessary equipment readily at hand to revive him. He would surely have been doomed had this happened at home or in his car.

I immediately applied the defibrillator paddles to his chest and shocked him once. Nothing. The monitor still revealed only the chaotic, undulating pattern of v-fib. I shocked him a second time, and then a third. Then…there was a faint *beep-beep-beep* coming from the monitor.

"Looks like he's back in a sinus rhythm," Jeff reported. And then pressing two fingers against the man's left carotid artery, he said, "And I can feel a faint pulse here. Sixty a minute, now seventy. Regular."

Our patient was responding. We watched as he took some deep breaths and began to look around the room, though still obviously confused. But his color was better and now he had a good, strong pulse.

One of our other nurses had come into the room and was now leading the man's wife out into the hallway, where her daughter and son-in-law were waiting.

"I'll be out in just a minute," I said to his wife, "and we'll let you know what's going on. For right now, he looks okay." I looked up at the clock on the wall: 5:35 p.m. The next hour or so would be critical.

We quickly determined that our patient, Wylie Stanfield, was indeed having a heart attack, his third. While we were doing the necessary things to stabilize him, our unit secretary was making arrangements to have one of our cardiologists admit him to the CCU.

I learned that Wylie had started having chest pain sometime in the mid-morning. Prudently, his wife, Margaret, had become concerned. They drove to their family doctor's office and, after sitting for an hour and a half in the waiting area, were taken back to an exam room. Their physician was equally concerned and recommended they drive the fifteen minutes over to the ER for testing. Our triage nurse had observed the low blood pressure and his cool, clammy skin. Wylie was brought immediately back to the cardiac room, where Jeff had met him. And here we were.

"Jeff, you okay here?" I asked him. "I need to step out and speak with the family."

"Sure," he answered. "He looks pretty good now."

In the hallway, Margaret Stanfield anxiously waited with her daughter and son-in-law.

"Mrs. Stanfield, I'm Dr. Lesslie," I introduced myself, not having had the time to do this in the chaotic cardiac room. I then informed them of our diagnosis, our current plan, and the seriousness of his condition. The daughter, Theresa Streeter, and her husband, Mac, stood on either side of Margaret, their arms around her, holding her steady.

We talked for a few minutes until I was sure they knew what was going on.

"Can Mother and I go in there with him?" Theresa asked.

I thought Jeff had had enough time to get things straight, so I said, "Sure, but we need to keep him calm." I said this while looking at Mrs. Stanfield. She seemed in control and nodded her understanding. The last thing we needed was for an emotional outburst to trigger another episode of v-tach, or worse.

The two women went into the room, and I was left standing in the hallway with Mac Streeter.

"What do you think, Doc?" he asked. "Do you think he can pull through this?"

"His chances are fair," I told him honestly. "After all, he is seventy-eight and he has a bad heart. We'll just have to see. Right now though, he's okay."

This seemed to satisfy him, and I turned, heading toward the nurses' station.

"Dr. Lesslie, do you have a minute?" he asked, tentatively. He was obviously concerned about something.

I stopped and said, "Sure. What's the problem?"

"Is there somewhere private we can talk?" He said this while glancing at the closed cardiac room door.

Curious, I looked down the hallway and thought a moment. Across the corridor, the ENT (ear, nose, and throat) room stood empty and dark.

"Let's go over here," I said, leading him away from the cardiac room.

I turned on the lights of the ENT room and closed the door behind us as we stepped inside.

I pointed to a stool in the corner of the room. "Have a seat, Mac. What do we need to talk about?"

Without any hesitation Mac Streeter began to tell me about the Stanfield family. "My first concern is for Wylie," he told me, "first and foremost," he stressed, looking squarely into my eyes. "And I don't want anything to happen here that might upset him and cause him trouble. I know he's not very stable."

And then he told me about the Stanfield's son, Phil. He was two years older than Theresa and lived with his wife and three children in a small town about an hour distant. Theresa had called Phil and told him of their father's condition. He was on his way, and his wife was staying at home with the kids. He would be arriving at the hospital shortly.

"The problem, Dr. Lesslie, is the relationship between Phil and his mother. They don't get along." I was soon to learn this was an understatement.

Mac explained that about five years earlier, something had happened at a family gathering. Words were said, misunderstood, and blown out of proportion. Phil and his mother were soon at odds and not speaking. It had been a trivial thing, but it soon became an open, festering wound. Attempts had been made to heal the break, but to no avail.

"You need to understand, Doctor, that while Margaret is a good woman, she is hardheaded. There's a side of her that's, well…She's just become bitter about this. She won't talk to Phil, won't answer his calls or return his letters. And she's put Wylie right in the middle of it."

"What do you mean, 'in the middle of it'?" I asked him.

"She won't let Phil talk to his father or see him. And if he does, she stops talking to Wylie and makes his life miserable. It's a real mess," he explained.

Mac and Theresa had tried to intervene, but unsuccessfully. Margaret was intransigent. The situation had worsened over the years and had taken its toll on all of them. Wylie had not been able to see his son or the three grandchildren, even though they lived only an hour away.

"I'm really afraid that when Phil gets here, we're going to have trouble," he continued. He shook his head. "Phil hasn't seen his father in five years. Or his mother. He's a good guy and I can't believe he would let anything blow up. But Margaret, on the other hand…I just don't know. We're going to have to keep them apart somehow."

What a mess. Wylie was barely clinging to his life, and this dysfunctional family dynamic was assuredly going to make things more difficult for everyone. Mac had been right to share the family skeletons with me. And we all had them. Some worse and some bigger than others, but they were there, usually hidden away. If a family thought itself immune to this, they weren't looking in the right closets.

We talked about the spiritual aspect of this situation. I opened that door with a simple question. "Have you and Theresa talked with a minister about this?"

Mac looked at me, seeming relieved I had been willing to ask this. He then told me he and his wife prayed about it every day. They prayed for reconciliation, and for Margaret's heart to be softened.

"We've talked with Margaret about this too, and she says she prays all the time about it and is just waiting for Phil to apologize. The frustrating part of this is that when Phil tries to apologize and make things right, she will have nothing to do with it. She says he's not sincere."

He paused and stared at the floor.

"You know, Dr. Lesslie, I believe in the power of prayer. I really do, and I've seen prayers answered. And I know the Lord can do anything. But when Theresa and I pray about this and put it in His hands, somehow…somehow…I know He can fix this, but I just can't see it happening. It's just so twisted and gnarly. We've tried everything, Theresa and I. And so has Phil. It's…just a real mess. And now this, with Wylie. I'm just afraid something bad is going to happen."

I assured him we would make every effort to keep Margaret and Phil apart, and to shield Wylie from any potential conflagration.

But it was not to be. As we stepped out into the hallway, I heard Mac moan behind me. "Oh, good Lord, we're too late!"

I glanced toward the door of the cardiac room and saw the back of a middle-aged man as he stepped into the room. Mac didn't have to tell me. I knew.

"It's Phil," he said. "Quick, I've got to get in there."

Phil was closing the door behind him, but I stopped it with the palm of a hand. Pushing it open, I stepped into the room behind him, along with Mac.

Phil never turned around. He stopped at the foot of the stretcher and looked down at his father. Wylie was lying there, quietly resting, eyes closed. Jeff was standing at the head of the bed, adjusting the rate of the IV fluids. Unsuspecting, he glanced over at the new visitor. Margaret and Theresa stood on each side of the bed, each gently stroking one of Wylie's forearms. They had looked up as Phil had entered the room. Theresa stood frozen, her eyes widening and her lips soundlessly parting.

Margaret stood completely still, staring at her estranged son. Then she patted Wylie's arm one more time and stepped toward the door. Mac and I were standing just behind Phil. I was blocking Margaret's exit, so I shifted toward Mac to get out of her way. She had reached the foot of the stretcher, when she stopped right in front of Phil. Their eyes met, and they both just stood there, staring at each other. Then she reached out and took her boy in her arms. And he wrapped his large arms around her, squeezing her tight.

"I'm so sorry," she sobbed.

His chest was heaving, and he struggled to whisper, "I'm sorry too."

And then there was silence, except for the *beep-beep-beep* of Wylie's heart monitor. And then the crying, from all of them. Mac and Theresa had watched in amazement, and now they huddled around Margaret and Phil, all of them hugging and sobbing.

Jeff looked at me, confused over what had just happened. He had no idea of the significance of this moment. Later, I would tell him.

There it was—my miracle. Wylie was lying quietly on the stretcher, not moving. But now his eyes were open and he was smiling.

I stepped out into the hall, wiping my own eyes and thinking of something that Mac had said earlier. He had put this whole thing in God's hands. But he had remained daunted by the enormity of the problem and its seemingly impossible resolution. *"The Lord can do all things, but...this one...I just don't know."*

Now he understood, as did I, that there is nothing beyond the power of God. There is no wall too high for Him to tear down, no situation too twisted for Him to straighten. He stands there ready and wanting to help, capable of softening the hardest of hearts, of resolving the thorniest of problems.

This, then, was my miracle. What greater wonder is there than the changing of a human heart?

9

Let the Little Children Come to Me

He took the children in his arms, put his
hands on them and blessed them.

—MARK 10:16, SPEAKING OF JESUS

I started medical school in the fall of 1972. In the last thirty-some years there have been a lot of changes in the field of medicine, both in the things we now know, and in the things we are able to do. For instance, some of the commonly used drugs then are no longer available, and some of the drugs we take for granted today were not even dreamed of then.

Back then as well, some things were only barely discussed in medical school, vaguely mentioned but not seriously considered. They were passed on as something to be aware of but not to spend too much time on. It wasn't that these weren't important topics, it was just that not much was known about them. One of these areas was abuse. First it was child abuse, later it was spousal abuse, and most recently, elder abuse.

In the mid-70s we were just getting a handle on child abuse. In fact, we didn't know how widespread the problem actually was, or the scope of things that were going on in our communities, both unseen and unheard. At first there was some confusion as to the nature of the problem, at least in the minds of some people. Was child abuse a disease, or was it a symptom of some larger disorder? Or was it a crime against a small, helpless human being? Those of us in the ER tended to see things as black-and-white. A six-month-old with two broken thigh bones from being thrown against the wall. A one-year-old with cigarette burns covering her buttocks because "she wouldn't use the potty." A three-year-old sexually abused by an uncle. These things were black-and-white.

As the magnitude of the problem became more apparent and the devastating consequences of child abuse became more evident, the thinking swung toward the ER view. There has been a much more organized and aggressive effort to detect abuse, protect the children involved, and prosecute those who are the abusers. Though human responses and actions are complex and multifactored, our primary responsibility is to protect our children. Those of us in the ER see ourselves as a line of defense, possibly the last and best hope for these young ones. Though it's true that the circumstances we encounter can sometimes be gray, they are too frequently black-and-white.

It was 10:30 on a Friday evening. Summertime, and the day had been especially hot. During the past few hours we had seen our usual seasonal complaints: a few really bad sunburns, a four-wheeler accident with a broken ankle, and a few minor boating injuries. I had just finished suturing the fingers of a seventeen-year-old who had badly cut them while slicing onions at a cookout on the lake.

Standing at the nurses' station, I signed the teenager's chart and handed it to Jeff. He was the nurse on duty this evening and would be working with me until 7 a.m.

"Jeff, would you put a bandage on this girl's hand and remind her to come back in ten days for suture removal? I've talked to her about what to look for in case it gets infected, but you might want to go over that again. Thanks."

He took the chart and was about to speak, when suddenly the ambulance entrance doors burst open. Into the department ran a young woman, carrying in her arms a limp and pale baby. Probably six month old. The child's limbs flopped haphazardly as she ran.

"Help me, someone!" the young mother shrieked, stopping a few steps from where I stood. "Something's wrong with my baby! Please, do something!"

She couldn't have been more than sixteen years old. She stood in front of us barefooted and dressed in a dirty white halter top and red short-shorts. Jeff was the closest to her and she thrust her baby in his direction.

"Here—please do something!"

Jeff put down the chart he was holding, took the baby in his arms, and headed immediately to the major trauma room. I was right behind him.

He put the baby on the trauma bed and put his hand on the child's chest, checking for any cardiac activity. The baby was dusky and not breathing, and I immediately reached for our pediatric ambu bag. As I glanced in the direction of our crash cart, I noticed that the young mother had followed us. She was standing just inside the doorway, her arms folded tightly across her chest, biting her lip. Tears rolled down her cheeks. Behind her, not yet venturing into the room, stood a tall, slender young man, maybe in his early twenties but no older. He wore sandals, a pair of old blue jeans, and a T-shirt that read simply, "The Man." He was impassive, and leaned against one side of the door opening, chewing slowly on a drinking straw.

I turned to the task at hand, positioned the baby's head so we had better access to his airway, and began using the ambu bag to blow air into his lungs. I quickly checked to confirm his chest was moving up and down, indicating good air exchange.

When I touched the child's face and head, I immediately looked up at Jeff. His huge hand was encircling half of the baby's chest, and he was effortlessly compressing the heart between his fingers and thumb. Jeff's eyes met mine and his eyebrows rose slightly. I nodded. The small body was cold—the baby had been dead for a while. We were not going to save him.

One of our techs had come into the room, and I asked her to put leads on the baby for the cardiac monitor and to check a rectal temperature. This effort was futile, but I wanted the mother to know we were doing everything we could. And as cruel as it might seem, I wanted her to see the flat line of the heart monitor and understand her baby was gone.

The tech attached the leads and slipped the child's diaper off to check his temperature. There was a brief glimpse of his buttocks, and I noted several bruises on each one. The marks were of different sizes and different ages.

"94 degrees," the tech reported, placing the baby's legs back on the bed. As she turned the switch on the heart monitor, the screen flickered and then became clear. A horizontal green line appeared. Flat. No electrical activity. I made sure the leads were connected to the baby's chest and looked at the monitor again. Nothing.

"11:14," Jeff quietly noted.

I nodded, and put the ambu bag on the bed beside the baby. Jeff removed his hand from the child's chest and gently laid him back on the bed. I looked in the direction of the doorway.

"Ma'am," I addressed the young woman. I didn't even know her name. "I'm afraid your baby is dead. There is nothing we can do. I'm sorry."

She turned pale and sank to the floor. The young man remained standing in the doorway, now more aggressively chewing the straw in his mouth. It was at that moment his eyes betrayed him. It was only a brief flicker, but he had glanced down the hallway as if determining his best avenue of escape.

The mother began to sob now, covering her face. Our tech helped her to her feet. Looking at me, she said, "I'll take them to the family room, Dr. Lesslie. Is that okay?"

"Yes, please," I answered. "I'll be there in just a few minutes."

She led them into the hallway and as they turned to walk away, the mother covered her mouth with one hand. With the other she weakly reached out in the direction of the stretcher. She started to step back into the room, but the young man grabbed her arm and pulled her back into the hallway. And then they were gone.

I closed the door to the trauma room and walked back over to the bed. Jeff was cleaning and putting up the equipment we had used.

"Doesn't look like SIDS, does it?" he stated.

"No, it doesn't."

While Jeff worked, I began to examine the young child. I checked the long bones of the arms and legs for any obvious evidence of an old or new fracture. I didn't find any. We would have to get X-rays to be sure. And I examined the bruises on his buttocks we had noticed earlier. It was difficult to estimate their ages—probably any time over the past one to three weeks. But there was a relatively fresh one on his right buttock, and the outline of the fingers of an adult hand could still be discerned.

Jeff was standing behind me as I made this observation.

"That son of a b———," he muttered.

"Who?" I asked, turning and looking at him.

"That guy standing in the doorway. It must be the kid's father. And I'll bet he's been the one doing this. Did you watch him? He just stood there. Never so much as blinked the whole time."

I knew Jeff was probably right. But that would be for someone else to determine.

"Call the coroner and get him over here," I told him. "And call DSS. They need to get involved right away."

I turned to the lifeless body of the baby, and then thought of something. "And we need to find out if there are any other children in the house."

"I'll go tell Amy," he said.

While we had been talking, I had taken the ophthalmoscope from the wall and focused its beam of light through the pupil of the baby's right eye, adjusting the distance up and down until the retina came into clear view.

Jeff was halfway to the door.

"Come here a minute," I said to him. "Take a look at this."

He walked back to the bed and leaned down, peering into the scope as I held it.

"Do you see the retina there, the pearly white sort of background?" He adjusted his head until the retina came into view. "Yeah, I see it. And there's some blood vessels running across it."

"Right—those are supposed to be there, and they're normal. But take a look at about three o'clock," I told him. "Tell me what you see."

He continued to adjust his head, shifting a little to one side.

His head stopped moving. "Hmm. I'm not sure what I'm seeing, but off to the side the retina's all blotchy. It looks like clumps of blood or something."

"That's exactly what it is. That's blood on the retina. Retinal hemorrhages."

Jeff straightened up and looked at me.

"What does that mean?" he asked.

I examined the child's other eye, attempting to confirm that these findings were present on both sides. They were.

"It most likely means that someone has been shaking this baby. Shaking him hard enough to cause the vessels in the eyes to bleed. And when that happens, there is almost always associated brain damage. There is no way this child died from Sudden Infant Death Syndrome. It looks like he was murdered."

Amy had called the coroner and he was on his way, as was a representative from the Department of Social Services. She had also notified the police. I walked down the hall to the family room. I would need to try to help the mother, to answer any questions she might have, and to help her contact people if needed. And I wanted a few minutes to talk with the two of them.

I reached the closed door of the family room and stopped. Looking down at the child's chart in my hands, I scanned the record for the name of his mother. "Angel." And the baby's name was "Zack." I tapped lightly on the door, opened it, and stepped into the room. Angel was sitting on one end of the sofa, her elbows propped on her knees, her head in her hands. Her hair cascaded wildly about her face, hiding it, and her shoulders heaved with her sobbing. The young man sat on the other end of the sofa with his legs crossed at the ankles. His knees were nervously moving up and down. He slouched into the cushions, one arm resting on the back of the sofa. With his other hand, he twisted the straw that still hung out of his mouth. He looked up, and his eyes met mine as I entered.

I closed the door behind me and sat down in the chair nearest it. I looked over at Angel.

"Angel," I began. "I'm Dr. Lesslie. I'm not sure I was able to tell you that earlier."

At this she sat up and brushed her hair out of her face. Her eyes were red, and her face was swollen. She didn't say anything.

I looked over at her partner. "And you are…?"

He continued to stare at me, and from around his chewed straw I was able to hear, "Timmy." His legs were moving a little faster now, and he chewed a little harder.

"Okay," I said, turning back to the mother. "Angel, can you tell me what happened to your baby this evening? Tell me about his general health, or about any problems he has been having. And when did you know something was wrong with him?"

Angel wiped her nose with the back of her hand and said, "He was fine most of the day. And he's been a good baby, really he has. Never caused any problems. Then this afternoon, he got a little fussy."

She stopped and looked at Timmy. He was no longer staring at me, but was absently gazing at the ceiling in the corner of the room. He was now sitting perfectly still.

"I think he was getting a virus or something," she continued. "He seemed to have a little fever, and then he had some diarrhea. I didn't have any Tylenol in the house, so when Timmy came over, I went to the store."

"Are the two of you married?" I asked.

"No. But we're gonna get married pretty soon. I live at home with my momma, and Timmy helps out with Zack whenever he can."

"Is Timmy Zack's father?" I asked, glancing at him.

"Yes," she stated simply. His legs were moving again.

"Was your mother at home this evening?" I asked Angel.

"No, she works third shift. I called her a few minutes ago, and she's on her way."

She began crying again, and I handed her the box of Kleenex that had been sitting on the small table.

Timmy stood up, put his hands in his pockets, and in the small space available at his end of the room, he began to pace.

"And then what happened?" I asked her.

"Well, I was only gone a little while, maybe thirty minutes. The store is just down the street. Zack was crying when I left, but he seemed okay. And then when I got home...he...he..." She covered her face with her hands and began sobbing again.

"Is that when you noticed he wasn't acting right? That he didn't seem to be breathing properly?" I asked her.

She nodded her head, saying nothing.

I sat back and was silent for a moment. Timmy was standing still now, studying the fire evacuation plan that was hanging on the wall in front of him.

I understood what had happened to Zack. Timmy had been left with a fussy, crying baby, and he had snapped. It may not have been intentional, but the outcome was the same. He had picked the baby up and shaken him in order to stop the crying. It hadn't worked, and he just shook him some more. And he continued to shake him until finally he was quiet. And now it would be time for the police to take over.

But I wanted to ask them one more question. Some part of me wanted to see how they would respond.

"Angel." I addressed her, but I watched Timmy. "There are some bruises on Zack's bottom. It looks like he's been spanked, and pretty hard. And more than once. Have you noticed that?"

She sat up and stared at Timmy. "No. I, uh, I have seen...he does fall a lot, and, uh, I guess he, uh, he bruises, and..." Timmy stood absolutely still.

"Angel, he's six months old," I reminded her. "Are you telling me he's been walking?" I was becoming upset, and I knew it was time for me to leave. Her head hung down now, and she was silent. I didn't need to hear any more.

I stood and opened the door. Turning back to them, I said, "Just stay here. Someone will be with you in a few minutes."

I closed the door behind me and stood in the hallway for a moment. I was angry, and I wanted to go back into the room and grab Timmy by his throat and...But I knew I couldn't do that. It was my job to be an ER doctor. It would be someone else's to bring justice for this innocent, dead baby.

The sound of approaching footsteps drew my attention. I looked up and saw two police officers walking toward me.

I will never forget the look in her eyes. It's been a little over twenty-five years, but I will never forget that look.

It was mid-December and a Thursday. Outside it was cold, and at six p.m., already dark. My shift would be over in another hour and I was trying to get the department in order for my replacement. So far, I was succeeding.

"Any big plans for Christmas?" Virginia Granger asked me. We were standing at the island of the nurses' station, just outside her office. She had been working on the nurses' schedule for the holiday, and I was writing up the chart of a guest in the observation unit. He had been practicing his seasonal celebratory imbibing.

"No," I answered. "Just plan to be at home with the family. It looks like you're having better luck with your schedule than I am with the docs'," I said, nodding at the clipboard in her hands. Her schedule was filled except for two openings. "It looks like I might be spending some of the holiday here," I added.

"Well, I hope not. Didn't you work last Christmas?" she asked.

I thought for a moment but couldn't remember. Holidays for an ER doc seem to all run together. I was about to respond when movement in the triage doorway drew my attention. Seeing me look in that direction, Virginia turned her head as well.

Lori was walking into the department, leading a young woman who was carrying a large picnic basket in front of her. She held the basket with both hands, leaning over slightly and straining with the burden. Lori turned around and held out a hand to help, but the woman shook her head, refusing the offer. Lori caught my eye and with a slight nod, signaled she needed me. I watched as she led her patient around the other side of the nurses' station and into room 3, closing the door behind them.

Virginia had watched all of this transpire, and she said, "Dr. Lesslie, you'd better go see what Lori needs. We'll talk some more later." She turned and walked into her office.

I left the patient's chart on the counter and headed toward room 3. Something was amiss here, but if it was a significant emergency, Lori would have been more insistent in her request for assistance. And yet, my curiosity was piqued about the contents of that picnic basket.

Pushing the door of room 3 open, I found Lori standing in the far corner beside bed B. The basket had been placed on the stretcher and she was leaning over it, carefully removing a small baby wrapped in a dirty piece of army blanket.

"And when was the last time you said you fed them, Hope?" Lori asked the mother as I closed the door behind me.

Them? I stepped over to the stretcher and looked down. In the bottom of the basket was another bundle of what appeared to be a piece of the same dirty blanket.

"An hour ago, maybe two, I guess…" Hope answered, her voice faint and her tone almost apologetic.

I took my first real look at this young mother. She was tall, maybe five-eight, and slender. No—she was skinny. Her long brown hair was matted and dirty, and it hung unchallenged into her face. She stood hunched over, staring down at her babies. Her arms were crossed over her chest and each hand grasped the opposite shoulder. She was rocking from side to side. Her blue jeans were worn, and torn at the knees. The stained sweatshirt she wore couldn't provide much protection from the frigid December air. She had no coat.

I glanced down and noticed she had on sandals but no socks, and her toes were blanched and colorless from the cold. Lori interrupted my observations. "Dr. Lesslie." With her head she motioned toward the doorway. She was holding the blanketed infant in her arms.

"Hope, stand here next to your baby for a minute, okay?" she instructed the mother, nodding at the basket.

"Okay," was the faint response. Hope edged closer to the stretcher, her arms still crossed on her chest.

Lori and I stepped toward the door and then turned back toward the bed.

She leaned close and whispered, "When I called Hope into the triage area from the waiting room, another patient stood up and walked over. She pulled me aside and asked me if I knew anything about Hope. I told her no, and she proceeded to fill me in. She seems to know her, or at least to know *of* her. Hope has been on the street for a while, it seems. She was a straight-A student in high school. Then she met some guy, got pregnant, and her parents kicked her out of the house. They won't have anything to do with her. She's lived with some friends, but that hasn't worked out. And she's been in and out of the shelters, but she usually just wanders off. It's strange, but I don't think we've ever seen her here before."

"What's the problem today?" I asked Lori.

"It's hard to say," she answered, looking down at the bundle in her arms. "She doesn't make a lot of sense. I think her main concern is that the babies aren't eating. I just brought them straight back, so I really don't know yet. I haven't even taken a look at them."

"Alright, let's see what's going on," I said to her, stepping back toward the stretcher. "How old did she say the twins were? They are twins, aren't they?"

"Yes, twins. Girls. And she said they were eight months old," Lori answered.

Eight months? That couldn't be right. The baby Lori was carrying was tiny.

She placed the first baby on the stretcher and began carefully lifting the other one from the basket. I unwrapped the child that lay on the stretcher and was stunned. The girl was the appropriate length for an eight-month-old, but she couldn't weigh more than ten pounds. Later, after we weighed the two of them, we would learn that this baby weighed eight pounds two ounces, a full five pounds less than her twin. She was emaciated, and listlessly rolled her eyes in my direction. She was diapered in a dirty piece of old sheet, the corners held in place with duct tape.

Lori looked over my shoulder and gasped. Then she placed her bundle on the stretcher and quickly unwrapped the second tiny girl. She was naked, dirty, and barely breathing. Lori immediately reached over to the emergency button on the wall and called for help, her voice shaking.

We shifted into a different mode. The second baby was clinging to life, but just barely. Two other nurses came into the room and we rapidly proceeded to resuscitate her. In short order we had secured her airway and had an IV going, and she was under a warming blanket. She was stable, at least for the moment.

One of the pediatricians on staff happened to be in the hospital and had come to the ER to help with this emergency. He was going to admit the child to the Pediatric ICU and had called in one of his partners to help with the first baby. Though her condition was not immediately life-threatening, she was still in a lot of trouble. With things under control, I was able to step out of room 3 and back to the nurses' station.

Lori was standing at the counter, writing on the chart of the first twin. She looked up as I walked over, obviously shaken and upset.

"What do you think?" she asked me. "Is she going to make it? The second one? I've never seen a baby so skinny, so wasted. It's terrible."

Lori had three children of her own, a boy and two girls. A moment ago she'd been focused on the task at hand, an experienced and effective ER nurse. Now she was a mother.

"So tiny," she whispered to herself.

I sat down, exhausted. An hour of an adrenaline rush will wear you out.

"I'm not sure," I answered. "She has no reserve, no body fat at all. And what was her temp—96? I thought that's what you said."

"Yes," she replied. "It was 96.2. She was cold."

"Yeah, she was cold. That either means exposure or an infection somewhere. Neither of which are going to be good. Where is the mother? And what about the other baby?" I asked.

"Hope is in the family room with the police, and the other child has been taken to the Pediatric ICU. She was starting to perk up a little after she got warm and we gave her a little bit of a bottle." She paused, and then, "And I think someone from DSS is on the way to talk with Hope after the police are finished with her."

"Hmm. I doubt she will ever see those children again, assuming they live," I observed.

"You're right," Lori agreed. "But you know, Hope is pitiful. I think she's devastated by this, but something just isn't registering with her. The look in her eyes is really spooky. She's just not there."

"I know what you mean. Is someone from Mental Health going to come down and talk to her?"

"Yes," she answered. "In the next hour or so."

We sat quietly for a moment, each of us reflecting on the events of the evening. Then Lori broke the silence. "You know, I had just a minute to talk to Hope when I took her back to the family room. Right before the police got there. I asked her how long her children had not been eating, and she just sort of stared at me. Then she told me her milk had dried up about two or three months ago, and she had started feeding them whole milk. She said they seemed to like it fine, but they weren't getting as big as she thought they should. And then she just looked at me and said, 'I didn't know what to do.'"

We fell silent again.

The first twin spent three months in the hospital and then was placed in a foster home. It remains to be seen if she will develop normally. The second twin died after two days in the ICU.

I don't know what's become of Hope.

> *He took a little child and had him stand among them. Taking him in his arms, he said to them, "Whoever welcomes one of these little children in my name welcomes me; and whoever welcomes me does not welcome me but the one who sent me."*
>
> —Mark 9:36-37

The **Still,** Small **Voice**

After the earthquake came a fire, but the LORD *was not
in the fire. And after the fire came a gentle whisper.*

—1 KINGS 19:12

S he began to pace. It was about nine in the morning, and up until
this point she had been lying quietly. Back and forth across the
room she walked, her bloated belly attesting to the fact that she was
full-term, maybe a few days late.

I watched her closely, keeping a reasonable, unintrusive distance.
From time to time she looked at me, her dark eyes at once fearful and
trusting.

But something was wrong. I was an ER doc and had delivered
dozens of babies. And though I wasn't an obstetrician, I knew something wasn't right.

She made another pass in front of me, and when she turned I could
see a small foot beginning to protrude. Then she walked over and lay
down on her side, panting now. Above and behind her, the faces of
my four young children were pressed against the panes of the French
doors that led onto the screened porch. It was here that Scooter, our
miniature dachshund, had chosen to give birth to her first litter.

The kids' faces were excited and they looked on with anticipation.
Barbara stood above them, bent over, hands on her knees. She was excited
also, but this was tempered with a measure of anxiety. She was concerned
about Scooter, but she needed to protect her own litter as well. This was
the toughest but most important audience I had ever had.

Earlier that morning I had called our vet, expressing my concern about Scooter's slow progress.

"Don't worry," she had tried to reassure me. "Dachshunds are notorious for having difficult deliveries. It's their long, low backs probably. And don't be surprised if you have a stillborn pup or two. In fact, maybe half won't make it."

"What?" I had asked, incredulous. "What am I supposed to do about that?"

"Nothing," she had answered. "Don't do anything. Just let nature take its course."

I was silent, considering what she had just told me. It was contrary to everything in me to just stand by and watch.

"Call me if there's a problem," she added. "But everything should be fine."

She had hung up, and I returned to the porch and Scooter's pacing, and the faces of my children.

Scooter lay with her back to the French doors, only inches away from the glass. We had tried to make her as comfortable as possible on a couple of folded towels. I stroked her head and neck and tried to encourage her, regretting that I didn't speak dachshund.

The tiny foot was now more visible, and then there were two. But something wasn't right. They weren't moving. Maybe that was normal, but...And then there was the pup. He was tiny, wet, and covered with a glistening membrane that Scooter immediately began to gnaw and bite. I watched with amazement as she nudged and cajoled her firstborn, stimulating the pup and trying to tear away this covering. How did she know to do this? I knew it was instinct, but still, it was amazing.

I glanced up at the kids, and their eyes were big as saucers. They were pointing and giggling and bouncing up and down.

Then I looked at Scooter. She had lain back down, seemingly exhausted, still panting. Another foot began to emerge from her birth canal.

And then I looked at the first pup. He was lying on the towel, completely still, not moving, not breathing. I rubbed him, trying to stimulate the little guy, trying to get him to breathe. But nothing happened. He was dead. Glancing up at Barbara, I saw the look of concern on her face. And then I looked at the children. They were just staring, no longer giggling and bouncing up and down. They knew something was wrong.

I picked up the pup and moved him out of their sight.

Meanwhile, Scooter had delivered her second puppy. She was again nipping at the amniotic membranes and trying to stimulate this little girl. Nothing. Same as before.

To heck with this.

"Okay, Scooter," I calmly spoke to her. "Let me see what I can do here."

I wasn't sure how she was going to respond, but she just looked up at me with those large, dark eyes and cocked her head. When I reached over and grabbed the pup, she didn't whimper or make any protective movement. She just lay there, watching me.

The puppy was a tiny, lifeless form in my hand, barely covering my palm. I briefly looked up at the faces pressed to the glass in front of me. Their expressions were wide-eyed and confused. As I watched, my older daughter's lips began to quiver. That was enough.

Using my thumbs, I peeled the slick and still-wet membrane away from the puppy's head. Then—and I still can't believe I did this—I put my mouth over the pup's nose and mouth and sucked whatever mucus I could get out of her airway. I rubbed her between my hands to try to get some response, but still nothing. Then I put my mouth over hers again and inflated her tiny lungs. Four, maybe five breaths. And then with my right thumb, I began doing chest compressions. I had no idea how fast they needed to be, I just did what felt right. After about thirty seconds I stopped and watched. Still nothing. And then…her tiny head moved, just a little. And her mouth opened, and she took a breath. I rubbed her a little more, and she rolled her head again. This time, after another breath, I heard a faint yip. Scooter heard it too and looked up at me and then at her puppy. Then she lay back down on the towel. There was more work to be done.

The puppy was now actively squirming in my hand. She was going to be fine. I laid her on the towel beside Scooter and watched as she gamely tried to stand.

The sound of clapping and cheering came from the other side of the porch doors and I looked up. The kids were jumping up and down and yelling. And then I saw that my wife was crying. Without words, she thanked me and told me she was proud of what I had just done.

Scooter would deliver five more puppies. Only two responded to her maternal ministrations. The other three required the same resuscitative efforts, and did fine. We lost just one puppy that morning, the first one. And the last little girl pup, Ivey, was the runt of the litter. She would be a member of our family for almost thirteen years.

That was a bright and shining moment for me, one I will never forget. But the experience would prove to be something else, something much more consequential.

2:00 a.m. Two weeks later.

Sheila Rice had just returned from Radiology. She had taken two auto accident patients around for some X-rays. Nothing serious, just a few bumps and bruises. At the moment they were our only patients.

She walked over to the nurses' station and sat down beside me. "Doc, I'm gonna need some coffee here in a minute. How about you?"

"No, I'm fine right now, Sheila," I answered, not looking up from the day-old newspaper I was paging through. "Maybe later."

Sheila was one of our regular night nurses. For some reason, working the graveyard shift suited her home life. But most important, she was able to sleep during the day. She had been doing this for a long time, ten or twelve years.

I was always glad to have her working with me. She had a lot of experience in the ER and was cool and calm in an emergency. Maybe most significant, she was a great Password partner. When we had some downtime, usually three or four in the morning, a couple of the lab techs would come over and challenge us to a game. The outcome was always the same, and they'd limp back to their department.

"Well, I'm going to the lounge, so should you change your—"

She wasn't able to finish her sentence. The door to triage had burst open and one of our business office secretaries came barreling towards us, pushing a young Asian woman in a wheelchair.

"You better come get this one!" she yelled in our direction. "I think she's havin' a baby!"

Sheila was instantly on her feet. "Madeline, take her over there to room 1," she directed, pointing in that direction.

Madeline put her back into it and gained even more speed with the wheelchair. She wanted no part of this and was determined to make her own delivery as quickly as possible.

It was then I noticed a young Asian man following them. He spoke quickly yet quietly to the young woman, in a language I couldn't understand. She didn't say anything, just nodded her head.

Madeline and Sheila transferred our patient from the wheelchair to the stretcher, and then Madeline escorted the man out of the department.

"Come on with me," she said to him. "We'll need to fill out some paperwork."

I had remained seated during all of this. Sheila would call me when I was needed. *If* I was needed. Usually when expectant women came to the ER like this, a quick assessment by the nurse would determine they either were not in labor, or were in its very early stages. In either circumstance, we would immediately send the patient to the OB floor to be evaluated. Only very rarely, maybe once or twice a year, would we deliver a baby in the ER or in the parking lot. And that was fine with me. It was fun to do this every once in a while, but we really weren't set up to handle deliveries, and it was always a stressful situation.

"Dr. Lesslie, get over here now!"

It was Sheila, and I was immediately on my feet.

I reached for the curtain but Sheila pulled it open for me, grabbing me by the arm and pulling me into the room.

"Here, do your thing," she said. "This baby's crowning. I'll go and get the delivery kit."

"Are you sure?" I asked her, still hoping we could just send this lady upstairs.

"Well, you tell me," she answered. She stepped to the side of the stretcher and gently spread the woman's knees. The top of the baby's head, covered with thick black hair, was just visible. What I could see was about the size of a 50-cent piece.

Whoa! Now it was more like a tennis ball!

"Get that kit, Sheila, and hurry up!"

I grabbed some gloves from a box on the countertop and snapped them on. Looking up at this patient, I suddenly realized she hadn't made a sound, not a moan or anything. And I realized I didn't know her name.

"Ma'am, everything's going to be fine here, okay?"

Ma'am? Where did that come from? She just looked at me, no evidence of pain in her face, no sound coming from her lips. She obviously didn't understand what I was saying, so I just looked at her and nodded. She smiled, and nodded back at me.

Sheila came up behind me, tearing the blue paper from the delivery kit. With one foot, she pulled an instrument stand from the corner of the room to the end of the stretcher. Then, throwing the paper on the floor, she opened the kit and dropped it on the stand.

The contents of the kit were limited and straightforward. There was an umbilical cord clamp, scissors, a pile of gauze, a couple of small blue towels, ring forceps, and a suction bulb for the baby's nose and mouth. If we needed anything else, we could quickly find it in the supply closet.

Then the young woman made the first noise we had heard from her. It was only a faint grunt, but Sheila and I both reacted to it. I stepped to the side of the stretcher and Sheila moved closer to the head. Then she once again gently spread the woman's knees, softly speaking words of encouragement.

"There, there, honey, it's going to be okay," she reassured her. "Now don't start pushing just yet."

Too late. I could see one ear now. It was time to deliver this baby.

I reached down, located one shoulder, and delivered it with ease. The second shoulder quickly followed. And then in one slithery, slippery instant, the baby, a little girl, was lying on the stretcher between her mother's legs.

I felt an enormous relief. While reaching for the suction bulb to clear the baby's airway, I quickly glanced at our new mother's face. Her forehead was glistening with sweat and a smile spread on her face. Her eyes met mine and she nodded, still silent, still calm.

"What in the world is that?"

Sheila's shocked concern immediately drew my attention back to the baby.

"What are you talk—" I stopped mid-sentence and stared at the newborn. In the midst of the precipitous delivery, I hadn't noticed.

"What is this thing?" Sheila asked again, now pointing at something that completely enveloped the baby.

My pulse quickened and my chest tightened. The relief I had experienced just seconds ago was now gone.

And then an image flashed before my eyes and I suddenly remembered. *Scooter.*

The newborn girl was covered with a transparent, glistening sac. It was still wet and slippery, and it would prevent her from breathing. "Intact membranes" is the medical term. I had read and heard about such a thing, but with our modern delivery techniques this was a rare occurrence. Rarer still for an ER doctor.

Dropping the green bulb on the stretcher, I told Sheila, "Get me a number 15 blade." The calmness in my voice surprised me. But I *was* calm. I knew what needed to be done, and I knew how to do it.

Almost without looking, Sheila reached behind her to a shelf on the wall and quickly located the needed scalpel. She peeled back the sterile wrapper and held out the exposed handle.

Taking the blade, I quickly made a careful incision through the membrane, and peeled the glistening capsule away from the little girl's head. Grabbing the bulb syringe, I then suctioned her nose and mouth. Then, thankfully, the three of us heard her first loud, strong cry. She was as tough and resilient as her mother.

Sheila picked up the baby and used one of the towels to remove the remainder of the membrane and dry her off. The cord was then clamped and cut, and Sheila placed the girl in her mother's arms.

I slumped onto the stool at the side of the stretcher, enjoying this moment as the remains of the adrenaline surge washed through my body.

"Have you ever seen anything like that?" Sheila asked me as she gazed down at our new mother and child.

"Nope, sure haven't," I answered. And then I thought about Scooter again and the back porch. "Well, as a—"

"But how did you know what to do?" she persisted. "I've never seen anything like it."

I was thinking of where to begin when the voice of the unit secretary interrupted us. "Sheila, we got one out here," she called from the nurses' station.

"Hmm," she sighed. "Well, let me go see what that is. I'll call OB and have them come down and take this lady upstairs. I guess we should call the pediatrician too."

She walked out of the room, pulling the curtain closed behind her.

Later, when it was again quiet, I would tell her. And Sheila would understand. This was not some fortuitous coincidence. I believe Einstein was wrong when he said that "coincidence is God's way of remaining anonymous." Our Creator doesn't choose to remain unknown or in the background of our lives. He wants us to know Him, and to walk with Him, and to talk with Him. And if we will listen, He wants to talk with us.

For that, this night, I was grateful.

Willis Stephens's head was trembling. Not badly, but sitting where I was in the pew behind him, it was noticeable. Subtle, but noticeable.

I had been studying the back of Willis's head for the past minute or so, and a strange thought crossed my mind. *What if Willis were to collapse? What if right at this moment, he slumped over in the pew?*

We were at a point in the worship service where such thoughts were not too intrusive, or at least not completely disturbing. The organist was playing some quiet music, and my ruminations were not distracting me from a prayer or the sermon.

I'm not sure why I was considering this possibility. When my wife and I had slid into this pew, Willis had turned around and offered me a solid, firm handshake. He was almost ninety and still going strong. For all of the years we had been members of this church, Willis Stephens had been a fixture, a bastion of the congregation. He was known for his humor and generosity, and for his love of young children.

Yet on this particular morning, something caused me to consider the back of his head, this mild tremor, and what I would do should he suddenly collapse in front of me.

What would I do?

I glanced beside me at my friend, Francis Wood. He was about my age and strong and agile enough. But how would we be able to help Willis?

The vestibule just in front of us, to the right of the choir loft, would be the logical place to take him. There was enough room there, there was a telephone for calling 9-1-1, and we could close the door behind us to shield the congregation. But how would we get him there? I had dealt with this before, the issue of "dead weight." If a person completely loses consciousness and muscle tone, he or she becomes extremely difficult to pick up and carry.

Once, before I had learned to call for a male nurse or any available EMT, I had run out into the parking lot of the ER to help get a patient out of a car. The person had apparently had a heart attack and collapsed on the way in. A young female nurse and I had reached the vehicle, followed by another nurse pushing a stretcher. What ensued was something I never want to repeat.

We tried to get a middle-aged man, weighing maybe two hundred pounds, out of the car and onto the stretcher. Arms and legs were everywhere. I thought I was in pretty good shape, but it was extremely difficult to maneuver the man onto the gurney. Somehow we managed to get this accomplished and get him into the ER. We were all exhausted.

Now, here was Willis. He probably weighed more than two hundred and twenty-five pounds. What would Francis and I do?

Then, like a flash, there it was, right in front of me: the "fireman's carry." That would do it. Let's see if I could remember…I would grab one of my elbows with one hand, and one of Francis's elbows with the other. He would do the same thing, creating a sort of chair seat made with our forearms. We would do this under Willis's slumping body and then be able to lift him with relative ease. Standing, we could then take him to the vestibule and carefully place him on the floor.

Having solved this dilemma, I relaxed just as our minister was getting to his feet and approaching the pulpit. I no longer noticed the continual shaking of the head in front of me.

We were a few minutes into the sermon when it happened.

There was a rustle of movement behind me. Not a lot, but just enough to distract my attention. And then there was a tap on my shoulder.

Turning to my left, I saw one of the young men of the congregation leaning into the pew behind me. He whispered, "Robert, we need you in the back. Something has happened to John Stanford."

I immediately stood up, and I looked beyond him to the back of the sanctuary. A few rows from the back wall, several people were huddled around the slumped-over body of John Stanford. A murmur of hushed voices began to sweep through the sanctuary, and somewhere in my subconsciousness I realized the minister had ceased speaking.

Making my way across the pew, I turned to Francis and said, "Come on, I'll need some help." John Stanford was in his mid-seventies and, like Willis Stephens, he must have weighed in excess of two hundred pounds.

My mind was racing as we hurried down the aisle. What had happened to him? Was he breathing? Had someone called 9-1-1? As we neared the back of the sanctuary, I watched as three or four men fumbled trying to get him out of the pew. This was not going to be easy, and I wondered how we were going to get him to the back of the church. We needed some space, and first we would have to get him out of the narrow confines of the pew. Then it struck me again: the "fireman's carry."

We reached his pew and I pointed to Francis and said, "Here, go in this row and get beside him." I made my way down the row behind John, stepping on a few toes as I negotiated my way.

Though John seemed completely unconscious, I quickly determined he had a pulse and was breathing. I said to the men standing around him, "Give us just a little bit of room." I then proceeded to instruct Francis in the carry. We fumbled with each others' elbows for a moment and then it all came together. It wasn't easy, but we were able to lift John and make our way down the pew and out the back to the foyer.

Gently, we laid him on the carpet and I again checked his pulse. It was there, but weak. He was pale, and his skin was clammy. Undoing his tie and unbuttoning his shirt, I asked Francis to raise John's legs to get more blood to his central circulation.

"Has someone called 9-1-1?" I asked the group in the foyer.

"They're on the way," came the response. "Should be here in about five minutes."

John was beginning to stir. His eyes opened, and he looked around him and then up at me. He was confused and afraid.

"John, everything's going to be okay," I told him. "Just relax and take some slow, deep breaths."

His color improved, and his pulse was stronger now. By the time the paramedics came through the foyer doors, John was talking and asking, "What happened?"

The EMS team had him on a cardiac monitor, an IV started in his right arm, and oxygen prongs in his nose within minutes. He was stable and was soon on his way to the hospital. He later told me that when visitors came to his hospital room, he would tell them, "The worst part of the whole thing was waking up on the floor and finding Robert Lesslie taking my clothes off."

As the ambulance siren faded in the distance, I turned to Francis and put my hand on his shoulder. "Thanks for your help. That was something, wasn't it?"

He was sweating, and I noticed that my shirt was soaked.

"Man, Robert, I didn't know how we were going to get him out of that pew. I'm glad you thought of…whatever it was we just did."

I knew then that, while those thoughts about Willis had been mine, they had come from some other place. I had never done the fireman's carry. I had never needed to—and to this day, I have never again performed it. On this particular day, however, John Stanford had needed some help, and I had been made an instrument. That was a humbling thought.

2:30 p.m. Wednesday.

The chart of my next patient read,

Brad Jenkins
42 year-old-male
sore throat, cough, and congestion

The triage nurse had placed him in our ENT (ear, nose, and throat) room.

This should be straightforward enough, I thought. No fever. Blood pressure was fine.

With the chart in hand, I turned to walk down the hallway.

"You might want these," Amy Conners suggested to me. She was shuffling and straightening some medical documents. They were recent ER records, copies of visits, which we kept in the department. The file drawer they were kept in had a folder for each of the previous 31 days, allowing us to quickly retrieve the records of each patient visit for the prior month. We had a few "frequent flyers," and this system allowed us to better track these patients and their multiple visits.

"Looks like he's been here a half-dozen times in the past two weeks," she added, sliding the stack of records across the counter.

That was a little unusual, and before I went to the ENT room I needed to take a look at these.

Multiple visits represented a potential red flag. One of the cardinal rules in the ER had to do with return visits. It also had a lot to do with attitudes and assumptions. A dangerous tendency among inexperienced ER staff members was to assume that an unscheduled return visit was a nuisance and probably bogus. This tendency would lead to a superficial examination and evaluation on the return visit, which in turn would sometimes result in disaster. The returning patient might in fact have something serious going on that had been missed on the first visit. It sometimes required discipline to remain objective and dispassionate, but these patients needed to be approached with a finer tuning of one's clinical radar.

Amy was right. Including today's, I counted six visits for Mr. Jenkins during the past two weeks.

Hmm. On the first visit, I had been the examining physician. He had complained of head congestion, drainage, and a mild cough. My diagnosis had been an "upper respiratory infection," and he had been treated with a decongestant and cough medicine. I looked carefully at this note, making sure his vital signs had been normal, and that I had not missed any subtle bit of information. Everything seemed routine.

On the next visit, two days later at midnight, he had been seen by one of my partners. His complaint then had been of persistent cough and difficulty sleeping. His vital signs again were completely normal, and nothing suspicious showed up in his health history. On this visit, he had received an extensive workup, including a chest X-ray and blood studies. Everything was normal. My partner had made a diagnosis of bronchitis and had given him an antibiotic, covering any potential underlying bacterial infection. Again, everything seemed appropriate. And he had again been instructed to follow up with his family doctor should he not improve.

Mr. Jenkins had come back to the ER three days after that visit, stating that he was no better. His complaint was "cough, congestion, fatigue." The next visit was for "nausea," and the ER sheet from yesterday simply read, "no better." Each time, his exam had been normal and he was told to follow up with his doctor.

Maybe he didn't have a doctor. Maybe he didn't have any insurance or the financial ability to afford follow-up elsewhere. I glanced at the demographic portion of today's record and noted that he was employed by one of the large companies in town. He had listed his job title as "regional manager."

This was unusual. "Thanks, Amy," I told her, attaching these records to his clipboard under today's encounter sheet.

I closed the door of the ENT room behind me and stood at the foot of the exam table. Brad Jenkins was sitting on the bed, leaning forward with his arms outstretched and his hands grasping the edge of the thin mattress that provided only a modicum of comfort. His legs swung in tandem beneath him and he looked up at me as I entered.

He seemed comfortable enough, and in no obvious distress. He wore khaki pants, a light-blue button-down collared shirt, and a red tie. Nothing struck me as being out of the ordinary.

"Mr. Jenkins, I'm Dr. Lesslie," I perfunctorily introduced myself. "What can we do for you today?"

He stopped swinging his legs but maintained his posture, leaning over and holding onto the bed.

"I'm sure you're aware I've been here a few times recently," he began, nodding at the clipboard in my hands. "I'm just not getting any better. Still feel lousy, with some congestion and occasionally a little cough." He cleared his throat after this last statement. "And I understand you're the medical director here, so I just want to say that each time I've been treated, the doctors and nurses have been very professional. I have nothing to complain about regarding my treatment, except that I'm just not getting better."

Six visits in two weeks—and he sat here in front of me completely calm, and actually complimenting us. I looked down at his chart again, making sure he didn't have a low-grade fever, or a slightly elevated heart rate—something, anything, that might tip me off to a significant underlying problem we were missing.

"Well, thanks," I responded. "But our goal here is to make sure you're okay, and to try to figure out what's causing your symptoms. Have you had any weight loss, or night sweats? Any unusual changes in your appetite or daily routine? Any bleeding?"

The answers to these questions were all in the negative. I continued to probe for any possible clue to his problem, any bit of information that would lead me to a correct diagnosis. I would be happy for something that just pointed me in *some* direction.

Nothing. Everything seemed completely normal, except for this slight cough and sore throat. And even these symptoms, when pursued, were vague and nonspecific.

His exam was completely normal as well. Ears, nose, throat, heart, chest—all normal. His muscle tone and neurological exam were also normal.

I rubbed my chin and looked at the previous visit's notation. He had had a CBC (complete blood count) done then and it was completely normal. No evidence of infection or anemia, or any problems with his platelets.

"Well, Mr. Jenkins," I began, having exhausted any thoughts and ideas, "I don't see anything bad going on today. And I'm sorry I can't give you a specific diagnosis as to what's causing your problems. Sometimes it just takes a little while to sort these things out. I think the most appropriate thing for us to do is have you seen by one of the ENT docs here in town. Maybe in the next week or two. We can help you set that up."

I paused, waiting for a response. He said nothing, just looked at me.

"Does that sound alright?" I asked him.

He lowered his head and stared at the floor, nodding.

"Hmm. I suppose," he said. There was resignation in his voice, but no frustration, and certainly no anger.

"Okay then," I responded. "Let me get some paperwork together and we'll be right back. We'll help you get lined up with one of our specialists."

There was no response, and I stepped out of the room.

As I walked up the hallway, I realized I had no sense of closure with Brad Jenkins. There was a small measure of release. I had taken a complete history and performed a thorough physical exam. I had done my job. Yet there was no closure. Sometimes that just doesn't happen in the ER and you have to move on to the next patient. But this was somehow different. There was something else going on here and I couldn't quite name it.

At the nurses' station, I stood at the counter writing on Brad Jenkins's record. Amy was reaching into the referral file to retrieve the slip of paper with the names, addresses, and phone numbers of our ENT doctors.

"What's going on with him?" she asked. "Seems like a straight-up guy, don't you think? But with all these visits…"

"Yeah, he seems straight-up," I agreed. "But I don't know exactly why he keeps coming back. Everything seems okay."

I put my pen down, struggling with what to write in the box entitled "Diagnosis." What *was* my diagnosis?

Something was bothering me, and I didn't like the feeling. Trying to shake off this unwanted emotion, I picked up the pen again. Its point hovered above Mr. Jenkins's chart, momentarily suspended while a thought formed in my mind. I don't know where it came from, but as it crystallized I knew what I needed to do.

Putting the pen in my lab-coat pocket, I returned to the ENT room. Brad Jenkins was still sitting on the exam table, but now he was leaning back against the wall, his hands folded in his lap. I closed the door and walked over to the stool in the corner of the room. Sitting down, I looked at him and our eyes met.

"Mr. Jenkins," I began, a little unsure of where this would lead, but determined to take this course. "I need to ask you a couple more questions."

"Sure, Doctor, what do you need to know?" he responded flatly.

"On one of your previous visits, you mentioned you were having trouble sleeping. You told me that it was due to some cough and congestion—but how long has that been going on?" I asked him.

"Oh, a couple of months, I suppose," he answered. "Why?"

"And tell me about your daily routine. What do you do for fun?" I pursued.

A puzzled look appeared on his face, and he was obviously struggling for a response. "I, uh, I...you know, I really don't know," he finally answered.

After asking a few more questions, I came directly to my point. "Brad, have you ever had any problems with depression? Ever felt really down and disconnected?"

He stared at me for a moment and then looked away, hanging his head.

When he didn't say anything, I asked, "Have you ever thought about hurting yourself?"

Upon hearing this question, his chest heaved and he whispered, "Yes."

This was painful for him, but I had to go on.

"Have you thought about how you might do that?" I asked him.

He took a deep breath and looked straight at me. "Yes, I have. There's a .38 in my car, and I was planning on leaving here and driving out to the lake. I can't go on like this anymore."

Brad Jenkins told me about his failing marriage, his estranged teenage son, and the ever-increasing stresses of his high-profile job. His life was coming unraveled, and he didn't know where to turn.

"We're going to get you some help, Brad."

He would be admitted to the hospital under the care of one of the staff psychiatrists. While Amy was making those arrangements, I took Mr. Jenkins's car keys and, with a security guard, walked out to the parking lot. We identified his car and unlocked the driver's door. I reached under the seat and felt the cold metal of a handgun.

God does speak—now one way, now another—
though man may not perceive it.

—JOB 33:14

11

Possessed

In the synagogue there was a man possessed by a demon, an evil spirit.

—LUKE 4:33

It was two o'clock in the morning, the middle of April. Remarkably, the ER was completely empty of patients. We had just discharged our last visitor, an alcohol-infused college student who had met a sidewalk up close and personal. He had sustained a laceration of his eyebrow, a badly swollen lip, and three fractured teeth. The morrow would be a tough one for him.

I was sitting at the nurses' station with my feet on the desk when the phone rang.

"Dr. Lesslie, it's for you," said Lynne, the night-shift secretary, handing me the receiver. "One of the ER doctors in York."

York is a small town fifteen miles from us, and they have a small but moderately busy ER. A phone call from there, especially in the middle of the night, was never a good thing. This would be no exception.

"This is Dr. Lesslie," I spoke into the receiver.

"Dr. Lesslie, this is Dr. Frost in York. I've got the duty here tonight, and I need a little help." He sounded young and a little perplexed.

"Okay. What's going on?" I responded, putting my feet on the floor and sitting a little more upright.

"Well, I've got a lady here, thirty-five or thirty-six, I think, and, uh, she needs some attention, and it's…it's more than we can provide here," he explained.

"What kind of attention?" I asked him, becoming curious and not a little apprehensive. "What's her problem?"

There was momentary silence.

"For one thing, she's crazy. I'm sure of that. But that's not her main problem," he stated with a newfound assurance. Yet there remained an undercurrent of consternation in his voice. Now I had a sense he was holding something back. When he had said "crazy," my mind had immediately shifted to a process that concluded quickly, with an acceptable and familiar disposition. The mental-health system in his county was a good one, and they were able to get people the psychological help they needed when they needed it. But he should know that. The York ER had its share of psychiatric emergencies.

"She, uh, she also has a medical problem that needs attention," he continued.

He waited for my response.

"And what is that?" I asked, now growing a little impatient.

"She swallowed her tongue," he stated flatly. "No, wait. She pulled it out first, and then swallowed it."

I sat there expecting more, but it was not forthcoming.

"She what?" I asked, needing clarification. "Swallowing your tongue" conjures up images of someone having a seizure and losing control of their musculature, with the attendant risk of their tongue limply falling back into the airway and causing a real problem. But of course no one "swallows" their tongue. And no one "pulls out" their tongue. It would be too painful and too bloody. This Dr. Frost on the phone must be nuts too.

"Just how bad is this injury, and how about her airway?" I gave him the benefit of the doubt.

"Oh, her airway's fine," Dr. Frost told me, now seeming more comfortable in this clinical dialogue. "And her tongue is pretty messed up, what's left of it. But it's not bleeding too much. She, uh, she won't let me get a good look. But she's breathing just fine."

I thought for a moment. "Well, it sounds to me like she needs an ENT doc, or maybe an oral surgeon. Have you called anybody?"

The medical community in York was rather limited, with mainly family practice physicians on the staff. There were no specialists, and patients needing the services of one were usually sent to Rock Hill.

"I tried a couple up your way, Dr. Woods and Dr. Smith, but they weren't interested," he told me. "They won't accept her in transfer. No luck there. They both thought she should be seen by someone from mental health first, and then some kind of decision could be made."

He should be able to handle this, but I sensed he was trying to make his problem mine, and I was determined not to let that happen. This was my chance. I would advise him to pursue this last option, the psych referral, and let them resolve his dilemma.

Before I could speak, he continued. "And I called mental health, but they said her medical problem had to be stabilized before they would get involved. See the predicament I'm in?" He was trying to hand this off to me, but I would have none of it.

"Well, it does sound like a tough situation. Have you tried anyone in Columbia or Charlotte? Maybe someone there would be able to help out. And what about your medical doctor on call in there? Maybe the patient has a family physician you could call?"

"Nope, I've tried all of those," he said. And then here it came. "I was hoping that—"

I interrupted him. "My advice would be that you keep trying. Or maybe keep her stabilized until morning, and see how things shake out then. It's usually easier to make some of these tough dispositions in the light of day," I advised him. Anticipating a rebuttal, I continued, "But I don't think we can help you here. It sounds like you've done everything we would do. I'd just keep trying and, well…good luck."

I had no qualms about my response to his predicament. He was working as an ER doctor and should be able to take care of this situation. Besides, there was an unspoken law among the brotherhood of ER docs: "Thou shalt not dump on one another." And this would really be a dump.

There was silence on his end of the phone. And then a resigned, "Okay, I'll keep trying and see what I can come up with. Thanks." He was clearly disappointed as he hung up.

Lynne looked up at me. "What was that all about?" she asked.

"The poor guy in the York ER has a real mess on his hands. He's got a psych case, and he's not sure how to handle it. I guess he was looking for us to bail him out, but this is something he needs to handle on his own. Hopefully."

"Hmm," was Lynne's response as she resumed work on her cross-word puzzle.

I went to our office for a cup of coffee and to continue work on next month's schedule. It had the promise of being a quiet night, one to be appreciated, and one that presented an opportunity to catch up on some paperwork.

Thirty minutes later I walked up the hall to check on things at the nurses' station. Kathy Neal, a recent graduate from nursing school, was restocking the minor trauma room as I walked by.

"Still quiet," she said, clearly relieved, and certainly hopeful. She had been in the department for only three weeks and was still green. She was maybe a little too sensitive, but the consensus was she would be a good ER nurse. She would need some experience, but the ER of Rock Hill General would provide that pretty quickly.

"Yeah," I responded. "It's been a good night." I looked at my watch. 2:40 a.m.

At the nurses' station, Lynne had set aside her puzzle and was organizing her work area, making sure the next shift would have plenty of the multiple forms and reports necessary to carry on the business of the unit secretary.

The ambulance doors suddenly opened, activated by weight on the outside floor mat. Reflexively, I glanced in that direction.

"Are we expecting something?" I asked Lynne.

"Not that I know of," she answered, looking up at the entrance. "Nobody's called me."

Through the doors came a stretcher guided by two EMTs, one holding onto each end. I immediately recognized the two young men and their uniforms. They were with the York Rescue Squad.

On the stretcher, sitting up and straddling the gurney with one leg dangling over each side, was a young woman. She looked angry, and her lower lip was protruding as she stared straight ahead. She seemed completely oblivious to her new surroundings. Her hands were folded in her lap, and on the top of her head, falling almost into her eyes, was a tattered and soiled blue rag. It appeared to be some sort of a small towel.

"Whatcha got?" I asked Danny, one of the EMTs. I already knew the answer to this obligatory question. *Dr. Frost.*

Lori had heard the ambulance doors open and had come back into the department from triage. She was having the other EMT wheel the patient to room 5.

Danny stopped at the nurses' station, releasing the stretcher to his partner. He had a clipboard tucked under his arm, and he placed it on the countertop. He opened the metal flip-top and began making a few notes.

"Well, Doc," he began, "got a call from the York ER to bring this lady up this way. Dr. Frost said he had talked with you and you would be expecting her."

I felt my face flush, but didn't immediately say anything. *Don't shoot the messenger* and all that. Danny had nothing to do with this. He was just doing his job. My first instinct was to pick up the phone and blast this young Dr. Frost. But what good would that do? Nothing, at least not at this point. I couldn't turn the stretcher around and send this woman back to York. She was mine now. But I would be having a chat with Dr. Frost in the not-too-distant future.

Danny told me the story, repeating most of the information I had been given earlier. But then he added some information he had gathered from the sheriff's deputies who had been in the York ER with this woman.

"It seems, Doc, this woman has a long mental history. She and her two sisters had been causin' some disturbances in town over the past couple of days. Approachin' people on the street and threatenin' them with voodoo stuff and whatnot. Went into one of the stores downtown and started singin' and chantin'. This patient here, Ethel, seemed to be the worst. Finally, the deputies locked 'em all up. Sometime yesterday, I think. And that's when it got weird."

He paused, glancing over to room 5. Lori and the other EMT had transferred Ethel from the rescue squad's stretcher to our bed. She seemed to be peaceful enough at this point, sitting calmly, her arms still folded, her blue towel securely in place. Kathy Neal had stepped into the room and was watching from a safe distance.

Before Danny started again, I spoke to Lynne. "Go ahead and call Security. We'll need someone to stay with her until we can figure out what to do."

I turned back to Danny, and he continued. "One of my friends at the jail told me he locked the three sisters in the same cell, and they just huddled up in a corner, and were just rockin' back and forth and mumblin' stuff. Then things got real quiet, and he went back to take a peek, to make sure everything was okay. Man, that must have been when it started. Ethel here, she had her fingers in her mouth, like she was trying to get somethin' out. And she was. She was pullin' out her tongue, piece by piece with her fingers. And she finally pulled it all out, every bit of it."

He stopped, shaking his head.

"She what?" I asked. Now this was a little far-fetched. I had seen a lot of tongue injuries in my years in the ER. Kids falling, landing on their chins, and splitting the tips or sides of their tongues. I had even had an eighteen-year-old who came in one night telling me his girlfriend had gotten mad at him, then professed forgiveness and kissed him. During this kiss she had bitten off and swallowed the tip of his tongue. But it had only been the tip, a dime-sized piece, and it had only required a couple of stitches to repair. But ripping out your own tongue with your fingers? Impossible.

"Yep," Danny went on. "Every bit of it. Gone. And the funny thing, Doc, is it didn't even bleed very much. I woulda thought she woulda bled like a stuck pig, but she didn't. I guess it clotted off or somethin'."

"Why in the world would she do something like that?" I asked him, studying Ethel from a distance. She had begun to slowly and rhythmically rock forward and then backward.

"Her sister told the deputy she was tired of evil spirits speakin' through her and was gonna put a stop to it. And that's why she's got that nasty towel on her head—to keep the spirits from getting in. Just try to take that thing off. She'll snatch your hand quick as a flash."

"Hmm," I mused. This was pretty interesting, even though I doubted the seriousness of her tongue injury. No one would be capable of pulling their own tongue out. But the fact remained that I would have to sort this thing out and find something to do with Ms. Ethel.

"Well, thanks, Danny. And if you find yourself in the York ER again tonight, thank Dr. Frost for me."

"Sure thing, Doc," he replied. His face showed puzzlement over this last remark.

A security guard was walking up the hall as I approached room 5. In this case, the term may have been a little self-contradictory. This seventy-plus-year-old gentleman might be a guard, but he didn't look too secure, nor did he inspire much of a sense of security. Our hospital was not unlike many others. In their attempt to hold down expenses, they hired the cheapest security group they could find, which meant we usually had retired individuals, unarmed and untrained. But they had spiffy uniforms. Ed was one of our regular night-time guards, and he was quiet and pleasant enough. But on the occasion of a real problem in the department he had the habit of disappearing. Hopefully, watching Ethel would not be too taxing a job for him.

"Ed, pull up a chair here and just keep an eye on her," I said, leading him into room 5 and pointing to a corner of the room.

Lori was taking Ethel's blood pressure as I walked over to the bed.

"Ms…" I paused, glancing at the clipboard lying by her side, "Jones.

I'm Dr. Lesslie. We're here to help you tonight, and to see what we can do for you."

She didn't respond. She just kept rocking and staring straight ahead. I glanced at Lori and she looked at me, shaking her head.

I needed to try. "So, Ethel, let me take a look at your mouth."

To my surprise, she stopped rocking, turned her head toward me, and opened her mouth. I mean *really* opened it. Not wanting to lose the opportunity, I grabbed the wall-mounted flashlight and took a look.

I was shocked! It takes a lot to surprise me, but I was truly taken aback.

"Holy—" I began, but stopped, catching myself. I was still the doctor here, and needed to at least appear calm and in control.

But, "Holy smoke," I muttered to myself. "It *was* gone!" Her tongue was completely ripped out. I leaned in and took a closer look. It had been torn out to its very root. There was nothing left, just a nub at the back of her mouth. To my amazement, there was no bleeding, just a few clots covering the stump.

Lori was peering over my shoulder and I heard a faint gasp. We looked at each other, but neither of us said a word.

I stood up and replaced the flashlight in its holder. Ethel closed her mouth and resumed her upright posture, staring straight ahead but rocking in a different direction now, from side to side.

I walked out of the room, Lori beside me. Ed was seated in the corner, his legs crossed and his arms tightly folded across his chest. He was a comical vision. His bright-red baseball cap was askew, its rolled bill pointing to his left shoulder. And his narrow navy-blue tie had flipped over and settled on the right side of his chest. Yet he was deadly serious about his assignment, not taking his eyes off his charge as he began his vigil.

"Wow," Lori said. "I've never seen anything like that."

"I don't think I have either," I agreed, stroking my beard and beginning to wonder just what I was going to do with this woman.

Over the next hour, the prospects of finding a reasonable solution to this dilemma became dimmer and dimmer.

I made a few phone calls to our local docs, to see if one of the ENT specialists would take a look at this woman. The doctor on call had already been contacted by Dr. Frost and told me the same thing he had told him. "Robert, it sounds like this lady needs to see a psychiatrist. That's probably where you should start."

And you can imagine what the psychiatrist offered. "Robert, this is a medical problem first. Get her squared away with that, and we can take a look at her later on. And good luck."

Yeah. Good luck.

I passed all this on to Lori and asked her to be considering what we might be able to do. For the moment I was stuck. But at least Ethel was calm, and she was stable. There was absolutely no bleeding from her mouth.

Ed had given Ethel a small pad of paper and a ballpoint pen. "Figger she can't talk to us, and if she needs somethin', she can just write it on that paper there." He pointed to the pad that lay at the foot of the stretcher, seemingly unnoticed by Ms. Jones.

It was then that Ethel started. I was standing at the nurses' station and absently looking in her direction. Slowly her right arm went into the air and her torso turned toward Ed. Her index finger was extended, curled, and began to slowly make circles in the air. Suddenly, she pointed directly at Ed, and her head began shaking violently. Her eyes were wide open, and she seemed to be mumbling something, though it was completely incoherent. I thought our security guard was going to fall on the floor. There was a look of complete and paralyzing fear on his face. He had pushed his chair back against the wall as far as it would go, but that wasn't far enough. He slowly stood and edged sideways out of the room, never taking his eyes off Ethel. And she never took her eyes off him. She tracked him out of the room with her finger, her head shaking, her silent lips working feverishly.

"She's puttin' some kinda voodoo thing on me, Doc. That ain't right. I don't got to put up with this. No, sir," Ed told me, stepping out into the hallway. He hitched up his pants and said, "I'll just stand right over here, if it's all right with you." He quickly walked around the corner, out of Ethel's gaze, and stood leaning against the wall.

Lori had stepped into room 5 and was trying to calm our patient. She patted her gently on her shoulder, and in a moment, all was again under control. Ed stayed in the hallway, out of Ethel's sight.

It wasn't long after that Ethel picked up the pad of paper and began writing. I was tempted to ask Ed to see what she had written, but thought better of it.

I walked over to her, and glanced down at the pad. "Bathroom."

"Lori," I called out. This was something I couldn't help her with.

A few moments later, Lori was leading Ethel down the hallway, and it was quite a sight. Lori held her by the elbow, or I guess it was her elbow. Ethel was a great moving mound of sheets which had been indecorously draped around her. She was barefooted, shuffling along and looking from side to side. On top of her head was the blue towel.

I watched as they approached Ed, who pressed himself into the wall as they passed, his chin tucked into his chest. I chuckled at this, and then was startled by a scream and the loud clamor of metal pans banging and clanging on the floor. I could see the shiny stainless steel basins and bowls as they cascaded out of the ENT room.

It seems that Kathy, our novice nurse, had been working in this room, restocking and straightening up. She'd been carrying an armful of pans when she stepped to the doorway, looked up, and saw Ethel standing in front of her. That was all it took. She had dropped everything she was carrying and run down the hall. Later, she would confess she had wet her pants.

At 5:45 a.m., Lori struck upon the idea that would save us. "Why don't you see who's on call for ENT at one of the hospitals in Columbia, and see if they will accept her? Maybe the doctor in York didn't really call anybody down there."

"Hmm, that's a good idea," I responded, glad for any help from any quarter. Dr. Frost had said he'd called some docs in Columbia, but given his irresponsible actions, there was a good chance he hadn't. Now I was *hoping* he hadn't.

"Lynne, why don't you call down to Columbia General, talk to the secretary in the ER, and see who's covering ENT for them tonight. See if you can get them on the phone."

Fifteen minutes later, the phone rang. Lynne answered. "Dr. Lesslie, it's for you. A Dr. Bissel in Columbia."

I had never heard of a Dr. Bissel, but it didn't matter.

I picked up the receiver. Dr. Bissel was on call for his ENT group, and I explained Ethel's circumstances to him. I told him she clearly had a psych problem, but the overriding concern now was the injury to her tongue. I'm not sure he was completely awake, because he agreed to accept her. He instructed me to have her sent to the ER at Columbia General and he would take care of things from there.

"Thanks a lot, Dr. Bissel," I told him. "We'll get her on the road."

I hung up the receiver and looked at Lynne and Lori. "Whatever happens, *do not* answer that phone. If Dr. Bissel wakes up and changes his mind, I don't want to know about it. Let's get her on the interstate as fast as we can."

"I've already called EMS," Lori told me.

Twenty minutes later, one of our paramedic teams had transferred Ethel to their stretcher and was wheeling her out of the department. They came by the nurses' station, where I stood with Lori, and paused while she finished completing the required transfer papers.

I looked down at the sad figure on the stretcher. What circumstances had brought Ethel to this point? Was it no more than faulty neural connections in her brain? Or were she and her sisters right about the demonic spirits? Whatever the cause, the effect was a destroyed life. There was a darkness here, and I sensed it was more powerful than any medication we could offer her.

Lori folded the completed documents. She put them in a large envelope and handed this to the paramedic standing at the head of the stretcher. Then she said, "Good night, Ms. Jones. I hope that everything goes well for you."

Ethel didn't respond. She just stared straight ahead, wrapped in a hospital sheet, the blue towel still on her head. Then she looked at me and held out her hand. She opened her fingers to reveal a crumpled, sweat-soaked piece of paper. I stared at it. At first I didn't move. She nodded, and thrust her hand closer to me. There was nothing to do. I took the piece of paper.

The stretcher was moving toward the ambulance entrance. Ethel twisted her torso and stared at me, her eyes large and unblinking.

Unfolding the piece of paper, I read, "It will turn green and fall off."

Somehow I knew she wasn't talking about my nose.

Looking up, I saw the doors closing behind Ethel and her entourage, and then they were gone.

Everyone in the department was going about their normal duties. I didn't say anything to anyone, just dropped the scrap of paper into a nearby trash can.

Voodoo? Black magic? Demon possession? Mental illness? Nonsense?

You'll have to decide for yourself from what I've told you.

But I know what I think.

If **Tomorrow** Never **Comes**

You do not even know what will happen tomorrow. What is your life? You are a mist that appears for a little while and then vanishes.

—JAMES 4:13-14

In his song "If Tomorrow Never Comes," Garth Brooks follows that phrase with "would you know how much I love you?" That's a very pointed question. If there were no tomorrow, would we have said everything we need to say and done everything we need to do?

Probably not. Most of us stay focused on tomorrow and not enough on today, and things go unsaid and undone. That reality comes crashing home almost every day in the ER.

The light turned green and Jill Evans pulled out into the intersection, turning left. She was driving safely but was a little distracted, still upset about the argument she had had with her husband last night. She was trying to remember how it started. Dan came home late from work and was going through the mail. There was the phone bill, the electric bill, and then the credit-card statement. That's what had done it. He had exploded when he opened the envelope.

She didn't see the pickup truck as it ran the red light, its driver looking down to locate a dropped cigarette. He never applied his brakes and the truck T-boned Jill's small sedan at full speed, caving in the driver's side and flipping the car over. When the police got to the scene, the pickup driver was standing by the crushed hood of his truck, rubbing his bruised and scratched left shoulder. Jill was on her way to the ER.

Jeff was waiting for the EMS team as they came through the ambulance doors.

"Bring her in here," he told them, standing in the doorway of major trauma. We had activated our trauma response team and they were on their way in. I followed Jill's stretcher into the room.

There was a flurry of activity as we moved her to the bed. She had one IV in place and another was being started. Blood was being drawn, and two X-ray techs were shooting films of her neck and chest.

Denton Roberts and his EMT partner had told us of the scene and of Jill's initial condition. She was unresponsive and had an obvious head wound and a crushed left chest wall. They had managed to secure her airway with an endotracheal tube and maintained her blood pressure with rapidly administered IV fluids. Her condition had worsened when she got to the ER. Her blood pressure was falling, and she was exhibiting signs of a devastating brain injury.

"Does she have any family?" I asked. I glanced down and saw that the fingers of her left hand were mangled and obviously broken. And I saw her wedding band.

"Her husband's on the way," Denton answered. "He was at work and should be here any minute."

We continued to work with Jill, inserting a chest tube to re-inflate her left lung and stabilize her chest. And we called Radiology to arrange for an urgent CT scan of her head. The on-call neurosurgeon and general surgeon were on their way down.

Virginia Granger pushed the trauma room door open and walked over to the stretcher.

"Her husband is here," she told me. "He's in the family room and only knows his wife was in an accident. He doesn't know how bad she is."

Sam Wright, our general surgeon, had followed Virginia into the room. As he began his examination of Jill, I filled him in on what had happened thus far.

Then I turned to Virginia. "Okay, I'll go talk with her husband. Do we know his name?" I asked her.

"Dan Evans," she answered. "And he's by himself."

It was another lonely walk down the hall to the family room. Jill wasn't dead, but her prognosis was very grave. Sam Wright had agreed with my assessment. "I don't believe she's going to wake up, is she?" he had observed. Her head injury was extensive, and I had to agree.

Dan Evans was on the sofa in the family room. He sat there with his head hanging down and his hands clasped together. He looked up as I entered, an expectant expression on his face. He was in his late twenties and was dressed in a dark business suit and red tie.

"Are you here to tell me about Jill?" he asked me.

I walked over to the chair beside him and sat down. "Yes, I'm Dr. Lesslie. And you are Jill's husband?"

"Yes, yes. I'm Dan Evans," he answered. "How is she? When can I see her?"

I held her chart in my hands and was considering how to begin this when he said, "We, uh, we had a big fight last night. It was about something stupid. A credit-card bill, I think."

He put his hands on his knees and stared at the floor, shaking his head.

"It was really stupid, something so small. But I blew it out of proportion, and we started yelling at each other. We didn't even talk this morning. Hey, I didn't even see her before I went to work. And now this."

He paused and I said, "Mr. Evans—"

He interrupted again, as if I were not in the room.

"I didn't even say 'goodbye,' or 'I'm sorry,' or anything. I just got up and got dressed and got out of there." He looked up at me and stopped shaking his head. "You know, we have a rule, Jill and I. We made a promise when we first got married that we would never let the sun set on our anger. I think it comes from the Bible, or somewhere. And most times we're able to do that. One of us will remember our rule and remind the other, and we'll take a minute and figure things out. One time we…" He seemed to lose his focus for a moment, gazing at the chart in my hands.

Then he looked up again. "Don't you think that's a good rule?" he asked me. "Anyway, last night, I didn't think about it and neither did Jill. We just yelled at each other, and then I went in the bathroom to take a shower. When I got out, she had gone into the guest room and locked the door. I went to bed, and that was it."

When he paused this time, I knew he had finished. But I waited a moment, just to be sure. He sat before me, silent, his eyes searching my face.

"Dan, let me tell you about Jill…"

Dr. Simmons was in the middle of his examination when he glanced over at his nurse. With a barely perceptible tilt of his head, he silently signaled for her to step over behind him. He shifted back and to his left so she could see through the pelvic speculum. Her eyes widened as she looked at the golf-ball-sized ulcerated mass that had engulfed this young woman's cervix. She looked at Dr. Simmons in disbelief and shock.

"Now tell me again, Christy," he said to the twenty-eight-year-old lying on her back on the exam table. "When did this problem start?"

Christy McKenna repeated her story. She had noticed some bleeding a few weeks ago, unrelated to her periods. At first it had not been very much, but over the past few days it seemed to be getting worse. She didn't have any pain and had no other symptoms.

"And when was your last Pap smear?" he asked.

She was silent, and Dr. Simmons's nurse looked up at her. Christy had flushed and avoided her eyes.

Christy had grown up in Rock Hill and had left town to attend college. She had been offered a job right out of school and stayed in that same community. She hadn't established a relationship with any physicians there. She had come home to spend a few days with her folks and to see Dr. Simmons. He had been her Ob-gyn doctor since she was seventeen.

"I've been real busy lately, Dr. Simmons," she told him. "You know I stayed in Columbia after college, and with my new job…I just haven't had the time. I know that's not a good excuse, but I've just been going in too many directions."

"Uh-huh," he murmured. "So, when do you think your last exam was?" he persisted.

"It would have been, uh, probably the summer after my sophomore year. I think that's when I was last here," she answered.

"Hmm, that would be six or seven years," he calculated.

"I didn't realize it had been that long, but I suppose you're right," she replied sheepishly.

"Well, Christy, we've got a problem here," he began to tell her. "You've got a growth on your cervix, and it's pretty angry-looking. It may very well be cancer."

He paused to let this thunderbolt have its effect. Christy was silent.

"We won't know for sure until we send some tissue to the lab and have one of the pathologists take a look at it. That should take a couple of days, so why don't we plan on seeing you again at the end of the week. Maybe Friday?" he asked.

Christy was still silent, shocked by this devastating news. *I've got to call Momma,* she thought.

"Christy, is Friday okay?" he repeated, not having received a response.

"Friday?" Christy echoed, trying to focus on what Dr. Simmons had just said. "Yes, Friday should be fine. And I'll bring my mother with me, if that's alright."

That had been six months ago.

"Christy, Mrs. McKenna, I think everything's in order," the hospice nurse told them. "Your pain medicine is right here, and if you need anything, just call me."

Polly McKenna, Christy's mother, walked the young nurse to the front door. It was already dark outside. Only six o' clock, but it was mid-January and the days were still short.

"Thanks, Jenny," she told the nurse. "Thanks for everything. You're so good with her."

"She's had a bad day today, hasn't she?" Jenny said.

"Yes, she has," Polly sighed. "And they seem to be getting worse, don't they?"

Jenny disappeared into the evening and Polly went back to her daughter's bedroom.

"Momma, you need to get some rest," Christy said, her voice a mere whisper now.

"Don't you worry about me," Polly said, making sure all of her daughter's medications were in order and easily accessible.

"You just haven't been sleeping much," Christy added. "And I don't want you to wear yourself out."

Polly looked down at her daughter. She was proud of the remarkable way Christy had handled the past few weeks. Her body had betrayed her, but her spirit had seemed to grow stronger with each passing day. Yet a bitter and unnamable fear was growing within Polly.

She had to look away from her daughter and busy herself. "Have you heard anything from Jane?" Polly asked her.

The turning aside of Christy's head was answer enough.

Jane was Christy's older sister. She lived in California with her husband, Jeremy, and their six-month-old son, Azure. The two sisters hadn't seen each other in more than five years, and they had only spoken once during that time. Even that one occasion had occurred by accident. It had been Christmas Eve and Jane had dialed her mother's house and Christy had picked up the phone.

"Let me speak to Mother," Jane had said.

The girls had been very close growing up, sharing clothes and friends, and occasionally boyfriends. Then Jane had gone to school in Los Angeles and met and fallen in love with a fellow student, Jeremy. He was a self-defined "free spirit," and when he had come to Rock

Hill to officially meet the folks and declare his intentions, there had been immediate friction. Polly and Mat McKenna had done the best they could to make him feel welcome and a part of the family, but there had been a growing rub.

It had all exploded one afternoon when Mat sat down with Jeremy and expressed his thoughts about marriage.

"Jeremy, I guess you know this is very important to us," he had told him. "I don't know about your religious convictions, but I think you know what Jane believes. She was raised in the Baptist church, and I assume she wants to be married here in Rock Hill."

Jeremy had sat quietly during this conversation, studying the backs of his hands.

"Our minister strongly recommends several premarital counseling sessions," Mat told him, "and he can meet with the two of you this Saturday, if that suits. He's a low-key guy and I think you'll like him."

Jeremy looked up and said, "Mr. McKenna, no offense, but I'm not into that stuff. I guess you would call me an agnostic, or maybe a universalist. Jane and I have agreed to disagree on that one. Anyway, we've decided to get married in California, at a friend's house that overlooks the ocean. It'll be a civil service, so I don't suppose we'll be needing to meet with your preacher."

That had started a widening rift. Mat and Polly had talked with their daughter and soon realized there was no common ground and no room for compromise. They were disappointed and concerned, but reluctant to be the ones to place a wedge between themselves and their daughter, who would be living a continent away.

Christy had not been as complacent and accepting. She and Jane had gotten into a bitter argument late one night, and hurtful things were said and cruel accusations made. In the end, Jane had felt she had to choose between Jeremy and her family, and she chose Jeremy. She faulted Christy for being what she saw as the "tip of the spear."

The couple had been married on a bluff overlooking the Pacific Ocean, with none of Jane's family members present.

"She hasn't called?" Polly persisted.

"No, she hasn't," Christy answered weakly.

"Well, maybe I'll—" Polly began but was interrupted.

"No, just leave it alone, Momma. She'll call when she's ready."

Polly wasn't sure about that. Jane was in some sort of denial and had been since the diagnosis of inoperable cervical cancer had been made. She and Mat had called her and tried to explain what was going on.

"Jane, your sister is very sick," they had told her. "Dr. Simmons performed a routine examination and found a tumor on her cervix. It turned out to be cancer, and a CT scan showed that it's spread through her abdomen and to her liver. He can't operate on it, so they'll be trying chemo and some other things. He said that if she had just had a Pap smear…"

Jane had been silent to that point and then she'd interrupted. "I had an abnormal Pap smear a few years ago, some inflammation or something like that. I just had to take some medicine and then it went away. Everything's fine now." And then she went still. That was all she said. No questions, no messages for Christy, nothing. And she hadn't called her sister in all these months.

This was a heartache that was hard for Polly and Mat to bear. They had called Jane on several other occasions, but the response was always the same. She didn't seem to be hearing them.

Polly kissed her daughter's forehead, told her goodnight, and quietly left the room. She made sure the night-light was on and the door was slightly cracked.

That night, they panicked. The people from hospice were wonderful, and they had clearly and accurately explained the dying process to Polly and Mat. The staff had been uncanny in their ability to map out these final few weeks and days, and had told them the end was fast approaching.

The McKennas thought they would be ready for this, but at midnight when Christy began making gurgling sounds and was no longer responsive, they panicked and called 9-1-1. Then Mat called Jane and told her Christy was dying.

I was in the ER when they came in. The paramedics took Christy to the Cardiac room and Jeff and I followed.

I had never seen Christy before, but it was obvious to me she was terminally ill. Her wasted frame caused me to look up at Denton, the lead paramedic, and start to ask a question.

His eyes and a nod of his head indicated I should look behind me. Mat and Polly McKenna had come into the room and were standing at the foot of the stretcher, their arms around each other. Polly was looking down at her daughter and was crying. Mat looked at me with reddened eyes and a hopeless and helpless look on his face.

They told me Christy's story, and I understood what needed to happen. She was near death, with agonal respirations and a slowing and weakening pulse. It would not be long. Once I was sure Mat and Polly understood what was happening and would be all right, Jeff and I left the room. The telemetry monitor at the nurses' station would tell me when it was over.

Jane had caught the first flight she could arrange out of Los Angeles, but there had been several delays. She made it to Rock Hill in time for the visitation and the funeral.

Stewart Donaldson was on his way in again. Denton Roberts had just called in on the EMS radio and given us a report: chest pain, shortness of breath, low blood pressure. We had been here before.

Stewart was 61 years old and was a retired chemist. He and his wife, Maggie, lived in a small house on the outskirts of town where they had raised their three children and where she maintained one of the finest rose gardens in the county. Five or six years ago Stewart had suffered a heart attack, a massive one. He had barely made it to the ER. I had been on duty that night, and we had struggled to stabilize him and then get him to the cath lab. The cardiologist told him he had small-vessel disease and it was not amenable to bypass surgery. They had placed a couple of stents in his coronary arteries, and this had worked for about a year. Then he'd had another heart attack, not as bad as the first, but it had knocked off a little bit more of his heart muscle.

Stewart had tried everything: medications, diet, exercise. Nothing seemed to be working. He'd continued to have episodes of chest pain and then several additional small heart attacks. With each of them he lost a little more of his heart. The last time he had been in the ER he'd been in congestive heart failure, his diseased heart failing to pump out the blood that was returning to it. His lungs had filled with fluid and he had almost died. He had survived that episode but now he was on a precarious balance beam, with any new stress or new development threatening to tip him into failure again.

Stewart and Maggie had considered a heart transplant but had decided against it. The chance of his surviving the surgery was too small, and the aftermath was too frightening. And they weren't even sure they could get on a waiting list.

They had resolved to deal with his heart condition as best they could and accept what each day brought. Recently, not many of those days had been very good.

It was a little after three o'clock in the afternoon when Denton wheeled Stewart into the department. Stewart looked up and smiled at me as he passed the nurses' station. His color was bad, and he was struggling for breath. Maggie followed a few steps behind.

Lori was waiting for them in Cardiac and helped Denton transfer him to our stretcher.

"The last reading I got was 60 over 40," he told her. That was a dangerously low blood pressure and would limit some of the interventions we would be able to try.

Lori attached his electrodes to our heart monitor and waited for the screen to come alive. An irregular beep…beep-beep…indicated that he was in an unusual rhythm and that his heart rate was rapid, somewhere around 120. None of this was good.

I walked over to the side of his stretcher and said, "Stewart, I thought you were going to stay away from this place."

He looked up and smiled. "Well, Dr. Lesslie, I tried. But I suppose I just wanted to come and visit."

He had difficulty speaking, and this brief sentence tired him. I patted his shoulder, noting that his skin was cool and sweaty.

"That's okay," I told him. "We're always glad to see you and Maggie." She had come into the room with him and was standing behind me, making sure she was out of our way.

"Are you having any pain today?" I asked him.

He shook his head, conserving his energy.

"Just the shortness of breath?" I pursued.

This time he nodded and as he did so, the nasal prongs that were delivering oxygen slipped from his nose. Lori reached over and gently replaced them, tightening the straps that went over his ears.

After I examined Stewart I said, "We'll need to get a chest X-ray and EKG. And we'll need to check some labs to see just where we are. That shouldn't take long."

Turning to his wife I told her, "Maggie, you can stay in here with him if you want. We're going to try a few things to help his breathing, but you won't be in the way."

"Of course," she said. "And I'll just stay right over here." She patted the countertop behind her and stepped closer to it. "Oh, and Dr. Lesslie," she added. "I brought you something."

She had a rose in her hand, its stem wrapped in aluminum foil. It was a single dark red bloom, and it was beautiful.

"I was hoping you would be on duty today," she said, smiling. "I remember you liked the darker roses, and my Black Magic is just now blooming. Here, this is for you." She handed me the flower.

I vaguely remembered talking with her at some point in the past about her roses, and I must have expressed my preferences. Her memory impressed me.

"Maggie, you didn't have to do this," I said, taking the rose from her. "This is really thoughtful."

"Just be sure to put it in some water," she instructed me, wiping her hands together.

I took the rose and stepped out of the room just as the X-ray techs entered, rolling their portable machine.

Thirty minutes later we had enough information to know that Stewart had suffered another heart attack and was in worsening heart failure. He had responded a little to the oxygen and the small amount of medicine we could give him to reduce the fluid in his lungs. There just weren't many options for him at this point.

I had called his cardiologist and he had mentioned trying the things we had already done.

"Well, Robert," he had told me, "there's just not much else we can do for Mr. Donaldson. If you want me to put him in the hospital, I will. But it sounds like this is going to be the end for him."

This was blunt, but his words were true. This reality had been hovering around me, but I had been unwilling to grapple with it. Now I must.

"Thanks. I'll give you a call if something changes."

As I hung up the phone, Lori asked me, "Did he have anything to offer? Any ideas?"

"No, nothing," I said. "Just pretty much what we already know. Stewart's not doing well, and I don't know if he is going to survive the evening. I need to go talk with them."

One of our techs was adjusting Stewart's monitor as I entered the room.

"Sandy," I said to her. "I need to talk with the Donaldsons, if you wouldn't mind stepping out for a minute."

She finished adjusting the leads and checked the rate of the IV fluids. "Sure," she said. "I'll be right outside."

She closed the door behind her and I was alone with the couple.

Maggie was standing by the head of the stretcher and was gently stroking Stewart's hair. He was still struggling for breath, though not quite as badly now. He was able to talk but not in long stretches.

"Well, Doctor, what does it look like?" he asked.

I pulled a stool over and sat down by his side, his chart in my lap.

"Pretty much what we thought, Stewart," I said to him. "And probably what the two of you thought. It looks like you've had another heart attack and it's tipped you over into congestive failure."

"Hmm," he mused. "We've been here before." He paused and caught his breath. "But this seems a little worse somehow."

Maggie stopped caressing her husband's head and said, "Dr. Lesslie, how bad is it? What do you really think?"

I glanced over at his monitor and noted that his heart rate had slowed a little, but it continued to struggle along in the 110-to-120-per-minute range. Still not good.

Looking at Maggie and then at Stewart, I told them, "You know, how bad it is really doesn't matter. Your blood work shows you've had more heart muscle damage, and we all know you didn't have much if any to spare. Any further heart tissue loss would be...would put you—"

"Am I going to die?" Stewart asked straight up. He was calm as he said this, and Maggie didn't flinch. I knew I needed to be honest with them and tell them what I thought and felt.

Still, it was difficult. I cleared my voice before beginning.

"Stewart, I don't think your heart can take much more. We've run out of options here to help you, and I...I think it's just a matter of time. Maybe not much time."

He didn't say anything but just raised his left hand in the air and Maggie reached down and grasped it. She was nodding her head and I saw that her eyes glistened, but there were no tears.

"Okay," he said with a new and surprising firmness in his voice. "Where do we go from here? We really don't want to be admitted to the hospital."

While he was catching his breath Maggie said, "How much time do you think we have? A day? Maybe two?"

I shook my head and said, "No, not a day. Maybe a few hours, or even less." It was difficult to say these words, but it was true. And they needed to know.

When she heard this, she took her husband's hand in both of hers and they looked at each other. He slowly nodded his head, wordlessly telling her that I was right.

For a moment the three of us remained silent. Then I stood up and walked to the edge of the bed.

"Let's do this," I began. "Stewart, I'm going to keep you here in the department for as long as I can. No, I'll keep you here in the department, period. And Maggie, you stay here with him. I'm going to have a more comfortable chair brought in for you, and if you need anything else, we'll be right outside the door. No one will bother you."

They looked at each other again and then at me.

Maggie spoke. "Thank you, Dr. Lesslie. We appreciate..." Her voice cracked, and I knew I had to leave the room. I turned away and walked to the door.

"Thank you, Dr. Lesslie," she said again.

Stewart and Maggie spent the next hour and twenty minutes together, talking and holding hands. They said the things they needed and wanted to say to each other, and then as Stewart's breathing became more labored, they fell silent.

Shortly after that, his monitor fell silent and Stewart was gone.

Later, after Maggie had gone home and the department had shifted into its usual evening rush of activity, I found myself walking up the hallway with three clipboards under my arms. There were new auto-accident victims in minor trauma, nothing serious, just a few bumps and bruises. As I neared the nurses' station, a flash of color caught my eye and I stopped.

On the countertop was Maggie's rose.

You're on My Last **Nerve**

*A man's wisdom gives him patience; it is to
his glory to overlook an offense.*

—Proverbs 19:11

I n the ER, if you have not mastered the skill of patience, you subject yourself to the risk of making unnecessary mistakes, distressing and disappointing those who look to you as a leader, and feeling pretty crummy at the end of your shift.

You feel crummy because some person or some situation has gotten the better of you. In the ER we are frequently tested in this area, and the testing usually comes in the form of an ER abuser. We need to make the distinction here between an "ER regular" and an "ER abuser." You have already met some of our "regulars," such as Slim Brantley. Slim means no harm and his ultimate motivation for coming to the ER is for food, warmth, and companionship.

An abuser, on the other hand, is frequently driven by sinister purposes. These purposes usually involve obtaining an injection of a potent pain medication, or even more desirable, the writing of a prescription for the same. The realization of these goals is achieved through deceit, deception, and sometimes violence.

Dealing with these individuals requires a large measure of patience and a diminished view of the importance of "self." These interactions are not contests between the ER doctor and a drug seeker. There is no moral or righteous high ground on which to plant our banner. There are no winners here—only the potential for all involved to be losers.

This was a difficult lesson for me to learn. I was amazed, as an intern, by the tenacity of these individuals, and by their audacity. My hackles went up when a "seeker" presented himself or herself to the department, and I believed it was my sworn and sacred duty to uncover and thwart their crafty and cunning efforts. I would not be bested.

11:55 p.m. I was at the nurses' station, contemplating the stack of charts of patients who were awaiting my attention. The double-cover doctor had left at eleven, leaving me with five or six people to take care of. Thankfully they all had seemingly trivial problems.

"Why don't you get this place cleaned out," Trish, our unit secretary said to me. She smiled, leaned back in her chair, and put her hands behind her head. "One of the nurses from 3North is going out for pizza and said she'll pick us up something if we want."

I was finishing up the record of a kid with strep throat and glanced again at the unseen stack of charts.

"Shouldn't take too long," I answered, unbothered by her gentle chiding. "Why don't you go ahead and get something organized. See what everyone wants."

After placing the kid's chart in the discharge rack, I picked up the record of the next patient to be seen. Room 3A: "Cough and can't sleep."

As I turned toward the door of room 3, my attention was drawn to the triage entrance. Jeff was leading a young man into the department. He was making a note on the patient's chart, and when he briefly looked up, his eyes caught mine. He lowered his head just a little and raised his eyebrows. This signal, unseen by the patient behind him, told me something was up.

The twentysomething man was dressed in jeans and a T-shirt that advertised "MYRTLE BEACH." His flip-flops slapped the tiled floor as he was led to room 4. Under his arm he carried a smudged and worn X-ray folder.

I turned toward my coughing and sleep-deprived patient. I was curious about our new visitor in room 4, but he would have to wait his turn.

It was almost 1:30 in the morning, and the stack of charts on the counter had been reduced to just one, that of the patient in room 4. I had not had a chance to talk with Jeff about this guy, and right now Jeff was back out in triage.

I picked up the chart and looked at the chief complaint. "Right leg pain. History of bone cancer."

Hmm. That was a little unusual.

His vital signs were normal. No fever and no elevated heart rate. A rapid heartbeat can be a reasonably good indicator of significant pain and stress. There was nothing else on the chart of any particular interest, except that he listed a city in Florida as his residence. Then I noticed that the ER business office had handwritten "No picture ID" on the bottom of his personal information sheet. This was beginning to smell a little peculiar, and instinctively my defenses were on alert.

Pulling the curtain aside, I stepped into his room. John Glover was sitting on the stretcher, his legs dangling over the side. He looked up as I entered and immediately began rubbing his right thigh.

"Hey, Doc. I hope you can help me," he implored.

I stepped across the room and sat down in the chair opposite his stretcher.

"I'm Dr. Lesslie," I introduced myself. "What can we do for you tonight?"

He continued to rub his thigh and looked down at this apparently painful appendage. "It's this leg, Doc. About eight months ago I started having some pain right here," he began, pointing to the mid-front of his thigh. "Not bad at first, but it just kept on hurting. After a few weeks I couldn't stand it any longer and I went to see a doctor."

At this point he stopped rubbing his thigh long enough to pat the X-ray folder lying beside him on the stretcher. "They got some X-rays and gave me some awful news. I've got bone cancer, and they say it's pretty bad."

He put his head in his hands and shook it from side to side. I was impressed.

"I'm on my way to see my sister in Virginia and I ran out of pain medicine. I just need enough for about two weeks. And if I make it that long, I'll be back home in Florida and can see my own doctor."

I was about to ask something when he spoke again. "Oh, and when it gets this bad, they usually give me a shot of Demerol and either Tylox or Percocet. That's what usually helps."

He looked at me expectantly and added, "Sometimes Oxycontin works the best."

Oftentimes I wonder just what people are thinking, and what they take us for. Do they think we wouldn't notice such a flagrantly inappropriate appeal? Or that we would immediately head for the drug cabinet and give them whatever they want? This guy obviously needed help, but it would be of a psychological nature, not physical. However, I knew he wouldn't be interested in anything at this point other than procuring narcotics. And in the ER, it was almost impossible to provide the sort of assistance he ultimately needed. My job was to sniff him out as a drug abuser, frustrate his perfidious efforts, and send him on his way.

I was up to the task, and I knew it.

"Well, we'll see what we can do to help," I assured him, considering my best course of action here. "Can I take a look at your X-rays?" I asked.

"Sure, Doc, help yourself," he answered, handing me the folder. "But could you please hurry? My leg is killing me."

"I'll be right back," I replied, and stepped out of the room.

Jeff was pushing a wheelchair into the department from triage, laden with a middle-aged man. This latest patient was having trouble breathing and was obviously struggling.

"Shortness of breath and a history of emphysema," Jeff informed me. "I'm taking him to room 6."

I knew it would take a few minutes for Jeff to get him on the stretcher and get things started. I would have enough time to look at Mr. Glover's X-rays.

"I'll be right there," I told Jeff. "Holler out if you need me."

I walked over to the X-ray viewing box, took out the two X-rays in the folder, and snapped them into the holders at the top of the box. I stepped back and looked at the films. The first thing I noticed was the top right corner, the area where the patient's ID information was usually included, had been cut away. Both X-rays were missing this same irregular rectangle. There was no way to identify the person whose images were before me on the screen. And then I noticed that at the bottom right-hand corner, completely contrary to any notational convention of which I was aware, someone had handwritten "John Glover" in black felt pen. No date. No identifying hospital. Hmm.

The X-rays were indeed of someone's femur. And that person, whoever and wherever they might be, was certainly unfortunate. The X-rays revealed a large bone cancer sitting squarely in the middle of his or her thigh. But it was impossible to know when these films had been made, or where. What was possible to know was that this person had either lost his leg or his life. This was a bad-looking tumor.

Where had John Glover gotten these X-rays? Was it someone he knew, maybe a family member? Did he have access to some Radiology department somewhere? My curiosity was morphing into anger as I realized the depth to which this young man had sunk in order to satisfy his need for drugs. Whether he was using them himself or selling them made no difference. Then I remembered the patient Jeff had just taken to room 6, and I knew I would soon be needed. I left the X-rays hanging on the view box and walked across the department.

It took about 45 minutes to get our patient with shortness of breath under better control. He had developed pneumonia, superimposed on poor lung function induced by 35 years of work in a cotton mill. He was in less distress now, but he was still sick and would have to be admitted to the hospital.

Stepping out of room 6, I walked to the nurses' station and remembered the X-rays John Glover had brought with him. I glanced over at the view box where I had left them. They were gone. The curtain of room 4 was drawn closed, so I assumed Mr. Glover was still there.

"Trish, did you see what happened to the X-rays I was looking at a little while ago?" I asked, motioning with my head toward the view box.

"Yeah," she answered, not looking up from the work she was doing. "The guy in room 4 came out and went over and got them. He stuck 'em back in his folder and went back to his room. He wanted to know how much longer it was going to be."

As I stood at the nurses' station I could hear Jeff's deep, reassuring voice coming from behind the curtain of room 6.

"You're going to be alright, Mr. Jones," he was saying. "You're breathing easier now, and we're going to be able to treat your pneumonia. You're going to be okay."

I couldn't make out Mr. Jones's response. But the thought suddenly struck me—here was a man who was struggling for his life. He had come to us for help, and we were giving him just that. We were doing what we were trained to do, and were doing it effectively. This is why we were in the ER at one o'clock in the morning.

Then I glanced at the curtain of room 4 and felt my face flush a little. This John Glover, or whoever he was, had no reason to be in this department. He was taking up our space and our time. I picked up his chart and walked across to his room.

For a passing moment, I considered flushing him out. I would go into the room and tell him that I had reviewed his X-rays and that he indeed had a very serious case of bone cancer. I would tell him I knew it must be very painful, but just to be sure where we stood, I was going to send him around to the Radiology Department for some current films. We would know more about the status of his cancer and be able to more effectively treat him. Then I would watch him squirm.

The moment passed, as did the temptation. As satisfying as that might be for me, I knew what I must do.

I pulled the curtain aside, and seemingly on cue he began rubbing his leg again.

"They haven't brought me anything for pain yet, Doc. Any idea when that's going to happen?" he asked. "This leg is killing me, and I really need to get on the road."

I clutched his chart to my chest and lowered my head, fixing my eyes on his.

"Mr. Glover, I think we both know what's going on here," I began. "Those are not your X-rays and you don't have bone cancer."

He immediately stopped rubbing his thigh, and his head tilted ever so slightly to one side. He continued to stare at me.

"You're not going to receive any pain medication here, or any prescriptions. You've taken up enough of our time, and I would suggest you leave this ER."

I stopped and waited for a response. For a moment he was silent, and he just stared at me. Then very calmly, he picked up the X-ray folder and stood up.

"Doc, you can just kiss my butt."

His shoulder brushed mine as he walked out of the room. I felt my face flush again, and I followed him as he walked toward the exit. I wanted to say something, something that would cut him to the quick, but I thought better of it. I was trying to regain control of myself and of this situation.

And then I remembered the X-ray folder. The doors to the exit had just closed and I hurriedly stepped toward them. What was I thinking? I needed to get those X-rays and destroy them. John Glover, probably using another name, would soon be in another ER, rubbing the same leg, asking for the same medicine, and exhibiting the same X-rays. Maybe even later this very night.

I was going to get those X-rays from him. That was the least I could do.

Stepping out into the ambulance area, I could just make out his shadow, retreating into the parking lot. There was no one else in sight.

"John," I called out to him. "Hold on just a minute."

I quickened my pace, determined that he not leave until I had what I wanted.

He stopped at the top of a small rise, silhouetted against the glare of a lamp post at the back of the large lot. Turning, he faced me, just forty or fifty feet distant.

"Hold up," I called. And then he did something that made me stop in my tracks. He was carrying the folder in his right hand, and slowly he transferred it to his left. Then, nonchalantly but with obvious purpose, he shoved his right hand into his pants pocket and withdrew something. It wasn't large enough to be a gun, but the fleeting glint of reflected metal registered somewhere in my brain. What was I doing?

He didn't step toward me, just stood there, waiting. Silent.

I remained there for a moment, torn between walking up the hill and confronting him and simply turning and walking away. I looked at his right hand and tried to discern what object might be hidden there. He wasn't that big a guy. How dangerous could he be? All I was interested in was getting those X-rays, nothing more. I wasn't looking for a physical confrontation, and I would bet he wasn't either.

Wait a minute! What was I thinking? There was no dilemma here.

I turned and walked back to the ER.

Once again at the nurses' station, I addressed Trish. "You might want to give a few of the surrounding ERs a heads-up on Mr. Glover. Let them know his age and that he's got some X-rays with him of someone with bone cancer. Drug seeker, and maybe dangerous. They can call me if they have any questions."

I had a few minutes to reflect upon this encounter. I began to realize how foolish my behavior had been, and that I had let my emotions cloud my judgment. This had been a potentially dangerous situation and I had put myself in harm's way. And for what? To prove to this man that I had sniffed him out as a drug seeker? That this was my ER and he was not going to walk in and make demands of us? That we were no local yokels, easily deceived and manipulated?

It was an issue of pride. I would have to overcome this and learn to be patient in these circumstances. I would need to learn to be more objective and more pragmatic. I would need to learn to control whatever it was that drove me to seek dominance in such a situation.

I was learning. But I wasn't there yet. Another lesson awaited me, and this would be one of those rare times when I would be able to gain some valuable insight from the misstep of another.

6:30 P.M. It was a busy Saturday evening. I was working with one of our young partners, Andy James. He had finished his residency training a few months earlier, and was bright, eager, and obsessive to an almost bothersome degree. He had come to us with a few rough spots, but we were all of the opinion these would soon enough be smoothed out. The ER of Rock Hill General had a way of doing that.

He was showing me the chest X-ray of a patient in room 5, asking for my opinion.

"Dr. Lesslie, does this look more like pneumonia or heart failure?" he queried, closely scrutinizing the films of this sixty-year-old man.

"First, Andy," I responded, "I want you to call me Robert, not Dr. Lesslie. Okay?"

I had requested this of him at least a dozen times since his arrival, and after each such request he would try to make the attempt at less formality. Eventually, he slid back into using this appellation, a remnant of his still-fresh residency training.

"Okay, Dr...I mean, Robert. What do you think?"

We were discussing the sometimes difficult distinction between these two different problems, when we both were distracted by the squawking of the EMS radio.

"General, this is Medic 3," the familiar voice of one of our paramedics announced.

Lori walked over to the phone and pushed the hands-free button, allowing her to speak to the paramedic and for us to hear what was going on. Andy immediately walked over to the counter of the nurses' station and leaned closer to the phone.

"Go ahead, Medic 3. This is the General ER," Lori responded, taking out her pen and preparing to make some notes. She glanced at the clock on the wall and jotted down the time.

The paramedic proceeded to tell us that he was in transit with three patients from a motor-vehicle accident. And that Medic 4 would be bringing in another three from the same accident.

Andy's eyes widened. He looked in my direction.

"Nothing serious," the paramedic announced. "Neck and back pain. We have a few of them in full spinal protocol."

"10-4," Lori responded. "Minor trauma on arrival."

"10-4 to that," the paramedic answered. "Medic 3 out."

Andy had been making some notes as well.

"Sounds like it could be something bad," he said to me. "That's a lot of PIs (personal injuries) in one accident."

"We'll see," I answered, not yet impressed. Putting three patients in one ambulance was an indication the paramedics working the accident were not too concerned with the possibility of significant injury. And then there was the relaxed tone of the paramedic's voice.

"We'll see," I repeated.

Twenty minutes later, six young men from the auto accident were crowded into our minor trauma room. Three were on backboards, their heads securely taped in a rigid position. They had complained of neck pain, and the EMS squads were taking no chances. The other three victims were casually sitting in chairs, rubbing various body parts.

As Andy and I walked into the room one of the paramedics pulled me aside.

"Doc, somethin' suspicious is going on here," he told me. "This was a one-car accident, in the middle of town. Couldn't have been going more than 25 miles an hour, and there's no obvious damage to the car." He scratched his head and surveyed the congested room. "Good luck with these guys."

"Thanks," I said, noticing that Andy was in the far corner, questioning and examining one of the patients who had been secured on one of the backboards.

"Where exactly do you hurt?" I heard him ask.

Lori came up behind me and tapped me on the shoulder. "Dr. Lesslie, I've got a seventy-five-year-old in Cardiac with chest pain and a blood pressure of 60."

I glanced once more at the confusion in minor trauma. No one seemed to be seriously hurt, and Andy should be able to handle this. Anyway, I was needed up front.

"I'm right behind you," I said to Lori as we headed up the hall.

Two hours and a bunch of X-rays later, Andy had managed to clear all six patients involved in the auto accident. Everyone had checked out okay. No one had any obvious injury, and all the X-rays were normal. He stood beside me at the nurses' station, writing up the charts of these patients.

"I think they're going to be okay," he told me. "I didn't detect any significant neurological injuries."

"Well, that's a good thing," I responded, suppressing a smile. We had known that from the first moment, "we" meaning everyone other than Andy. But something still wasn't right here. Things didn't quite add up. I had been too busy to try to sort this out, but that moment of clarity was fast approaching.

We were still standing at the counter, when a police officer walked up. He was accompanied by a diminutive, bespectacled forty-year-old man. He shuffled along with the officer, looking down at the floor.

"Doc," the officer said. "I need to talk to you about the auto accident downtown, and about those guys involved. Mr. Grant here has some interesting information for you."

Andy immediately stopped what he was doing, looked up at the officer, and edged closer to where we were standing.

"What's going on here, Mr. Grant?" I asked him. "Do you have something to tell us?"

Mr. Grant fidgeted and put his hands in his pockets. Reluctantly, he looked up at me.

"I don't want to get into any trouble," he began. "And I don't want anyone else to get into trouble," he continued, nervously looking down the hallway. "But there's something you need to know."

The police officer was silently nodding his head.

"That accident, the one with all those people…" he began. "It didn't exactly happen the way they said it did."

I glanced at Andy. He had a troubled look on his face.

"What exactly do you mean?" I asked him.

"Well, I know they told you they ran into a telephone pole, and they were all thrown around inside the car and everything. And they told you that two of them had been crossing the street when the car knocked 'em down. That's how they said they got hurt."

"You're right, Mr. Grant. That's what they told us," Andy excitedly interjected. "They all told us the same story."

Mr. Grant looked in his direction and then back at me.

"Well," he started again. "I was there, and I saw what happened."

"You were in the accident?" I asked him. "You were in the car?"

"No, no. I was walking down the sidewalk when it happened. I saw the whole thing."

The police officer was nodding his head again, and smiling.

"Yeah, I saw the whole thing," our volunteer witness continued. "It was like in slow motion. I was walking down the street, and then here comes this car, headed straight for the curb. The driver wasn't paying attention and the car clipped a couple of parked vehicles and then came to a stop. Barely bumped those cars," he added, shaking his head. "But the main thing is there were only two guys in the car. The driver and a front-seat passenger. That was it."

"Wait a minute," Andy said, becoming a little agitated. "There were six people in the accident. You can go back there and count them."

"I know what they told you," Mr. Grant responded. "But there were only two people in that car. The other four were standing on the sidewalk when it happened. They must have known the driver of the car, 'cause as soon as it happened, two of them ran over and piled in. And the other two just sorta looked around and then fell down on the ground, right in front of the car. Then they all started rubbin' their necks and rolling around."

"You're kidding," I said, amused by their audacity.

"They did what?" Andy asked angrily. "You mean these guys weren't even in the accident? They're committing fraud?"

"That's exactly right," Mr. Grant said. "Nobody was hurt in that fender bender, and it's all a hoax. That's why I came down here. And that's why I found this officer and told him the story." He stood a little straighter now, and a little taller, having told us the truth and assisted in the now-inevitable triumph of justice.

There was a moment of silence as this new revelation registered, and then I addressed the police officer. "What do you plan to do here?" I asked.

"Have you people medically cleared them?" he responded. "Are they free to go?"

"Yes," Andy said. "They're medically cleared and ready to be released. You're going to arrest them, aren't you?" he asked. "I mean, this must be some sort of a crime, isn't it?"

"Sure, there's misrepresentation and all of that. And probably some sort of fraud issues, I suppose," the officer said. "I dare say the insurance people will be interested in this, and I can assure you we're going to have a word of prayer with them down at the station."

"You mean this was all about collecting insurance money?" Andy asked, incredulous. "They've wasted our time—and the EMS call… What if someone had truly needed an ambulance and none was available because they were responding to this bogus accident?"

I was going to try to calm Andy, but when I turned to face him, he had already headed off down the hall toward minor trauma.

"Uh-oh," I said, and followed him. The officer was right behind me.

Andy stood in the doorway of the crowded room with his hands on his hips and began to harangue the miscreants. Freed from their backboards, they were all huddled in the back left corner of the room, either sitting or standing.

"What were you people thinking?" he began. He then lined out their multiple crimes against humanity and the great risk they had imposed upon the people of this community. He dwelt at length on the possibility of truly needy patients not being able to receive care from the EMS system because they had been inappropriately tied up.

Amazingly, the six gentlemen stayed where they were and calmly took this diatribe. To be sure, there was open hostility on the faces of a few of them, and one or two stared blankly at the ceiling. Then I looked behind me and understood the reason for their acquiescence. The police officer was standing behind us, a good head-and-a-half taller than Andy. The look on his face clearly commanded their silence.

Andy finished, his face red with righteous indignation. Then he turned and walked past us. He didn't notice the wink the officer gave me.

I understood the anger Andy felt in this situation. Blatant abuse is hard to deal with, under any circumstance. But in this instance I was able to be a spectator, and I was able to analyze what had happened here over the past few hours. Andy was justified in his indignation, but what had this confrontation accomplished? Andy might have felt some sense of relief, having blown off some steam and calling these guys out, but I doubt it. He would still be stewing about this when he drove home at seven in the morning. And the six perpetrators? They had no sense of wrongdoing. Their concern now was the immediate repercussions of their actions, nothing more. Their core values had not been altered by Andy's admonitions.

So everyone here had really been a loser. Wait—there was the police officer. He might be the only winner. He had gotten a little chuckle out of the happenings in minor trauma.

I was going to remember this.

You have to have a lot of patience to learn patience.
—STANISLAW LEC (1909–1966)

On **Crossing** the **Bar**

When the perishable has been clothed with the imperishable,
and the mortal with immortality, then the saying that is writ-
ten will come true: "Death has been swallowed up in victory."

—1 CORINTHIANS 15:54-55

For those of us in the ER, dealing with death in our own depart-ment is difficult enough. But from time to time we are also called upon to deal with a death that has occurred elsewhere in the hospital. When someone dies, a physician is needed to certify and then docu-ment that a death has actually occurred. This responsibility clearly falls to the treating physician. However, if it's late at night or the middle of a weekend and that patient's physician is not in the hospital, the ER doc on duty might seem a reasonable alternative. After all, he or she is in the hospital, awake, and "available."

Pronouncing the death of a patient is something we had performed in the past as a courtesy extended to the medical staff. However, as the medical staff and hospital census grew, this practice became onerous for the ER physicians.

It isn't only that we are pulled out of the department at inoppor-tune times. After all we don't lock the doors to the ER while we are gone, and patients don't stop coming in. Imagine the response if we called the involved physician when we returned to the department and asked him to come in and help because we had gotten backed up.

The real objection we have is that on occasion we go upstairs to find the recently deceased surrounded by a room full of family members.

These people are complete strangers to us and they are understandably upset and distraught.

And then come the questions:

"Who are you?"

"Where is his doctor?"

"What caused her to die?"

"Do you think he suffered?"

"What do we do now?"

These are all things we are, in most cases, unprepared to answer. (I can usually handle the first one.) It is always an awkward moment for the family and for us. Our current policy is that we will go upstairs when practicable, document the person's death, and then note the time on the death certificate and in the patient's chart. This should only take a few minutes, and then we are able to return to the ER. It is the responsibility of the patient's physician, coordinating with the unit charge nurse, to be sure the family has been notified and left the patient's room. This is not a perfect solution, but it is a reasonable compromise.

In the past, there were a few members of the medical staff in particular who seemed to always forget the part about taking care of the family. And there we would be, opening the door and being confronted by grieving strangers.

Dr. Bill Jones, whose patient I was to deal with very early one morning, did not fall into this group. He was appreciative of our help and always made that clear. He understood the position we were in, and the potential dilemma. Still, it was a hassle.

Yet isn't it interesting that something you view as a hassle, something that is a real nuisance or inconvenience, can actually become a profound and meaningful experience? These things happen when we least expect them. They present themselves at unusual times and places. I think you need to be at least a little receptive to such a possibility—or the opportunity passes, forever lost. I wonder how many of these opportunities I have missed.

Bill Jones had called and asked me to go upstairs and pronounce one of his patients.

"Sure, Bill," I responded. "Mr. Blake in 432?" I confirmed, making a note on a scrap of paper.

"Yes, that's right," he answered. "Eighty-two years old, I think. Cancer of the pancreas. The family has already gone home. They were expecting this, and I'll talk with them in the morning."

"Okay, I'll take care of it," I told him, and handed the phone back to the unit secretary.

I took a look around the department, and stepped out into the triage area. Jeff was on duty here and was standing at the reception desk, talking to the third-shift secretary and our security guard for the evening. The waiting room was empty.

"Looks pretty quiet?" I observed.

He turned to me and said, "Yeah, knock on wood. We're under control."

"Good," I said. "I've got to go upstairs and pronounce a patient for Dr. Jones. Up on 4East. If you need me, just have the operator page. But I should only be a couple of minutes."

"Will do," he answered, then returned to his conversation.

The elevator ascended smoothly, and for a moment I was alone with my thoughts. *How many times have I done this? Too many.* And I suspect there will be many more. It is a perfunctory task. Check for a pulse. Check for any respirations. Note the time on the chart. Almost always, these are people I don't know and have never seen. Sometimes I will find myself pronouncing a patient I had seen in the ER a few days earlier and who had then been admitted to the hospital for a serious problem. Occasionally it would be someone I had seen and who had then been admitted with what seemed to be a routine and non-life-threatening condition. Those deaths surprised me. They were unexpected, and I would wonder what might have gone wrong.

And rarely it would be a friend or acquaintance of mine—usually an elderly individual whose presence in the hospital caught me unaware. These are always somber times for me, and the only occasions when I don't mind family members being present.

The doors of the elevator opened slowly and I stepped onto the fourth floor, facing the nursing station. The upper floors of the hospital were designed as a large "wheel," with the nursing area in the center and four "spokes" extending outward. These "spokes" contained the patient rooms, and were designated North, East, South, and West. I stepped over to the central counter, a circular structure where one of the unit nurses was sitting and writing on a chart. She looked up as I walked over.

"Good morning, Dr. Lesslie," she welcomed me, smiling.

I looked at the clock on the wall behind her. *2:35 a.m.* It didn't feel like it, but I guess in fact it *was* morning.

"I suppose you're here for Mr. Blake in 432." She closed the chart she had been writing in and handed it to me.

"Yeah, that's Dr. Jones's patient, right?" I asked, taking the chart. Reflexively, I checked the room number and patient name on the top of the clipboard. "432—Blake." Just wanted to be sure. On more than one occasion I had been handed the wrong patient chart and had walked into a room with family members present and proceeded to look pretty goofy. I never wanted that to happen again.

"That's right. We checked on him a little while ago, and he had passed," she confirmed. "He was a real nice man," she added.

"Thanks," I tucked his chart under my arm and walked toward the east spoke of the wheel.

The even-numbered rooms were on the right side of the hallway, and 432 was about halfway down the hall. The door was partly open and I stepped through, pulling it closed behind me.

The room was dark, illuminated only by the pale fluorescent glow of a small fixture over the head of the bed and the faint light of a new moon as it shone through the open window. It took a moment for my eyes to adjust to the change.

I walked over to the edge of the bed and looked down. Mr. Blake lay peacefully, covered with a blanket that had been tucked neatly under his chin. His head rested on a pillow, his eyes were closed, and his mouth was partly open. I watched him for a minute and could not discern any respirations. I put my stethoscope in my ears and, pulling the blanket down, exposed his chest. I checked for any cardiac activity or movement of air. None. After carefully replacing his blanket I opened his medical chart, found the appropriate page, and struggled in the faint light to make a few notes. "No respirations. No cardiac activity. Pronounced dead at 2:27 a.m."

That was it. I had officially documented the death of this complete stranger. He had been born eighty-some years ago, and now he was gone. I stepped back from the bed and found the scene strangely peaceful. It was completely quiet, and the moon shining through the window added a surreal touch. Then it occurred to me that I was an interloper. This was a profound moment, the ending of a man's life. And though I was on official business, I was in fact a stranger.

I turned to the door and jumped, when from the far corner of the room I heard a man's voice. "He's at peace now."

Stopping in my tracks, I stared in the direction of this voice and tried to determine its source. In the shadowed right-hand corner of the room, I began to make out the form of a man sitting in a chair. He shifted in his seat, clearly declaring his presence.

"Yes, he is," I answered. "I'm Dr. Lesslie. And you are…?"

"I'm his son, Paul Blake," came the response.

We were silent for a moment. Strangely this unexpected interruption didn't bother me, though now even more than before it occurred to me that I indeed was interrupting this scene.

"Yeah, he's at peace now," Paul repeated. "It's been a tough couple of weeks. Cancer of the pancreas is a…" He paused, searching for the words that could somehow sum up his father's last weeks of pain and suffering. There were no adequate words for this, nor for the loss that Paul had anticipated and that was now crushing him. "He suffered a good bit the last few days. But last night he was real calm, and we talked for a good bit. And his pain seemed to be better."

Paul Blake shifted again in his chair. "At about midnight, Rachel—that's his wife, my momma—told him it was time and it was all right to let go."

He paused and collected himself. "And that seemed to release him. He got real quiet and peaceful. And in a little while, he just stopped breathing."

He was silent, and I wasn't sure I needed to respond. But somehow this was an unusual moment and I was led to say, "You know, sometimes that's what it takes. When nothing else can be done, it's the words of a wife, or husband, or some other loved one that can make the difference. And you're right about 'release.' Sometimes that's what has needed to happen. And it takes a strong person to be able to release a loved one."

"You're right," he answered. "Momma was a strong person. And right now, I miss her something awful. She's been dead five years."

What had I just heard? I looked around the room to be sure no one else was present. His mother was dead? And then I understood.

"Your daddy thought he was talking with his wife?"

"No. He didn't *think* he was talking with her. He knew he was. He was sort of muttering to himself, when he just stopped and looked straight at me. And then he was as clear as a bell. He told me what she'd said, and that it was going to be all right. And he told me he loved me. Then he was quiet. And that was it." Paul's voice was shaking at the end.

We were again silent. It was time for me to leave, and I cleared my throat and began to turn toward the door.

"That's why I'm sitting here, Doc." His voice pierced the shadows. "I'm waiting. I want to talk to my momma. I'm hoping she will say something to me, just like she did to Daddy."

I peered into the corner, trying to make out the face of this man. And then I looked again at his father, lying on the hospital bed. I put

Mr. Blake's chart on the bedside table, pulled up the remaining chair in the room, and sat down.

Leaning forward with my elbows on my knees, I said, "Paul, I think I know how you feel."

"You do?" he asked. "I was about to give up and go home. But somehow, I just kept hoping. It seems like she's just so close right now."

"She is," I answered. "I don't know how, but I know she's right here. And she's with your daddy."

I could see his head nodding. "I know. But I just need something I can see, or feel. Something I can hear, so I can be sure. You know what I mean?"

"Yes. I know what you mean," I answered, knowing painfully too well.

"I know that Momma loved the Lord, and so did Daddy. And I know where they are right now. But it's awful lonely right here in this room. I'm not ready to lose them both. I'm not ready to be alone, without them."

I did know how that felt. My mother had died when I was fourteen, and my father had died several years ago. In a very real way, Paul and I were orphans. Our parents are no longer here to counsel us, to hold us, to give us advice. It's part of the cycle of life, but it's a painful part.

"Paul, I know we don't know each other, but let me share something with you."

I could see him settling back in his chair, his hands grasping the arm rests, his legs extended in front of him, crossed.

"As a physician, I'm trained to approach things from a scientific viewpoint. You stake out a theory and then you try to prove it. And if you can't prove it, if the evidence is not there, then you discard the idea and move on to another one. Now, scientific evidence is something we can see or feel. It's something that can be reproduced over and over again. If something is true here in Rock Hill, really true, then you should be able to observe the same thing, the same findings, in Chicago, in London, and in Australia. If you can't, then you're probably barking up the wrong tree."

I paused for a moment.

"Yeah, I understand that, Doc," Paul said.

"Well," I continued. "I have come to understand that there are things in this world, in this life, that don't fit that model. There are things that happen, things that are absolutely real that you can't put in a test tube, or see, or feel with your hands. But you know they are real, and they are true. Like your mother tonight, communicating with your daddy. I believe that is real. I don't think it was some semiconscious thought or some long-ago memory being awakened. I believe it happened."

Paul interrupted me. "Doc, I want to believe that too, and I think I do. But why can't I experience it? Why can't I talk with Momma just like Daddy did? I've been sitting, and waiting, and praying. And nothing. Just me in this room, alone, until you came in."

I leaned back in my chair now and looked out the window. The sliver of moon was now partially obscured by some quickly passing clouds, and the room had become darker.

"I understand what you're feeling," I told him. "But somehow, things don't work that way. There are definite moments of communication, of a sense of the real presence of a loved one, but they come at times of their own choosing. We can't command them or force them to occur. And I think it happens when it's supposed to happen. I think for a lot of us, it happens and we don't expect it, we don't understand it, and we don't accept it. You've seen it here tonight, with your father. And you know that it was real and you accept it as being real."

We were again silent, and I contemplated whether I should continue.

Paul gave me my answer. "You said you wanted to share something, Doc. What was that?"

It occurred to me that I was sharing some of my deepest thoughts and feelings with a complete stranger, in a darkened hospital room, in the middle of the night. Yet it was the right thing to do, the right moment.

"I told you my father died several years ago. He was in his mid seventies when that happened. He was an organic chemist, a professor, and the smartest man I have ever known. He had a lot of interests, but one of his passions was birds. He wouldn't allow any cats around the place, because they would bother the birds and drive them away. And his favorite was always the bluebird. I'm not sure why. Maybe their color, or their personality. But whatever the reason, wherever he lived he would build houses and feeders and work hard to attract bluebirds. And he was always successful. When I would visit and we would walk through the yard and talk, he would never fail to point out a particular birdhouse and describe 'the bluebird family' that lived there. I never quite understood his fascination with these birds, but I accepted it as part of who he was.

"He's buried about twenty minutes from here, in the cemetery behind the Neely's Creek ARP church. My mother is buried there too. About a year after Daddy died, I found myself on a highway not too far from the church. I had some time, so I drove over to the cemetery. It was a weekday afternoon and no one was around. It's a beautiful old cemetery, wide open, with a large magnolia near the place my parents are buried. I walked over to their graves and just stood there for several minutes. I read their headstones and it struck me that our lives, it seemed, could be summarized in just a few words and a few dates. But of course that's not true. These were my parents, and a life-time of memories came to my mind. They were good memories, and yet after a while, they became sad and painful. And I found myself feeling just like you described. I was without parents in this world. My mother and father were gone. I knew those pieces of granite didn't truly mark their presence. They were somewhere else. But they were not in a place where I could see them, or feel them, or talk to them. And at that moment, I was alone and lonely.

"I turned around and looked at the magnolia tree. It was tall and strong and graceful. And I knew my father would have liked it. All of a sudden, a movement caught my eye and I turned back around, facing the two headstones. And there it was, a bluebird. It had come from who knows where and perched itself on Daddy's headstone. It just stood there, looking at me, cocking its head from side to side. And I just looked at it. A coincidence? A fluke? No. You will never convince me of that. It was a moment I will never forget. After a minute or two the bird flew away, and I was alone again. But the loneliness was gone and the sadness had disappeared. I still miss them, my mother and father. There are times when I miss them more than others. But when I feel their absence the most, I can draw on that moment, on that experience. And I know I'm not really alone."

"Hmm," Paul murmured. "You know, I don't think that was a coincidence either. And that's all I'm looking for. Some kind of sign, something that's real for me, just like that was for you."

"And you will have it, Paul," I told him. "It will come in its own time. Let me tell you one more thing, something that recently happened and that I've only shared with a few people.

"Not too long ago, one of my sons and I were cleaning out the attic. We've lived in our house for more than twenty years and have accumulated a bunch of stuff. Mostly things that should have been thrown out a long time ago. Anyway, I found a big cardboard box way back in one of the corners and was moving it toward the steps, where there was better light. I had no idea what was in it. As I was moving it, the bottom broke and a lot of stuff spilled out. There was a stamp collection I'd had when I was nine or ten years old. And there were my Boy Scout things—merit badges and an old cap. And there was a plastic department-store bag, sealed with some dried-up Scotch tape.

"I picked up the bag and opened it. Inside, I found a bunch of old letters. It was hot up there and I was curious about these letters, so I told my boy I was going downstairs for a minute. If he wanted to take a break, he could go ahead. I went down to our empty guest room and spread the envelopes out on the bed.

"Before I go on, I need to explain a little about what was happening in my life at that time. Or at least in my professional life. My business partner and I were experiencing a difficult situation, one that was requiring a lot of time and thought. And it was becoming very uncomfortable. We were faced with making a decision that could cost us a lot if things didn't go well, but that could eventually put us in a better circumstance. At any rate, we were in a tough spot, and a lot of my mental and emotional energy was consumed with trying to figure out the right thing to do. And sometimes I just wasn't sure.

"Anyway, I looked at these letters and realized they were all addressed to me, and they had been written by my father. The postage dates were during the years I was in medical school, almost thirty years ago. I picked up one of the letters and opened it. It had been a while since I had seen my father's handwriting, and somehow this stunned me. I don't know why it did, but seeing his handwriting…it…it…a lot of things suddenly came back to me. And then it was as if he were right there in the room with me.

"I don't know why I picked up that first letter. I just grabbed one and started reading it. After the first paragraph, I realized why he had written it. I was in my first year of medical school, and during that fall, I was really down. Not that I was having trouble with school. Sure it was tough, but I was doing fine. I was just wondering whether I was in the right place, doing the right thing. I had talked to him about it and told him I was even thinking about doing something different. Looking back on it, and being a father myself as I read that letter, I had a moment of regret for having burdened Daddy with this. But now I realized he had been listening, he had taken me seriously, and he had taken the time to sit down and write this letter to me.

"At that moment, he was right there with me. I could see his face and hear his voice coming to me from the pages I held in my hand. At first, he talked about some of the hard times he had experienced. And then about the difficult situations other family members were going through. Finally, he addressed my situation. And his message to me was clear. I was in the right place and I was doing the right thing. And one thing he said stood out and struck a chord. 'You won't be able to experience the joys of 1974 and 1975 if you don't endure the hardships of 1973.' I remember reading this letter when I was in medical school, and I had known he was right. I had endured that period of my life and had found the other side of that difficult time to be much better and much brighter.

"And suddenly I realized he was talking to me about my present circumstance. He was talking to me right then, thirty years after he wrote those words. He was telling me to endure—to pick the right course and stay with it. To remember that it might exact a cost, but that a better day would come. And I knew then my partner and I were doing the right thing. It was the advice I needed at that moment, the confirmation I had been looking for. And I thanked my father."

I was finished. I wondered if I had said too much to this stranger. But I felt a strange and rare calmness, and was grateful for this moment.

There was no sound from the corner of the room. I got out of the chair, paused briefly by the bed, and turned towards the door.

"Thanks, Dr. Lesslie."

I stopped and looked back at this man, still faceless in the darkened room. "No, I need to thank you, Paul," I told him.

I stepped out into the hallway and closed the door behind me. For a moment I stood there alone, in the quiet. What had begun as an inconvenience had become a gift, a blessing. It was unexpected to be sure, but it was a true blessing.

I walked to the elevator, my father at my side.

Who Is My Brother?

On one occasion an expert in the law stood up to test Jesus.
"Teacher," he asked, "what must I do to inherit eternal life?"

"What is written in the Law?" he replied. "How do you read it?"

He answered: "'Love the Lord your God with all your heart
and with all your soul and with all your strength and with all
your mind'; and, 'Love your neighbor as yourself.'" "You have
answered correctly," Jesus replied. "Do this and you will live."

But Jesus was questioned further: *"Who is my neighbor?"*

In answer he tells the story of the man beaten by robbers and left
for dead, and the response of three different passersby, including the "Good Samaritan." Then he questions his listener:

"Which of these three do you think was a neighbor to the man
who fell into the hands of robbers?" Jesus asked. The expert
in the law replied, "The one who had mercy on him."

Jesus told him, "Go and do likewise."

—FROM LUKE 10:25-37

Most of us are seldom exposed to the reality of the truly destitute,
the truly unfortunate, and the truly untouchable. We see it
only through the aseptic medium of the TV screen or the computer
monitor. In the ER, our exposure is up close and personal. We have
to approach these circumstances from a dispassionate and technical
standpoint, doing the things we are trained to do: stabilize, diagnose,
treat. And then, in a quieter moment, we are left to sort out the more
human and philosophical meaning of what we have just experienced.

Sometimes, we can't even begin to imagine.

"ER, this is Medic 2. Is the doctor nearby?"

I was sitting at the counter of the nurses' station, finishing up the chart of the patient I had just seen in room 3. It was a two-year-old boy with a temp of 104. He had a rip-roaring ear infection but would do fine with antibiotics and something for pain.

Lori picked up the radio receiver and glanced at me, raising her eyebrows in question.

I nodded and glanced at the clock across the hallway. *10:30.* It had been a quiet evening, especially for a Monday. But it was cold outside, low twenties. And though normal for mid-January, cold weather sometimes kept people indoors and at home.

"Medic 2," Lori answered. "Dr. Lesslie is right here. Just a second."

She handed the receiver to me and then walked over to the child in room 3. I placed the receiver in its cradle and punched the speakerphone button.

"This is Dr. Lesslie," I said. "What's going on?"

It wasn't unusual for one of the paramedics to ask to speak to the doctor on duty in the ER. Usually they would be requesting clinical advice for a difficult situation. Sometimes it would be a touchy circumstance, maybe a domestic problem or someone who really didn't need to be transported to the ER by ambulance. I continued to write on the chart, anticipating a straightforward response.

"Doc, Denton Roberts here. We've…" He paused, his voice unsure and troubled.

The puzzling response by the paramedic piqued my interest. I stopped writing and put the chart down.

"Go ahead, Denton. What's going on?"

"It's, uh, a little unusual." He paused again. And then, "We're bringing in a forty-seven-year-old male. Stable, vital signs are okay, but, uh…could you meet us outside, at the ambulance entrance? Our ETA is about five."

Now this *was* an unusual request. The last time I had been asked to meet an ambulance outside the doors of the ER I'd found myself delivering a screaming, full-term little girl. That wasn't going to happen this time, though. There was no panic, no sense of urgency in Denton's voice. Yet something out of the ordinary was going on.

Amy Conners was the unit secretary tonight, and she had been listening to this communication. She pivoted in her chair and looked at me, her lips pursed in puzzlement.

"Uh, sure, Denton. If that's what you need," I responded.

"I would really appreciate it, Doc. We'll be there in four to five. Thanks."

Amy reached over and hit the speaker button on the scanner, ending the call.

"Now what do you think's up with Denton?" she asked me. "He sounded sorta upset."

"He did, didn't he? I guess we'll find out in a minute."

I finished the last notations on the record of our two-year-old, placed the chart in the discharge basket, and walked to the ambulance doors. As I stepped on the activating mat, the doors slowly opened inward. I was buffeted by a blast of cold air, a reminder that it was winter and I was not dressed for lingering very long outdoors.

The lights of the approaching ambulance played over the few cars in the Emergency Department parking area. I glanced up, remarking to myself the clearness of the night sky. I found the new moon, which had just edged past the treeline beyond the parking lot. Just down and to the right…that would be Venus. Bright, stately. And Jupiter would be—

Medic 2 pulled to a stop in front of me, ending my all-too-brief reverie. Glancing through the driver's window, I saw Seth Jones at the wheel. He waved and nodded, then killed the engine. Seth, an EMT, had been Denton's partner for the past five years.

My attention was drawn to the back of the ambulance, where Denton had opened the double doors from the inside. He stepped down and greeted me as I walked to the rear of the vehicle.

"Thanks for meeting us out here, Doc," he said. "I just thought it would be better if we talked a minute before we bring the patient inside. You might not want to bring him in at all when you, uh..."

"No problem, Denton," I responded, moving toward the open doors.

He grabbed my arm and I stopped, looking directly in his face.

"Before you step in there, Doc, you need to know something," he told me, his eyes meeting mine.

"What's going on here?" I asked, shivering in the cold night air. I was beginning to lose my patience.

"We got a call to Oak Park from a neighbor of this guy," he began, tilting his head in the direction of the ambulance. "The neighbor said we needed to pick this guy up, that he needed some help. Nothing more specific than that. Then he hung up. So we went over and found this fella in a trailer. No electricity. No heat. Just a kerosene space heater that was out of fuel. Said it had just run out. Maybe he was telling the truth, 'cause the place was cool, but not freezing."

He paused and stamped his feet in the cold air. I shivered again.

"The trailer was in a vacant lot," Denton continued, "surrounded by nothing but trash."

Oak Park was an area well known to EMS and the staff of the ER. It was an unfortunate neighborhood, run down and left behind by a city that was expanding in different and more affluent directions. EMS runs to Oak Park were frequently dangerous, with an inordinate number of gunshots, seizures, and stabbings.

"Says his name is Charlie," Denton informed me. "No last name. No ID. No nothin'. The trailer was a wreck. Just a few empty cans of beans on the floor. Oh, and there were two cats and a mangy dog inside. Didn't even get up when we walked in. Just sorta looked at us." He stopped and rubbed his hands together.

I was trying to decipher the importance of the dog, when Denton continued.

"Charlie's got some kind of skin problem. Had it for a long time, and it's really bothering him now. Itching somethin' fierce, he says. That's the main reason the neighbor called us. That, and the—"

He hadn't finished this last sentence when I broke from his grasp and stepped up into the ambulance. I was cold, and it was time to get me and this patient inside.

The overhead battery-powered lights were on. They were dim, but I could make out the form of our patient lying under a blanket on the ambulance stretcher. The blanket was tucked under his scruffily bearded chin and his large dark eyes were agitated, glancing from side to side. His hair stood in shocks, interspersed with irregular bald areas. The scalp that was visible was a blotched, angry-red color. He was filthy, and had a peculiar odor—a combination of musk, sour clothes, decay, and something else I couldn't quite identify.

My eyes were drawn to his blanketed torso, where I could make out the furious movement of his arms and hands. He was violently scratching himself. And now I could hear his faint moaning. It was a pitiful sight and sound.

"Charlie, I'm Dr. Lesslie," I said to him. "I'm here to help you."

I reached down and grabbed the edge of the blanket. Denton had stepped into the ambulance and was standing behind me. He whispered in my ear.

"I'd be careful with that, Doc," he warned. "Like I said, it's not just the itching that's bothering him…"

I had stopped as Denton said this, but now I lifted the edge of the blanket, pulling it toward me and exposing Charlie's scantily clad body. His dirty and tattered plaid shirt was open, revealing his chest and abdomen. The light was not very good, but I could see that his skin was wrinkled and scaling. That strange odor was stronger now, and I noted oozing from the deep furrows that seemed to be everywhere.

Then I froze and just stared. There was…movement. His skin was moving, writhing, somehow alive. And he was scratching himself everywhere. What was I looking at? I leaned closer. Were those—

"It's the ants, Doc," Denton said. "They're everywhere. All through the trailer, and all over his body. They're itching him to death."

Reflexively I stepped back, dropping the blanket over his body. His eyes caught mine and correctly interpreted my revulsion. Yet his gaze didn't waver.

"Help me," he pleaded.

I collected myself and thought for a minute.

"Denton, ask Seth to take him to room 4. It's empty and he'll have some privacy. Then we'll need to figure this out."

"Sure thing, Doc." He was obviously relieved to be passing the responsibility of this unfortunate man on to someone else. "Seth," he called out. "Come on back here."

Seth rolled Charlie through the ambulance entrance and toward the waiting bed of room 4. I glanced over and watched as Tina Abbott, a young nurse from one of the staffing agencies, followed them into the room. Denton and I stood just inside the automatic doors and he told me what he had learned from the neighbor who had placed the 9-1-1 call.

Charlie had been living in town for about two years. Apparently he moved around a lot, never staying long in any one place. The neighbor owned the lot and the trailer, and one day Charlie had knocked on his door, asking for work and food. He gave him some odd jobs to do and let him mow the grass. The run-down trailer wasn't being used, and he let Charlie stay there for free.

"Not a bad guy," Denton said of the neighbor. "Apparently he took pity on Charlie and would bring him meals every few days. That's how he got to know about him and his problem."

Charlie had been born somewhere in the Midwest, and from about six months of age his parents knew something was wrong. His skin began to wrinkle and then to crack and ooze. At first they were told their child just had a bad case of eczema. They tried various steroid creams, but nothing helped. His skin just got worse. Eventually the correct diagnosis was made. It was a condition called *ichthyosis. Ichthy* refers to fish, and their scales were descriptive of this disease. This particular variety spared the face, palms, and soles of the feet. But the rest of the body was affected with varying degrees of scales, cracking, and furrows. There was no cure, and depending upon the severity it could be very difficult to endure. Skin infections were common, as was itching. Interminable itching.

Charlie had a severe case, the worst I had ever seen. When he was two years old, Denton told me his parents had had enough. The constant draining sores, the crying, and the stares and disgust of all who saw him became too much for them to bear. They tried to leave him at several orphanages, but none would accept him. Who would be willing to adopt this child? So finally they just abandoned him. Left him on a park bench and took off.

He had grown up in a series of foster homes, being home-schooled, if it could be called that. No public school would accept him because they thought his skin condition was contagious.

And then he had just wandered from town to town, working where he could find employment. The neighbor didn't know much more than that.

"Just a pitiful creature," he had told the EMTs. "I just finally had to call you guys."

I thanked Denton for the information, and then I noticed a small black ant climbing up his right shirtsleeve. I pointed to it and he brushed it away.

"Aaaah!" The scream came from the direction of room 4. We both looked over in time to see the curtain fly open and Tina Abbott bolt from the room. She had both hands held to her mouth and ran bent over. Running blindly, she stumbled into the soiled-linen cart and knocked it over, spilling its contents.

"Aaaah!" she screamed again, and then began to vomit in the middle of the nurses' station.

Lori had just walked back to the counter from triage, having sent our two-year-old with the ear infection on his way.

"Could you step into room 4?" I asked her. "Seth is in there, and he may need some help."

Without asking any questions, she started in that direction. First she helped Tina sit down on one of the chairs at the desk.

I then turned to Amy Conners. "Would you check the cleaning closet and see if we have any insect spray?"

"What the—" she began.

I just shook my head and said, "Please, just see if we have any, and bring it to room 4."

Lori was attempting to wipe some of the ants off Charlie as I entered the room.

"Hmm," she murmured as I walked over.

The light here was better and now I could see just how severe Charlie's skin condition had become. There were deep crevices everywhere, with no apparent area of healthy skin except on his face, hands, and feet. And the ants were everywhere as well. They were crawling in and out of these cracks and fissures, apparently having made their home there. All the while, Charlie was scratching and quietly moaning.

After ordering something for the itching, I left Lori with Charlie and walked over to the nurses' station. I sat down and began to ponder my options. First, we needed to get these ants off him. But how? Enough insect spray to kill all of these ants would probably be toxic. We couldn't scrub him down—the ants were buried in his skin. Alcohol? Betadine? That wouldn't work.

"What about the Hubbard tank in PT?" This came from Amy, who had sensed my quandary and had come up with the obvious remedy. "You know," she added. "The one over in physical therapy."

This was the perfect solution. This large stainless-steel tank, when filled with warm water, was used to treat patients with burns and other skin injuries. You could suspend a person in the tank and gradually submerge them. In Charlie's case, the ants would either drown or have to flee for survival.

"That's a great idea!" I told her. "Thanks. Could you get the nursing supervisor on the phone and we'll see if we can get this going?"

"That would be May Flanders," she informed me with obvious skepticism in her voice.

"Hmm," I muttered. "Well, get her on the phone, and we'll see."

May Flanders was sixty-two years old and had been a nursing supervisor for about seventy years, it seemed. I had never seen her touch a patient, much less offer any constructive help to our staff, even in the worst of circumstances. Most puzzling was that she always carried a ballpoint pen in one hand and a clipboard in the other. Yet never in all my encounters with her had I ever seen her make any sort of notation on that pad of paper.

Fifteen minutes later, Amy's phone rang.

"ER, this is Amy," she answered, followed by silence as she listened to the caller. "Yeah—well, okay. But why don't you tell him that."

She handed me the phone, shaking her head and silently mouthing, "May Flanders."

I took the receiver. "Ms. Flanders, this is Dr. Lesslie. What did you find out?"

"I talked with Jim Watson, head of PT," May solemnly informed me. "And he said, 'No way.' It will not be possible to use his tank for this purpose. Cleaning it, and…and…you know. Just impossible. So the answer is no. You will just have to find some other means of—"

"There are no other means," I interrupted. My face was flushing, and I was becoming angry. "Why don't you just come down here and look at this guy, and then tell me what we're supposed to do."

There was silence. And then, "I suppose that is your problem, Dr. Lesslie." Then she hung up.

I wanted to throw the phone across the room. But somehow I managed to calm myself and hand it back to Amy.

She hung up the receiver and then looked at me as she tapped the eraser end of her pencil on the desktop.

"What about the administrator on duty? I can find out who that is, if you want," she volunteered.

That was another good idea. It would be going over the head of May Flanders, but that was of no consequence to me at this point.

Charlie needed to be taken care of, and we were getting nowhere. And this was just the start. First we had to rid him of the ants, and then we would need to find a physician on staff to admit him to the hospital. That was going to be another significant challenge.

It was 11:45 when Amy again answered the ringing telephone.

"Mr. Waterbury, this is Amy Conners in the ER. Sorry to bother you this late, but Dr. Lesslie needs to speak with you."

Nodding my thanks, I took the receiver. "Ken, Robert Lesslie." Ken Waterbury was one of three assistant administrators. Thirty-five years old, he had made his way through the hospital ranks, having started in the dietary department. I wasn't exactly sure what he did as an assistant, but he had drawn the duty for administrative coverage this night.

I explained Charlie's situation to him and the problems we were having obtaining access to Physical Therapy and the Hubbard tank.

"Well Dr. Lesslie, this is a pickle, isn't it? Have you considered sending him back to his home and notifying social services in the morning? That might be the best solution. After all, you say he has no ID, and I'm sure he has no insurance. We don't want to saddle him with a huge hospital bill, now do we? Perhaps—"

"Ken, this man *has* no home," I explained, feeling my face once again turning red. That's part of my Scottish ancestry, and unfortunately it makes it very difficult for me to disguise my emotions. "If we send him out, he'll die in the cold. And we have to do something about his skin condition. He needs to be admitted to the hospital." I was adamant with this last point.

"Well…" he responded. From the tone of his voice, I knew where this was headed.

"Just a minute, Ken," I said, and then held out the phone at arm's length but where I was sure he would be able to hear what I was saying.

"Ms. Conners, who is the chief of medical staff this year? Isn't it Dr. Burns?"

"Yes, that's right. Dr. Burns," she answered. "And he's on call for his group tonight. Do you want me to get him on the phone?" She had quickly picked up on what I was doing and spoke loud enough for the administrator to hear.

"Yeah, would you? I need to talk with him about this problem."

Ken Waterbury was saying something over the phone, and I again held it to my ear.

"What was that, Ken?" I asked. "I didn't hear you."

"Don't, uh, don't call Dr. Burns just yet. Let me, uh, let me check on a couple of things," he stammered. "I'll get right back to you."

He hung up. I had pushed a button, and knew it. The one thing an assistant administrator didn't want to do was create a big problem, especially in the middle of the night. And Dr. Sandy Burns would do just that. He was the head of the largest orthopedic group in town and had been one of the leading admitters to the hospital for more than twenty years. More important, he was an outspoken champion of patient care and didn't mind butting heads with anyone who stood in the way of achieving that end. Ken Waterbury knew where Sandy Burns would come down on this issue.

As it turned out, I never had to talk with Sandy. Miraculously, somehow, we were able to send Charlie to PT and have him treated in the Hubbard tank. And thankfully this worked. He was soon free of the ants that had plagued him. There was an occasional confused insect that would crawl from a hidden crevice, but it would be quickly removed. He was much more comfortable now, with the ants gone and with the medicine Lori had given him to control his itching.

We managed to find someone to admit him to the hospital for a dermatological evaluation and hopefully some form of treatment. I had no illusion he would be cured—or even substantially improved. But I hoped he could at least be made more comfortable, and that whatever support systems we had in the community for a person like this could be brought into play.

My work schedule didn't bring me back to the ER for three days. When I got the chance, I went upstairs to check on Charlie. He had been admitted to the medical ward on the third floor, room 314.

When I got there, the bed was empty. I asked the head nurse of the unit about Charlie. She shook her head and told me he had been discharged two days earlier. She didn't know anything else—not where he went, not about any follow-up. He was just gone.

A few days later, Denton Roberts brought a patient into the ER again, and I had a chance to ask him about Charlie.

"Seen anything more of the guy with the ants?" I asked.

"Nope, Doc. In fact, we were on Oak Park yesterday, and I noticed the trailer was gone. That whole lot is empty. Looks like it was bull-dozed. Don't know what happened to him."

No one did. I never saw Charlie again. And to this day, have heard nothing about him. I sense that he's out there somewhere, alone and miserable.

But we can't fix everybody. Sometimes I wonder if we can really fix anybody. We couldn't fix Charlie. He was one of the invisible people who drift among us, unknown and unloved, one of the "untouch-ables." One of the ones we are called to touch.

I picked up the next chart on the counter. "Sore throat and fever."

What value has compassion that does not take its object in its arms?
ANTOINE DE SAINT EXUPÉRY (1900–1944)

Angels in the ER

*Do not forget to entertain strangers, for by so doing some
people have entertained angels without knowing it.*

—Hebrews 13:2

I f you don't believe in angels, you should spend some time in the
ER. You will soon learn they do in fact exist, and they manifest
themselves in a variety of forms. Some are nurses, a few are doctors,
and many are "everyday people," passing through our doors and into
our lives. Sometimes you have to look hard for their wings. And sometimes you have to shield your eyes from the glow that surrounds them.

Macey Love came through the triage door in a wheelchair. She was
leaning forward, tightly gripping the handles of the chair as Lori
pushed her into the department.

"We're going to 5," Lori said. "It's her asthma again."

I was standing on the other side of the counter and had looked up
as they entered. Macey saw me and smiled, nodding her head. She
was struggling for breath, and I could hear her wheezing from across
the room.

"I'll be right there," I told Lori. And then to Amy, "Give Respiratory Therapy a call and tell them Macey is here."

Macey Love was well known to the staff of our emergency department. She was a sixty-two-year-old woman who had suffered with
asthma all of her life. Over the past decade or so the disease had wors-

ened, necessitating frequent visits to the ER. Usually we could turn one of her asthmatic attacks around with aggressive treatment, keeping her in the department for several hours and watching her closely. She didn't want to be admitted to the hospital and made her feelings perfectly clear on that point. "Dr. Lesslie, I've got to get back home and take care of my two grandchildren, so you'd better get me tuned up," she would tell me, sometimes shaking her index finger for emphasis.

On a few occasions she was too sick to go back home, and we would have to send her upstairs for a few days. Those occasions had become more frequent of late.

Still, we would do everything we could to get her "tuned up" and back home. We knew about her grandchildren and the responsibilities she had with them.

The two girls, eight and ten years old, had been living with their grandmother for the past six years. Their mother had decided to move to New York and had abruptly left them with Macey. She hadn't returned. Sometimes at night or on a weekend, the girls would come to the ER with Macey. We didn't want them sitting in the waiting room alone, so they would come into the ER with their grandmother. They were neat kids, friendly, smiling, and well-behaved.

Macey had devoted this time of her life to caring for these girls. Before asthma had robbed her of her lung capacity, Macey had been the choir director for the largest AME church in town. Each Sunday morning she had made sure her two granddaughters were in the choir loft with her. And on Wednesday night they would be there for choir practice.

Macey was proud of them. It was easy to see that, and they loved her dearly.

The girls weren't with her this day. It was around noon on an April Thursday, and they were in school.

Lori was starting an IV in Macey's left hand as I walked into room 5.

"Pulse ox is 87 percent," she informed me. This number came from a device that was placed over one of her fingertips, pressing gently over the nail bed. It measured the amount of oxygen in Macey's blood, and while 87 was low, I had seen her much worse. "Oxygen going at three liters a minute," Lori added. "Do you want a blood gas?"

Macey winced when she said this, anticipating once again the painful needle stick in her wrist as blood was drawn from the radial artery. It would give us a more complete picture of her oxygenation status, much more so than a simple pulse ox measurement. But it was pretty painful.

"No, let's hold off there and see how she does," I told Lori, to Macey's obvious relief.

Her lungs were really tight today, with audible wheezing but not a lot of air movement. After listening to her chest, I stood back and looked down at her, my arms folded across my chest.

Before I could say anything, she raised her hand and shook a finger at me. She didn't have to say anything, and would have found it difficult to do so between her labored respirations.

"I know, I know, Macey," I said. "We'll do everything we can to keep you out of the hospital. But you're pretty tight this time. You know that."

She nodded, and she was smiling as Lori fitted a mask across her mouth and nose. The mask was connected to a machine that was delivering a vaporized concoction of oxygen, water, and a bronchodilator. Macey knew the routine and was sucking the misty medicine as deeply into her lungs as she could.

We started some other medicine through her IV, and I ordered a portable chest X-ray. We would need to know if a pneumonia or some other problem was contributing to the problem.

I told her what we would be doing and she nodded her head, smiling through the steam that was escaping from the mask on her face.

It was the smile that always struck me. But it was more than just a simple and pleasant smile. There was a twinkle in Macey's eyes, and a glow that seemed to surround her. It didn't matter how sick she was or how bad her asthma was. She was always smiling, and through that smile she was expressing her love. I could clearly see that with her grandchildren. But amazingly, I could see and feel it with us as well, the staff of the ER. I didn't know anyone who was not affected by this, and who didn't want to help take care of Macey when she had to come in for treatment.

Virginia Granger was affected by that smile. But that had been going on for more than fifty years.

Virginia and Macey had both grown up in Rock Hill. When they were in grade school, back in the forties, the schools were segregated. Any "mixing" of the races was frowned upon, if not strictly forbidden. Macey's father had worked at one of the large textile plants in town, as had Virginia's. The two girls had met at one of the company functions, where they had inadvertently bumped into each other. They had become fast friends and had managed to see and play with each other on a regular basis. Macey's disarming spirit and Virginia's tenacity, which brooked no meddling in her personal affairs, withstood the stares and occasional slurs of less enlightened "friends" and townspeople.

This relationship had grown and flourished until time and life choices intervened. Macey finished high school and took a job at a dry-cleaning establishment in town. Virginia had dreamed of becoming a nurse, and she left Rock Hill for college to pursue that career. For years they hadn't seen each other. Only chance had brought them back together. Chance and Macey's asthma.

Several years earlier, Macey had come to the ER in the midst of a severe asthma attack. Virginia and I were working that day, and she was taking care of Macey when I entered her exam room.

"I'm just so glad you are here today, Ginny," Macey had said, looking up at her friend. "I'm glad you'll be the nurse taking care of me."

I had glanced over at Virginia upon hearing this. *Ginny.* Now there was something I could use. Then Virginia looked at me over the top of her glasses, and I knew for certain I would never utter that nickname in her presence.

"You know, Ginny," Macey continued between her gasping respirations, "the Lord has blessed me mightily. He truly has."

She paused to catch her breath and I listened carefully, curious as to how she would continue this thought. She was in the ER, in significant respiratory distress, and suffering from a disease that was not going away. And yet she spoke of being blessed.

I would soon learn about the blessings of Macey Love. She told us about her granddaughters and the many things they did together. She reminded Virginia about her father and the tireless days and nights he had worked to provide for his wife and children. And she told us of her complete lack of fear as she faced the uncertainties of her worsening asthma and failing health. And in the midst of all of that was her smile, and those twinkling eyes.

The only time I had seen that smile even hint at fading was one morning when the two of us were talking about her granddaughters. She was going to have to be admitted to the hospital on this occasion, and she seemed more aware than ever of the gravity of her medical condition.

"Dr. Lesslie," she had said to me. "If something happens to me, I just don't know what will happen to those girls. They're all the world to me, and I'm afraid I'm just about all they have. There's Patrice, my sister, but…I just don't know."

And then she was silent, thinking. She closed her eyes, and after a moment she nodded her head. She opened her eyes, and the smile was back.

On this particular visit, Macey was responding to our treatments. Her breathing was much less labored and her oxygen saturation had improved to 95 percent. We would continue the inhalers and the medications, but I was planning on being able to send her home in an hour or so. She would be relieved, and I walked over to room 5 to let her know.

I pulled the curtain back and Macey looked up at me, smiling. Sitting by the side of her stretcher was Virginia Granger. She glanced up as I entered and then looked back at Macey.

They were holding hands.

I stood there for a moment, watching these two women, these two friends.

"I'll be back in a few minutes," I stammered, and backed out of the room.

Macey is gone now. She died during an asthma attack at home one night before one of our EMS units could reach her. It's been more than fifteen years since I last saw her in the ER, but I can see her face before me now as clearly as if she were in the room with me. I will never forget that smile, those twinkling eyes, and the special feeling we all experienced in her presence.

The writer of the book of Hebrews advises us to always be hospitable, lest we be in the presence of an angel and not realize it. With Macey, I knew.

And with Virginia.

Emma and Sarah Gaithers lived in one of the older neighborhoods in town. The two sisters, both in their eighties now, had lived in the same house all of their lives. Their father had been middle-management in the largest textile mill in the city, and he had built their home when large and square and white was the thing to do.

The family had lived four or five blocks from the mill, comfortably located between the homes of the hourly mill workers and the exclusive neighborhood of the mill owners, the bankers, and the town's doctors.

The textile plant was gone now, and the neighborhood had been left to do the best it could. Many of the houses had been torn down or boarded up, and "For Sale" signs dotted distressed and overgrown yards. The exclusive neighborhoods were now located in the suburbs, but the Gaither sisters remained. In reality, they had nowhere to go. Their parents had died forty years earlier, leaving them with a mortgage-free house and little else.

The fact they had been able to stay in this house was remarkable. Sarah had been a schoolteacher and had taught long enough to qualify for state retirement benefits. But Emma had never been employed. She had suffered some unspecific accident during her delivery and had never developed normally. Her mental age was probably around three or four years, and she had been confined to a wheelchair since the age of five. Her legs were twisted and useless, as was her left arm and hand. She was able to use her right hand, but she had never developed any significant dexterity. After her mother and father died she had been totally dependent on her sister.

Sarah assumed this responsibility unflinchingly. She had attended college and earned her teaching degree, but she had never married. If there had ever been a romantic interest in her life, it was a closely guarded secret. Emma was her only family and had been the focus of her life.

Now in her mid-eighties, Sarah was having a more difficult time taking care of her sister. While Emma did not have any chronic medical problems, Sarah had developed diabetes and hypertension. This was beginning to take its toll. In spite of her dedicated and indomitable spirit, she was growing weaker, and the daily routine of taking care of Emma was becoming more difficult.

"Come on this way, Sarah," I heard Lori say, but I didn't look up.

I was sitting at the foot of bed D in minor trauma, trying to get a suture into the squirming, curling great toe of a noncompliant four-year-old. It was summer, and he had been swimming at the lake and had the misfortune of stepping on a broken bottle. So here he was. For a split second, his toe extended and I grabbed my chance. The curved needle with the suture went through one edge of the laceration and out the other. I cinched the thread firmly, tied it securely in place, and leaned back on the stool.

"There, Momma," I said to the young mother who had ineffectually been trying to control this youngster. "That should do it." She was relieved, as was I.

I looked behind me and diagonally across the room to bed B. Lori was transferring Emma Gaithers from her wheelchair up onto our stretcher. It was an awkward undertaking, helped only by the fact that Emma weighed a little less than 90 pounds. Sarah stood at Emma's side, helping steady her.

Before I could get my gloves off and cross the room to help, Lori had managed to get Emma on the bed and was pulling up the guard-rails. Sarah looked up as I approached.

"Good afternoon, Dr. Lesslie. Good to see you," she said to me. She was holding Emma's alpaca sweater in her hands, gently smoothing the worn garment over her forearm. A sweater, in the middle of July.

"Hello, Sarah," I answered, meeting her eyes and then looking down at her sister. "What's the problem with Emma today?"

The answer seemed obvious. Lori was using sterile gauze to gently clean Emma's forehead. A large laceration extended from her hairline to the bridge of her nose. Blood had clotted in the wound, and the front and collars of her blouse were soaked.

"Hmm," Sarah murmured. "Emma was having her bath, and I was getting her out of the tub. I guess my strength just gave way and she slipped. Her forehead struck the edge of the tub, and…well, you can see what happened," she explained, pointing to her sister's forehead.

Emma was looking up at me while Lori cleaned her face. She was smiling, but it was a vacant smile, and as always I wasn't sure how to respond. I've never known how much she comprehends. Sarah would say that she recognizes us, that she knows the people in the ER. But I've never seen any evidence of that.

Leaning closer to her, I smiled and nodded. "Hello, Emma. Looks like you've got a little cut there." I gently examined the wound, checked her eyes, and looked for any other obvious injuries. Other than the laceration, she looked okay. "We'll get that fixed up in just a minute," I said, patting her shoulder. She continued to smile, but made no sound.

Turning to her sister I said, "She'll need some stitches, probably quite a few. Has she acted like anything else was hurting her?" I asked.

"No, other than that she's fine," Sarah responded. She would know. To my knowledge, Emma had never uttered a word. Yet she and Sarah communicated in some unspoken way. If Sarah said she was okay, that was enough for me.

"Good," I said. And then I noticed a small but brilliant sparkle of light in the middle of Sarah's left eye.

"Sarah, I thought you were going to get that cataract fixed," I said with feigned sternness. I looked closer and noted that it had gotten larger since she had last been in the ER.

She just shook her head and didn't say anything.

"How's the vision in that eye?" I asked her, taking the ophthalmoscope from its holder on the wall. "Open both eyes real wide," I instructed her while examining her right eye. A cataract was starting in the lens of that eye as well and would soon cloud what remained of her vision.

"Not very good, is it?" I answered for her.

"Dr. Lesslie, how am I supposed to have eye surgery? Who will take care of Emma? I just don't have the time right now. Maybe...maybe in a couple of months or so...We'll just have to wait and see."

"Sarah, it's not going to get better on its own," I gently scolded. "And how are you going to take care of Emma if you can't see?"

We had been down this road before, and we both knew there was no good solution to the dilemma. Sarah and Emma had no other family members, and what few friends they had were either long since dead or were in nursing homes.

One of my younger partners had made a significant mistake on this issue. That mistake had brought the only instance I had ever known Sarah to demonstrate anything resembling anger.

Emma had fallen from bed one night and Sarah had brought her to the ER. After examining her carefully and determining that no serious damage had been done, Jack Young had asked Sarah to step out in the hallway with him. He wanted to speak privately with her about Emma.

"Ms. Gaithers," he began. "Your sister is going to be alright tonight."

"Well that's a relief, Dr. Young," Sarah responded. "I was so worried."

"She's alright *this* time," he went on. "But what about the next time she falls? Or what if something worse happens?" he asked her.

Sarah was startled by the question, and for a moment didn't know how to respond.

Jack Young misinterpreted the pause as an invitation to offer his guidance and wisdom. He proceeded to tell Sarah that it was time for Emma to be placed in a home of some sort. She should be in a place where she would be properly taken care of. In fact, this probably should have happened years ago.

Sarah's face had flushed and her back had stiffened.

"Dr. Young, you don't know me," she had firmly declared. "And you don't know my sister. We have been together for more than eighty years and nothing is going to change that now. I will take care of Emma for as long as the good Lord allows me to."

She paused here and leaned close to his face. "And that, young man, will be His decision and not yours."

She had collected herself, softened, and then said, "If we're finished here, I suppose I should be getting Emma home now. Thank you for your help."

Jack didn't make that mistake again. And while I knew the time for such a move was rapidly approaching, I was not willing to tread there. Not just yet. Sarah would know when her ability to take care of Emma had come to its end.

Several months earlier, I thought we had reached that point. On this occasion Sarah had been the patient and Emma her companion. EMS had brought the two of them to the ER after Sarah had called complaining of cough, fever, and shortness of breath.

We had quickly determined she had a severe pneumonia and would need to be admitted to the hospital for IV antibiotics and supportive care. It would be dangerous to do otherwise.

"Dr. Lesslie, that will be impossible," she had told me, shaking her head. "I cannot stay in the hospital," she stated emphatically. "Who will take care of Emma?"

I again explained the seriousness of her situation, and that should she die, there would be no one to take care of Emma. I got nowhere. She refused to be admitted, and I knew we could not force her.

Exasperated, I left her room and walked over to the nurses' station. Virginia Granger was sitting behind the counter and listened as I voiced my predicament.

She stood up and straightened the starched, pleated skirt of her uniform. "Dr. Lesslie," she said. "Give me a couple of minutes with Sarah."

She walked over to Sarah's room and pulled the curtain closed behind her. I waited. A few minutes later she walked out and around the nurses' station. I caught her eye and was about to speak when her right index finger, pointing upward, silenced me. She went to her office and closed the door behind her.

For fifteen minutes she was on the phone, calling people in administration and on the medical floors. She was calling in every bargaining chip she had, and she had plenty.

When she walked out of her office she was smiling.

"Well, here's the situation," she began telling me. Amy Conners pressed close behind me, curious as to what wonders Virginia had been able to bring about. "The administration has agreed to let Emma stay on a cot in the room with Sarah. The staff on the medical floor will make sure she's fed and taken care of. Sarah should be alright with that, don't you think?"

I didn't know what to say. This kind of thing just didn't happen, not in this hospital.

"Virginia…" I started, and then paused.

"Well, are you going to tell Sarah, or do you want me to?"

Another slight hesitation on my part, and Virginia was on her way to Sarah's room. She agreed to be admitted to the hospital under these terms, and after a week of aggressive therapy, she and Emma were once again at home.

This afternoon's visit to the ER would be more straightforward. We would repair the laceration of Emma's face and the two of them would be on their way.

"Okay, Emma, let's get your forehead taken care of." I spent the next forty-five minutes suturing her laceration. Sarah stood by her side holding her hand, and all the while Emma just stared at the ceiling, smiling. The only indication of any discomfort had been a slight furrowing of her eyebrows as I numbed the edges of the wound.

"There, that should do it," I said, taking off my gloves and tossing them onto the surgical tray.

"Why, Emma," Sarah said, leaning close to her sister, "your forehead looks fine. I think Dr. Lesslie should have been a seamstress."

Emma just smiled. Lori was giving Sarah instructions for wound care as I left the room.

A few minutes later they came up the hall behind me, Sarah pushing the wheelchair and Emma once again in her sweater.

They stopped at the nurses' station and Sarah said, "Thanks again for all your help." She patted her sister's shoulder and added, "And Emma thanks you too."

"You're welcome, Sarah," I answered. "And you too, Emma," I added, looking down at her upturned face. "You two take care of each other."

Sarah nodded and smiled. Then she turned and began pushing the wheelchair again. She paused, confused as to which way she should go. I was about to speak, when Sarah leaned over her sister and said, "Here we go, Emma. This way." They moved across the hall and disappeared through the triage door.

Truly here was a ministering spirit, an angel passing through this life and touching ours.

The ambulance doors opened and Willie James was wheeled into the ER by two thirtysomething women. They were his daughters, and they were pushing his wheelchair toward the nurses' station. One of them looked up at us and said, "It's Daddy's heart again. He's havin' trouble breathin'."

Virginia had just come out of her office carrying the beginnings of next month's nursing schedule. When she saw Willie, she put her stack of papers on the countertop and walked straight over to him.

"Having some trouble tonight, Willie?" she asked, stepping between the two women and taking control of the wheelchair. "Let's just head over this way," she added. She looked at me and nodded in the direction of the Cardiac room.

Willie James was 63 years old. He had suffered a pretty significant heart attack three years ago, leaving him with a little less than half of his cardiac muscle. Since then he had teetered on the edge of heart failure, sometimes doing well, and sometimes slipping over into dangerous and deadly territory. Too much salt, too much stress, too much physical activity—any of a number of things would overload his heart, and fluid would back into his lungs. He would become more and more short of breath, unable to walk short distances or even lie down without gasping for air. Then a frothy foam would form on his lips. Patients sometimes describe this as a feeling of "drowning in your own secretions," and it is understandably very frightening.

Tonight Willie had slipped over the edge, but he was calm, and he even managed to smile up at Virginia as she had walked over to him. He was too short of breath to answer her question and only nodded his head as he leaned forward in the wheelchair, tightly grasping the handles and gasping for breath. The telltale foam of congestive heart failure was evident on his lips.

Willie was wearing an old T-shirt and well-worn plaid trousers. His feet were covered with white athletic socks, one of which had fallen halfway off. Its tattered and dirty toe was dragging on the floor. I got up from behind the counter and followed him and Virginia into the Cardiac room.

Without being asked, Amy said, "I'll get X-ray down here. And the lab and someone from Respiratory."

"Thanks," I responded, glancing at the clock on the wall. *10:35 p.m.*

Willie was in bad shape. He had waited a little too long this time before asking for help. He wasn't responding to our usual treatments, and his condition was deteriorating right before us. And he was getting tired. Virginia was setting up an airway tray, anticipating we would soon have to intubate him and put him on a ventilator. That would be the next step, but I wanted to avoid it if at all possible. Willie did as well. He glanced at the tray with its various equipment and tubes, and his eyes widened. He looked up at me. He couldn't say anything, but his eyes spoke for him.

We were all thankful when he began to improve. His oxygen saturation began to move upward and his pulse slowed a little. We continued our treatments, and within forty-five minutes it was evident he was moving in the right direction. He would avoid the ventilator tonight but would obviously need to be admitted to the hospital.

"Willie, isn't Angus Gaines your doctor?" I asked, making sure that only a movement of his head was required for a response. I was pretty certain that was correct.

He nodded in affirmation.

"Good. I'll give him a call and tell him you're here," I went on. "You'll need to come into the hospital tonight, alright?"

It wasn't a question, and Willie again nodded his head.

A few minutes later, Amy had Dr. Gaines on the phone.

Angus Gaines was in his early seventies and was still practicing medicine full-time. He had been in Rock Hill for more than forty years, and while technically a GP (general practitioner), he took care of just about everything. He didn't do any surgery now, but he had more patients than any other physician in the area, and he wanted to be involved in their care. I knew he would want to know Willie was in the ER. He would probably come in and see him, and then have one of the cardiologists on staff admit him to the CCU.

Angus always came in to see his patients. It didn't matter what time of day or day of the week it might be. We'd give him a call, and within a matter of minutes he would come walking into the department. That wasn't necessarily the rule for other members of the medical staff. In fact, it was becoming the exception.

Only a few days earlier, a forty-year-old woman had come to the ER complaining of fever, chills, and chest pain. She had a history of worsening lupus—an inflammatory disease of the internal connective tissues—and had recently been diagnosed with kidney failure. We determined she had pericarditis complicating her lupus. This was an infection of the outer lining of her heart, and could prove fatal. She would need to be admitted to the hospital. She gave me the name of her family physician and I asked Amy get him on the phone.

A few minutes later she handed me the receiver and I talked with her doctor.

After explaining the circumstances of this patient, I was told, "Well, Robert, we do see this lady in the office, but she owes us money now, and...well...I just don't think we're going to take care of her anymore. Why don't you have the person on call for 'unassigned medicine' admit her."

I was incensed. His response was totally inappropriate. But I knew this was not the time to fight this battle.

I glanced over at our patient, glad she had not been able to hear this conversation. Trying to control my anger and my tongue, I looked at the on-call board, which was located on a column in the nurses' station. It listed the physicians responsible for various specialties: surgery, ortho, pediatrics, medicine. These medical staff members were required to take care of patients who didn't have a doctor.

Locating the "medicine" slot, I read—

"Yeah, Robert—just have the on-call doc—" he began, repeating himself.

"Well, just a minute, Jake," I interrupted him, with not a small feeling of satisfaction and sense of divine justice. "That would be you. You're on call tonight for unassigned medicine."

"Wha..."

We would never get such a response from Angus Gaines. In fact, I had never heard him utter a cross word or show any sign of frustration with his patients or with being called in to the hospital late at night.

This night was no different. I was standing in front of the counter, when Amy handed the phone to me. "It's Dr. Gaines," she told me.

"Angus, this is Robert Lesslie in the ER," I said, wondering if we had waked him. "I've got one of your patients here, Willie James. He's in congestive heart failure again, and he needs to come in."

While I waited for the response, I slid Willie's chart over so I could read the information at the top of it. I knew what was coming, and I wanted to be ready.

"Willie James, you say." The gravelly voice sounded in my ear. Angus seemed wide awake, so maybe we hadn't disturbed his sleep. "Does he live at 122 Bird Street?"

I looked for the address on the chart. "Yep, that's right," I answered. As always, I was amazed by his memory. He knew where just about every one of his patients lived, and there were a lot of them.

"And he was born, uh, sometime in April of 1930," he added.

I looked at the chart again. "Birth date: 4/18/30." How did he do that?

"Yes, you're right again," I told him.

"Okay, yeah, I know Willie. I'll be over directly."

I handed the phone back to Amy, knowing what "directly" meant. He would be here within fifteen minutes.

But how did he do that? How does someone have that kind of memory? I have trouble remembering my wife's anniversary date, and that should be easy, since it's the same as mine.

Still, for Angus Gaines at his age to possess such a memory was an impressive thing. It occurred to me that a large part of his motivation for remembering these things was the genuine care he had for his people.

The ambulance doors were hissing open, and I looked up at the clock. *12:22 a.m.* It had been eleven minutes since I had hung up the phone, and here was Angus coming through the doors.

"Good evening, Robert," he said. "Where is Willie tonight?"

I motioned toward the Cardiac room and stepped in that direction.

Anyone not knowing Dr. Angus Gaines would probably have been startled by his appearance. Amy and I were accustomed to it and we barely noticed.

Angus walked toward Cardiac. He was wearing a knee-length charcoal overcoat, and under the coat the legs of his pin-striped pajamas were clearly visible. On his feet he wore brown leather bedroom slippers. He took off his gray derby hat and tossed it on the countertop.

"So you think he's doing a little better?" he asked me.

I was giving him a brief update as he pushed open the door and we stepped into the room. Willie's daughters were now with him, and one stood on each side of his stretcher. All three looked in our direction as we entered.

You would have thought it was Christmas morning. When they saw Angus Gaines, their eyes lit up and smiles spread across their faces. One of the daughters ran across the room and hugged him. "We're so glad you're here!" she said.

Thirty minutes later they were all on their way to the CCU. Angus picked up his hat at the nurses' station and turned to me. "Thanks for looking after Willie. I'm just going upstairs to make sure he gets settled in. I'll have one of the cardiologists come and take a look at him too."

Then everyone was around the corner and gone, with Angus padding down the hall in his slippered feet.

The rest of my shift was uneventful, with only a few patients scattered during the early morning hours. My relief walked into the department at five till seven, and I grabbed my briefcase and headed out the ambulance doors.

The early morning air was clean and cool, and the sun was trying to peek over the trees at the far end of the doctors' parking lot. I walked up the hill toward my car and for the first time realized how tired and sleepy I was. I looked forward to getting home, taking a shower, and going to bed.

My attention was drawn by some movement behind and to the left of me. I stopped and turned around. Someone was walking across the far side of the parking lot. I could make out the figure of a man dressed in a dark overcoat and derby hat. It was Angus Gaines. He was just now leaving the hospital, having spent the entire night in Willie James's room, unwilling to leave his side until he knew everything was stable and Willie was going to be all right.

His hands were thrust deep into his pockets, and he shuffled along in his bedroom slippers, obviously deep in thought. For a moment I looked on in admiration as he slowly made his way up the hill. And then something strange and amazing happened as I stood and watched. A single beam of early morning light made its way through the trees, and it shone directly on this remarkable man.

> *We are like children, who stand in the need of masters to enlighten us and direct us; God has provided for this, by appointing His angels to be our teachers and guides.*
>
> —THOMAS AQUINAS

Notes

Page 48: "Every man naturally desires…" Thomas à Kempis, *The Imitation of Christ* (Peabody, MA: Hendrickson Publishers, 2005), p. 4.

Page 193: "You have to have a lot…" Stanislaw Lec, *Unkempt Thoughts* (New York: St. Martin's Press, 1962) p. 110.

Page 217: "What value has compassion…" Antoine de Saint Exupéry, *The Wisdom of the Sands* (New York: Harcourt Brace and Company, 1950), p. 26.

Page 235: "We are like children…" Thomas Aquinas, *Summa Theologica* (Denton, TX: Christian Classics, reprint ed. 1981).

ANGELS
ON CALL

To Lori, Rob, Amy, Dave,
Robbie, Jeffrey, Katie—
the arrows in my quiver
(Psalm 127:5).

...And to the memory of Virginia Granger.

Contents

Introduction for *Angels on Call*

W ho would have thunk that a tall, gangly teenager, growing up in Due West, SC, would one day write a bestseller? Certainly not me, that gangly teenager. But it happened. And when, not long after "Angels in the ER" had been released, my editor called and asked if I was ready to write another one, I didn't have to think very hard. Of course I would! There were more stories to tell, more experiences to share, and more people to introduce.

But I had a growing sense that I needed to do something different with this book. As I got further into my writing, I understood what that "something" needed to be. As I finished chapter 11, "Stand By Me," I realized more than ever how fortunate I have been to have people in my life who have stood by me. And the idea of "being on call" became firmly planted in my mind. After all, these were people who had been "on call" for me when I had needed them. Sometimes they were there without even being asked.

And then there was Duncan MacKinnon in my final chapter— dying with cancer yet resolutely clinging to the knowledge that he was not alone, that there was One standing beside him. The words of the hymn he was singing still echo in my heart: "It is well with my soul".

But I knew there was a larger, more important question here. Who are we on call for? Who do we go out of our way to help and to serve? Who do we stand beside, no matter what?

Have you ever asked yourself that question? If so, what was the answer? We all need to ask ourselves this every day. And if like me you sometimes struggle for an answer, the men and women in this book will help you find the way.

First Things

The ER has a lot to teach us about living and dying, about other people, and about ourselves. It's a classroom that never closes.

In these pages, I share some of my experiences from over two decades of working in the emergency department. Throughout all those years, I learned that one thing never changes: Every person who walks, or is wheeled, or is carried into the ER is unique and has a story to tell. Each has something to share. And most importantly, each has something to teach us, if we only take the time to listen.

One of those lessons is that we all need someone to lean on. At some point each one of us will ask, "Who can I turn to when I'm in trouble?" "Who can I count on when all hope seems gone?" "Who is on call for me?"

Maybe you know who those people are, or who that Person is, in your life.

And maybe you have come to understand that the more important question is, "Who am I on call for?"

Into the Deep End

*Then you will understand what is right
and just and fair—every good path.
For wisdom will enter your heart,
And knowledge will be pleasant to your soul.*

PROVERBS 2:9-10

Thursday 7:05 a.m. Jack was standing at the nurses' station rubbing his eyes, as if that would clear the cobwebs from his brain. He was not used to getting up this early. His "early" classes the past two semesters at Appalachian State had started at 10 a.m., and the alarm clock this morning had been an unpleasant intrusion.

This was the first morning he was going to spend in the emergency department with me this summer. He wanted to see how his father spent his time as an ER doc, and he wanted to get an idea if a career in medicine was something he wanted to pursue. He would be a senior next fall, and he was twenty-two years old. Hard to believe.

"Wake up, buddy!" Amy Connors chided him. "Things are gonna get hoppin' here in just a little while. EMS is already out on a couple of runs."

Amy was our unit secretary this morning. And she was the best I had ever worked with. She was in her late twenties and had been in the department for the past six years. Nothing seemed to bother her—no amount of stress or being yelled at by impatient physicians (of course, that wouldn't be any ER doc), or even an overwhelming workload. She just rolled with whatever came her way. What I really appreciated was her anticipation of what needed to be done, regardless of the situation. She always seemed to be one step ahead of me, which is what every emergency physician needs.

I was drinking my first cup of coffee, and I looked over at Jack as Amy needled him. He smiled at her and said, "I'm awake, Amy. Don't worry about me."

We had gotten to the ER a little before seven, relieving Tom Anders, the overnight doc. He had left me a clean board, and the department was empty.

Jack sat down beside me, behind the nurses' station.

"Dad...or Dr. Lesslie," he hesitated. "Which should I call you? I hadn't thought about that."

"Why don't you call him what we do?" Amy impishly suggested. "In fact, you could take your pick from a couple of names."

Without looking in her direction I said, "Amy, don't you have something to do?"

And then I said to Jack, "You know, we need to think about that. It might be best to call me Dr. Lesslie. That way, none of the patients would be confused or bothered."

Before Jack could respond, our attention was drawn to a commotion coming from the triage area. The voices of several men could be heard, and they sounded pretty excited and angry. Over this din, I could hear the voice of Jeff Ryan, our triage nurse. He was trying without success to calm down the boisterous group.

"Hold on just a minute!" I heard him shout.

"We ain't holdin' on!" someone responded angrily. "Johnny needs some help and he needs it right now!"

Then the door from triage burst open and a tangled mass of people spilled into the department. Amy and I just sat and watched, but Jack immediately stood up and stared in surprise. I noticed his mouth had dropped open.

The group stumbled over to the nurses' station, and it was then I noticed they were all dressed in bikers' garb—blue jeans, chaps, and leather jackets. A few still had their helmets on. In the middle of this group stood Jeff Ryan, still trying to regain some semblance of order.

"Alright, guys," he bellowed. "Just hold it right here, and we'll get Johnny taken care of!" His voice reached a new level of intensity, and even this cantankerous audience stopped where they were and listened.

"We're going to take him to the trauma room, and I want two of you—*just two*—to come with me. Everybody else needs to go back to the waiting room."

There was some murmuring and muttering from the group, but slowly they began to do as instructed. These were all big men, and pretty intimidating. Most had long, unkempt beards and seemingly perpetual scowls on their weathered faces.

But Jeff was not intimidated by them. He was thirty-six and had been working in the ER for over twelve years, starting just before our family had moved to Rock Hill. He was a big, seemingly gruff mountain of a man, intimidating in his own right in size and demeanor. His mere presence usually calmed the most belligerent and rambunctious of our patients. And if his presence didn't calm them, a firm hand on a shoulder would quickly bring them into line.

Jeff's reddening face was a sure indication that he meant business, and the bikers must have sensed this as well. They were finally beginning to follow his instructions. It was then I noticed the knot of men standing behind Jeff. Three of them were holding a companion in their arms, trying to be as gentle as possible. That must be Johnny, their injured friend.

As the other members of the group began to shuffle out of the way and back toward triage, Jeff turned around and said, "Alright, three of you then. You guys follow me down the hall." Then he turned and headed briskly toward the trauma room.

We got a glimpse of Johnny as they passed by the counter. He was moaning in pain and his face was a pasty white color. He was clutching his left hip, grimacing with each step taken by his carriers. I stood up and walked around the nurses' station, motioning Jack to follow me.

Jeff directed the group to the side of the trauma stretcher, which was positioned in the middle of the room.

"Here, put him down gently," he told them. They tried their best, but Johnny gave out a loud, anguished cry as they laid him on the thin mattress.

"Oww! My hip!"

His three buddies stepped back from the stretcher, and I tapped the one nearest to me on the shoulder. He turned around and I said, "Tell me what happened here."

"You the doc?" he asked.

"Yes, that's me," I answered him. "I'm Dr. Lesslie. What happened to your friend here?"

"Dr. Lesslie?" he remarked. "I think you're the one who sewed up my head last summer." As he said this, he took off his helmet and began parting his hair, searching for his scar.

"That's great," I said. "I probably did, but tell me about your friend. How did he get hurt?"

"Oh, yeah," he muttered, sheepishly putting his helmet back on. "Johnny busted his leg this morning in a swimming pool."

He paused, as if this were all the information I needed.

"A swimming pool?" I finally prodded him.

"Yeah. We were comin' in late from Atlanta and were staying at the Sleep EZ Inn. Johnny sees the swimming pool and says he's gonna jump it. Done it before—but not quite that big a pool, and it wasn't six in the morning, and the other pool had water in it."

"The pool was empty?"

"Yeah, they must have been cleaning it or painting it or something. Anyway, it was empty, and there was a fence around most of it, and we didn't think he could get up enough speed to clear it. Told him that, but it didn't make no difference. He was determined to try, and sure enough, he couldn't get up enough speed."

He started giggling, and turned a little more toward me, making sure Johnny couldn't see his face. "Actually, it was pretty funny… almost like slow motion. He backed up, gunned his hog, and hunkered down. When he hit the edge of the pool, he tried to pull up the front of the bike, but it just kind of froze in space and headed straight down. I didn't see him hit the bottom—it was in the deep end—but boy did I hear it. That was awful. That bike is all busted up, probably done for. And Johnny was throwed off and into the far wall. Must have hit it with his left knee, 'cause that's what hurts. Should have hit it with his head, then he'd probably be alright now." He started giggling again and quickly glanced behind him.

"Was he knocked out?" I asked.

"No. In fact, he tried to stand up, but he couldn't. Said his leg was comin' off and started hollerin'. That's when we threw him on the back of one of the bikes and brought him here."

The thought of that ride made me flinch.

"Okay, why don't you and your two friends head out to the waiting room, and we'll take care of Johnny," I told him.

Reluctantly, he and his two fellow bikers left the room, and Jeff, Jack, and I were alone with Johnny.

He was a big man, and in a lot of pain. Jeff was trying to get him quieted down on the stretcher, but it was difficult for him to find any comfortable position.

"It's my hip, Doc!" he moaned. "It feels like it's comin' off!"

We got him undressed, and as Jeff was carefully removing his jeans and chaps, I could see the source of his problem. His left hip was swollen and already bruised, and its angle of attachment to the socket was clearly abnormal. It was either severely fractured or dislocated, or both.

I asked Jeff to start an IV and then pushed the intercom button for the nurses' station.

"We need some portable X-rays in trauma," I told Amy. "Hip and pelvis, and a chest."

"Got it," Amy replied.

Jack was standing against one of the counters, being careful to stay out of our way. I explained to him what I thought was going on and what we needed to do.

Once Jeff had the IV started, we gave Johnny some pain medication, and then something to help him relax. Because of his size, it took a couple of doses before he seemed a little calmer.

When the X-rays were developed and brought back to the trauma room, I put them up on the view box and stood back, studying them.

"What do you see, Doc?" Johnny asked from the stretcher. "Is it bad?"

It was in fact the best of several bad possibilities, and was what I had hoped for. The hip was dislocated, but there was no fracture. The upper leg and pelvis were fine. Just the dislocation was the problem. That would be better for him in the long run. When he fell into the pool, his left knee must have hit the side wall, driving his upper leg and hip back and out of its socket. It takes a lot of force to do that, especially with someone as big as Johnny. And it was going to take a lot of force to get it back into place.

I told Johnny what the X-rays showed, and that we would need to get it back in place as quickly as possible.

"Once we do that, your pain should be gone," I told him. "You're going to be pretty sore for a while, but this should heal quickly."

His chest X-ray was fine. There was no evidence of any other injury, other than some scattered scrapes and abrasions. He was one very lucky guy.

Jack tapped me on the shoulder and asked, "How are you going to get that hip back into place? Will you need to knock him out?"

"We'll sedate him as much as we can," I explained, "and then we'll have to put some traction on it in order to get it reduced. You'll see. But we need to get it back in place as fast as we can. The longer it's out, the greater the chances for complications and problems later on."

This was an unusual injury, and I had treated only a few myself. I had been able to get all of those reduced, but some had proved to be very difficult, especially the cases involving a big, muscular person like our biker patient.

Johnny was still pretty uncomfortable and not yet relaxed enough, so I asked Jeff to give him more sedating medication. Then I showed Jeff what I wanted him to do.

"Here, let's get Johnny flat on his back," I told him. "And then I want you to stand beside him and hold his pelvis flat on the bed. You're going to need to put all of your weight into it, understand? He's going to try to come off the stretcher."

Jeff positioned himself beside our patient and then placed his hands firmly on Johnny's pelvis, one big hand on each side.

"This what you want?" he asked me.

"Perfect," I said. "Just be sure to hold on."

Then I climbed up on the stretcher and stood over Johnny's legs. There wasn't much room up there and it felt pretty precarious, but there was no other way to do this. He was drowsy, but was still awake enough to mutter, "What the…" Then he closed his eyes and his head turned to one side. Good.

I glanced over at Jack. He was staring at me in disbelief but didn't say anything.

Carefully bending over, I grasped Johnny's injured leg at the knee, and slowly brought it up until it was perpendicular to the stretcher. His thigh was huge, and his calves were enormous. I nodded at Jeff and then bent down further, hugging our patient's calf tightly against my chest. Johnny moaned a little with this movement, but then grew quiet. That was when I noticed the multicolored tattoo on his left thigh, right in front of my face: "MOTHER." I looked up at Jeff and he just grinned and nodded his head.

"Alright, here we go," I told him.

Jeff straightened his arms and applied all of his strength, determined to keep Johnny's pelvis flat on the stretcher. I began to pull up on his leg, raising his knee at a 90-degree angle to his pelvis.

Johnny moaned and began to twist on the bed, but Jeff was able to keep him in place. And I kept pulling, but nothing was happening. His muscles were knotted, and they seemed determined to keep his hip out of its socket.

I started sweating. This was hard work, but I couldn't back off from the traction. I would need to cause his muscles to fatigue and then relax, allowing me to pull the ball of the hip joint over the edge of the socket and back into place. So far, his muscles were fatiguing *me*.

I glanced at Jeff. His face was red too, and beads of sweat were forming on his forehead.

Then I thought I felt a little give. It was subtle, but I was sure I'd felt it.

"Hold on tight, Jeff," I encouraged him. "I think we're—"

Before I could finish, the hip suddenly slipped back into place, and I almost fell off the stretcher. As it did so, we all heard a loud clunking noise, followed immediately by a relieved "ooooooh" from Johnny.

It was the clunk that did Jack in. I heard some metal pans rattle on the countertop, and I looked over just in time to see him reaching behind himself with both hands. He was trying desperately to find something to grab, something to keep him from sliding down to the floor. I watched as his face went from a peculiar greenish color to a pasty and almost ghostlike white. Then his knees buckled. Jeff had seen this too, and with one large arm he reached out, grabbed Jack around the waist, and helped him gently to the floor.

"Just sit here for a minute, boy," he told him. "Take a few deep breaths, and you'll be okay in just a minute."

I climbed down and moved to the head of the stretcher.

"Johnny, how do you feel?"

"Doc, I feel great," he slurred, still under the influence of our medication. "I can move my leg again, and it doesn't hurt."

He tried to pick his leg up from the bed but I quickly put my hand on his thigh and held it down.

"You'll need to be still for a while, Johnny," I spoke loudly. "We don't want that hip going out again."

"No…don't want that," he mumbled, shaking his head and again closing his eyes. This time he had a smile on his face.

Then I turned my attention to Jack. He was sitting on the floor with his head in his hands. His color was a lot better, but not quite back to normal.

He looked up and quietly said, "I…I don't know what happened. I was fine until you pulled on his leg and that…that sound. That was awful. And then the room starting spinning…I'm sorry, Dad, I don't know…"

"Don't worry, Jack," I told him, suppressing a smile. "This happens a lot, and with bigger men than you. You'd be surprised how often. Anyway, just sit there until you feel better. And when you're ready to get up, let Jeff or me know and we'll give you a hand. We don't need another dislocated hip."

From the still-somnolent biker on the stretcher, we heard, "That's for darn sure."

11:45 a.m. Jack had made a full recovery, and Johnny had been discharged on crutches in the company of his friends. He was instructed to follow up in the morning with the orthopedist on call. He would do fine if he didn't push himself. And if he didn't try to jump any more empty swimming pools.

It had been about an hour since Johnny and his friends had left the ER. We were standing at the nurses' station with our backs to the ambulance entrance. I heard the doors open behind me, followed by the quiet clicking of the wheels of a stretcher as it was rolled into the department. Busy with the chart in front of me, I didn't turn around.

Then the clicking stopped and I felt a light tap on my back.

"Robert, I'm so glad you're here today."

The voice was of an elderly woman, and I recognized it.

Turning around, I looked down at the stretcher behind me and saw Myra Donalds.

She stretched out her slender hand to me and said again, "So glad you're on duty today."

Myra Donalds was easily in her nineties. When we had first moved to Rock Hill, she was active in teaching the children in the church we joined. In fact, she had taught all of our own kids in Sunday school, including Jack. Her husband had died four or five years ago, and Myra had moved into one of the retirement centers in town. She had trouble getting around, and I hadn't seen her in church in a long time.

"Myra Donalds," I said, taking her hand in mine. It was tiny, and weak. She had aged since I had last seen her, and she had lost weight. Myra had always been slender, always prim and proper. But she knew how to handle the young people in our church, especially the more difficult ones in the middle-school years. It wasn't her size, or commanding voice, or gruff demeanor. She had none of those. It was because they knew she cared about them, and they cared about her. She was a favorite of all of our children, especially Jack.

It was unusual, really. Jack had been having a typical rebellious phase in the sixth and seventh grades, about the time he started attending Mrs. Donalds's Sunday-school class. Other teachers had tried various ways of dealing with him, but like his father before him, he had spent a good bit of time in trouble. Or at least until he sat down in Myra's classroom. It all changed then. Something clicked between the two of them, and his demeanor and behavior completely changed. And so did his life.

"What brings you to the ER today?" I asked her. "I hope it's just a social visit."

I knew better, having glanced down at her right hip and seeing its awkward angle and the way she was trying to hold it still.

"I wish it were, Robert," she said, smiling. "But I'm afraid it's this hip of mine," she explained, gently patting it. "I tripped over a rug in my apartment this afternoon and fell. I landed right on it. I'm afraid it's broken."

Denton Roberts, the paramedic who had responded to the call, was standing at the head of the stretcher. I looked over at him and he silently nodded his head.

Denton was one of our best paramedics. He was in his mid-forties and had been with the EMS for the past fifteen years. Tall, slender, and always smiling, I trusted his judgment in the field and frequently leaned on his experience. He had seen a lot.

He reached down and patted Myra on her shoulder. "This is one tough customer, Dr. Lesslie," he said respectfully. "Obvious hip fracture, but she didn't want anything for pain. Just wanted to be brought to the hospital. And she apologized for not having tea and something to eat for us."

"Well, young man," she said, straining to look back at his face. "If I could have gotten off the floor, I would have."

I laughed at this, knowing she meant it. Then I said, "Myra, we need to get you back to one of the exam rooms and get you taken care of." Then suddenly remembering Jack, I said, "And look who's here with me today."

Jack had been standing near Denton, and Myra had not yet seen him. He moved around the other side of the stretcher until he stood beside her.

"Mrs. Donalds, it's Jack Lesslie," he said, laying his hand on her elbow. "It's been a long time."

There was a mixture of emotions on his face. He was genuinely glad to see her, but at the same time he was surprised at how much she had changed. She seemed much older than when he had last sat in her classroom. Once he had started high school and now college, he had lost contact. Seeing her like this must have been a shock.

"Jack? Is that you?" Myra asked, her face brightening.

"Yes, Mrs. Donalds. It's me," he answered, now smiling himself, and more relaxed.

Myra let go of my hand and reached up and patted Jack on his cheek.

"My, my! You have grown up, young man," she said with obvious pride. "You're not a young boy anymore."

"No ma'am, I'm not," he said. "I'm in college now, and spending some time with Dad in the ER this summer."

"Well, I bet you didn't count on seeing an old lady like me, did you?" she kidded him.

"I…well…" he stuttered, taken off guard.

"Myra, let's get you on back to a bed and get you more comfortable," I said, coming to his rescue. "Denton, I think the first bed in ortho is open. How about taking her back there?"

Myra Donalds did have a fractured right hip, and it would need to be operated on, probably this evening. For a woman over ninety, she was in remarkable health. And perhaps even more remarkable, she was not taking any regular medications. This should be a routine admission

and surgery, and then a routine discharge back to her retirement center. But I knew better.

After the orthopedist had examined Myra and written orders for
her admission, Jack went back to talk with her before she went upstairs.
After about twenty minutes, he came walking up the hall and stopped
beside me at the nurses' station. I had just picked up the chart of my
next patient, and I turned to him and asked, "Did you have a good
chat with Mrs. Donalds?"

"I did, Dad," he answered, looking at the countertop and nodding
his head. "It's been a long time since I've seen her, but she really hasn't
changed at all. Not really. She's still as funny and sharp as ever. And
somehow she knows just the right questions to ask you. She doesn't
beat around the bush, does she?"

"No," I answered. "*That* she doesn't do. And she never has. Maybe
that's why the two of you have always gotten along so well. She came
into your life when you needed someone to shoot straight with you,
someone outside of our family."

"Hmm," he mused. "You know, I think you're probably right. I
didn't realize back then how much I really…liked her, I guess."

I studied his face for a moment, "Did you tell her that this afternoon?"

"It's funny, but I did." He looked up at me. "It was just so easy to
talk with her, and she asked about everything I was doing, and what
was going on in my life. It just came so naturally, and I wanted her to
know how I felt about her."

He paused and looked down again.

"I'm just glad it's only her hip that she's injured," he told me, breaking this brief silence.

"What do you mean?"

"Well, it's just her hip," he began to explain. "Like that other guy this
morning, the biker. He really hurt his hip bad but then he was able to
go home on crutches. Like you said, he's going to be okay."

He waited for my response, and I said, "Uh-huh," wanting him to
go on.

"I mean, she's going to be alright after this, isn't she?" he asked. My hesitancy seemed to concern him.

I put the chart in my hand down on the counter and looked into the eyes of my son.

"Jack, I know it seems like sort of the same thing, these two hip injuries," I began. "Johnny the biker goes home and should completely recover. But Myra, well, *this* hip injury is a completely different story. If Johnny had broken his hip instead of dislocating it, he still would have been okay. He would have been admitted to the hospital and had it operated on. And then he would have gone home and done fine. But when someone Myra's age breaks a hip…well, it can be the beginning of the end."

"The what?" he exclaimed. "She seems fine now, and it's only a hip… and…"

"I know that's what it seems," I explained. "But Myra is ninety-two years old, and even though she lives in a retirement center, she's still very lonely. She and Bill had been married for over sixty years, and when you lose a spouse after that long…well, it's really a hard thing to get over. And it was especially hard for Myra because she and Bill were so close."

I stopped and let Jack think about this for a moment.

"You mean Mrs. Donalds is going to give up?" he asked me.

"I don't know that it's *giving up* exactly," I answered, searching for the right words. "I think it might be coming to an understanding that you've reached a place in your life…a place where things really get difficult and you just wonder why you're fighting so hard. And then you come to a peaceful place, and you're ready to accept what comes next. Unfortunately, not everyone finds that peace. And don't misunderstand me—Myra might go back to the retirement center and do just fine. It's just that the odds are against her, and I sense…well, I sense that's where she is."

Jack just looked at me. And then he said, "Dad, now I understand what she was saying."

He stopped. I just waited.

"When I was back in the room talking with her, she said, 'Jack, it's important to live well, and it's important to leave well.' I didn't understand her, and I think she knew that because she said it again. She wanted to be sure I heard her, and that I remembered. Now I know what she meant."

Myra Donalds. Always teaching, always supporting, always thinking of someone else. She continued to be an amazing woman.

Over Jack's shoulder I could see her being wheeled out of the ortho room and around the corner toward the OR. I didn't say anything.

"And she said something else," Jack added. "She reminded me of a verse from the book of John. She had us memorize it when we were kids, but after all these years, I can't remember it. I'll have to look it up when we get home."

I picked the chart up from the countertop again and started down the hallway.

"When you look it up tonight, son, let me know."

Now before the feast of the Passover,
when Jesus knew that his hour had come
to depart out of this world to his Father,
having loved his own who were in the world,
he loved them to the end.

JOHN 13:1 RSV

Choose Life

Light is sweet,
and it pleases the eyes to see the sun.
However many years a man may live,
let him enjoy them all.
But let him remember the days of darkness,
for they will be many.

ECCLESIASTES 11:7-8

6:58 a.m. I walked through the ambulance entrance just as Sally Carlton was being brought in from triage in a wheelchair. Jeff Ryan was our triage nurse this morning, and he was pushing her down the hallway to room 4.

"Sally's here for another transfusion," he told me as they passed the nurses' station.

"Hey, Dr. Lesslie," she said, looking up. "Sorry, but it's me again."

"Sally," I said, smiling. "You know we're always glad to see you. Let Jeff get you settled and I'll be back with you in just a minute."

Jeff and Sally continued down the hallway, and I looked for Tom Anders, the nighttime doc I was relieving.

He stepped through the curtained entrance of room 2 and walked over to the nurses' station. Shaking his head in disbelief, he tossed the patient's chart onto the countertop.

"Twenty-one-year-old college student," he told me. "Too much beer and too much sun yesterday. You ought to see this guy's burns. Woke up a little while ago, or more correctly *sobered* up, and realized how much pain he was in."

Tom made some notes on the chart, wrote a prescription for pain medicine, and tossed the clipboard into the discharge basket.

"He's going to have a tough couple of days," he said. "Maybe he'll learn a lesson here."

"Doubt it," Amy Connors muttered, not looking up from the patient ledger she was studying.

"Yeah, you're probably right," Tom agreed. "Anyway, that's all I have, Robert," he said, turning to me. "Everything's taken care of."

"Thanks," I told him. "Now go get some rest."

He turned and headed toward the ER entrance. "See you tonight," he called over his shoulder.

Lori Davidson was walking up the hall with Katie Matthews. They were intently studying a notepad, and I could hear Lori explaining to Katie the importance of making sure each room was restocked at the beginning of a shift.

They were an interesting contrast. Lori had been working in the ER for almost ten years and had become one of our steadiest and most dependable nurses. She was a little more than thirty, yet had the judgment and patience of someone much older. Her presence in the department was calming, a rare quality in such a chaotic and stressful environment. Perhaps her greatest strength, though, was that she genuinely cared for her patients, and they quickly sensed that.

Katie, on the other hand, was twenty-two years old and had just completed her nursing degree, graduating with honors from the program at Clemson. She had grown up in Fort Mill, a small town just a few miles from Rock Hill, and had spent some of her college summers in the ER as a tech. She was enthusiastic but inexperienced. Lori would be a good teacher for her and a good role model.

"So, you think you've got that, Katie?" Lori was asking her. "This is our check-list, and when you're finished, just be sure to initial what you've done."

"I understand," Katie answered. "That way, if something's not right, you'll know who's responsible."

She was quick, and for the few weeks she had spent in the ER as a full-time nurse, she was catching on quickly.

Jeff walked back to the nurses' station and handed me Sally Carlton's clipboard. He had taken her to room 4 and was helping her get settled on the stretcher.

"Here's Sally's chart," he told me. "I'll get things ready."

As he turned and walked to the medication room, it occurred to me that this might be a good opportunity for Katie to meet Sally.

She was standing on the other side of the counter, still talking with Lori, and I interrupted them. "Katie, if you've got a minute…"

They both looked over at me. "Sure, Dr. Lesslie," Katie said. "What is it?"

"There's somebody I want you to meet," I told her. "She's in room 4, Sally Carlton. But I want to tell you about her before we go in there."

Lori nodded as I said this. "That's a good idea, Katie," she told her. "You'll like her." She walked around the counter. "I'll be out in triage."

I motioned for Katie to follow me into the empty observation room. In a quiet voice, I began to tell her about Sally.

Sally Carlton was twenty-five years old. Three years earlier, when she was a senior at the University of South Carolina, she had come home on Christmas break and complained of fatigue. Sally had always been healthy, and her parents were concerned enough to take her to their family doctor. He told them it was probably the stress of a heavy schedule and advised her to get some rest over the break. A week later she came to the ER feeling worse, and running a low-grade fever.

I had been on duty that day, and remembered that first meeting. She was a pretty girl, of medium height and slight build. She had long, dark hair and a spontaneous and infectious smile. But it was her eyes that grabbed your attention. They were alive, and there was a sparkle behind them. Here was a spitfire—and someone who didn't like the idea of being sick.

But it was also those eyes that bothered me. Below each of them were dark circles, almost bruises. And as we talked, I became more concerned about her and about her fatigue.

This had started a few weeks earlier and had begun to affect her ability to get around the sprawling USC campus.

"I can't go up and down stairs now," she told me. "I just seem to give out."

Her parents had been in the room with her, her father standing with his chin cupped in his hand, her mother nervously patting her on the shoulder.

She had no history of any medical problems and was on no medication. Her father described her as "the picture of health."

"We don't think this has anything to do with the pressures of being in school or stress or anything like that," he told me. "I don't think Dr. Jones has any idea what's going on, and he's wrong about that."

"Hmm," I mused. "What about any bruising, Sally? Anything unusual like that?"

She had looked up at her mother and then back at me. "You mean like this?" she answered, pulling up the right sleeve of her blouse and revealing several large, purplish areas. They were irregular in shape, and the multiple shades of blue and purple indicated they were of different ages. This had been going on for a while.

"When did you notice this?" I asked. Her parents leaned closer, staring at her arm. This was something new for them, as she had apparently tried to keep it hidden.

"I guess it started about two weeks ago," she answered sheepishly. "I thought I must have bumped into something and that it would go away."

"But it didn't, did it?" I remarked gently.

"No, and then these…" She pulled up the left leg of her loose-fitting slacks, revealing more extensive bruising about the outside of her thigh. Her mother had gasped, putting her hand to her mouth. And her father had just stood up straight, staring at his daughter's leg.

A CBC had given us the answer nobody wanted. Sally had leukemia, and was in trouble. That evening she was at Duke, under the care of a blood-and-cancer specialist. Within a few weeks, she would have a bone-marrow transplant.

And for a while, she had done well. The medication was working and her blood counts had returned to normal. Most importantly to Sally, her energy level had returned and she was able to go back to school and her classes. She wanted to finish her degree and pursue a career in nursing.

But that had lasted only a few weeks. Her white-blood-cell count started to rise again, indicating more problems. Then the fatigue returned, and her fevers. The specialists at Duke tried everything, and she would sometimes seem to be improving, to almost *will* this disease into remission. Then the blood work would be bad again. First it was her white count, exposing her to what could be a catastrophic infection. And then her hemoglobin began to fall, with the resulting anemia causing a fatigue that never seemed to leave her.

It was the anemia that had been bringing her to the ER. She would come in for a transfusion of a few units of blood and would then feel better for a few weeks. But it was always there, this thing that had destroyed her bone marrow, and her visits to the ER had become more frequent. It was all that could be done at this point. And there was no way of knowing how many more times we could do this, and how much more time she had. It probably wouldn't be very long.

"So there's really nothing anybody can do?" Katie asked. "I mean, how about another transplant?"

"No, I'm afraid she's run out of options," I told her. "But you wouldn't know that by talking to her. You'll see."

We walked around the nurses' station to room 4. Sally was lying on the stretcher, her blanket drawn up to her waist. She had folded her arms across her chest but now raised her right hand and waved as we entered.

She smiled and said, "I'm glad you're on duty today, Dr. Lesslie. And who is this with you?" she asked, looking at Katie.

"This is Katie Matthews," I said. "She just recently finished her nursing school and has started working here in the ER with us."

Sally held out her hand. "It's good to meet you, Katie," she said as they shook hands. "I'm sure Dr. Lesslie has a few things to show you. And I'm sure he has plenty of stories to tell you," she adding, winking at me. "You know, I'm going into nursing myself."

Out of the corner of my eye I thought I saw Katie tense just a little. But Sally's words were spoken with conviction, and her smile and expression did not change at all. She meant what she was saying. And yet she knew the reality of her condition.

"Where did you go to school?" she asked Katie.

"Well, that will give you two something to talk about," I told them. "Sally, we'll get your blood going as soon as it comes over from the lab."

Jeff had come back into the room and was preparing to start an IV.

"Want to give me a hand?" he asked Katie.

"Sure," she answered. "I'll be happy to."

Sally would be in good hands, and I stepped to the doorway. "I'll check on you in a while," I told her. "Keep these guys straight."

"Don't worry about them," she answered. "I'll make sure they behave."

As I stepped out of the room, I saw Virginia Granger standing in the doorway of the head nurse's office. She motioned for me to join her.

Virginia had been our head nurse for a lot of years, longer than I had been in Rock Hill. No one knew her real age (no one was brave enough to ask), but she must have been in her mid-sixties. The early part of her nursing career had been spent in the military, and her bearing continued to be rigid, overtly professional, and quite intimidating. She always wore a dazzling white, freshly starched uniform, and white scuffless shoes. And this morning, as always, her pointed nursing cap was bobby-pinned to her dyed-jet-black hair.

She commanded respect from her staff and demanded that we all take our jobs seriously and focus on the needs of our patients. That's what she did, and we were to do nothing less. Yet behind this rigid exterior, behind this intimidating façade, lived a woman with a big and warm heart. She didn't show that side to a lot of people, and I'm not sure why. But I knew it was there. I had seen it.

"Dr. Lesslie," she said to me. "Close the door, would you? And have a seat."

She pointed to the chair in front of her desk, and I sat down.

"Tell me about Sally."

I knew Virginia didn't want to know temperatures or blood pressures or blood counts. She wanted to know how Sally was handling things, how she was *really* doing.

We talked for a few minutes and I told her I would get back with her before Sally left the department.

"That one's a fighter," Virginia said, slowly nodding her head.

Two hours later, Sally had finished receiving her blood transfusion. Jeff was wheeling her toward the exit. She was laughing at something he had said, and I noticed that her color was decidedly better. This time she was able to go home, but the time was soon coming when that would no longer be an option.

Her father had gone out to bring the car around to the ambulance entrance, and they were waiting for him to come back into the department.

Katie had walked up with them. They all stopped beside me at the nurses' station.

"Sally, are you feeling better?" I asked. "You certainly look like you do."

"I feel like a million dollars," she said, smiling at me. "I've had expert care this morning. What else would you expect?"

The ambulance doors opened, and her father stood beside the passenger door of their car. Jeff began pushing the wheelchair once again, with Katie walking close behind them.

Sally twisted around in her chair and waved at me. "I guess I'll see you next time." Then she turned and said something to her father as they disappeared through the closing doors.

A moment later, Katie walked back into the department and over to where I stood.

"You know, Dr. Lesslie, you're right. She really is a special person. Do you think she understands how sick she is?" she asked.

"Of course she does. It's just that she's not willing to give in to it. She wants to live. You can see it in her eyes. The day that's gone, the day that fire's not in her eyes, that's when I'm going to worry."

She stood there for a moment. "How much longer do you think she has?"

"There's no way of knowing for sure. But it's going to be measured in days and weeks, not months."

That seemed to bother her, but it was the truth.

"But you know, Katie, whatever time she has left, she'll make the most of it. She has a spirit I wish we all had. She appreciates every moment she has."

Katie was about to say something but was interrupted by the crackle of the EMS radio.

"Rock Hill ER, this is Medic 1. Is the doctor nearby?"

That's when it started.

Amy Connors picked up the receiver and handed it to me.

"Medic 1, this is Dr. Lesslie," I answered.

"Doc, this is Denton Roberts. We're at the scene with a twenty-six-year-old woman, complainin' of not feelin' right. She seems a little bit confused, but all her vital signs are good and she seems stable. Normally we wouldn't bring her in, but somethin' doesn't quite seem right. Any problems if I go ahead and transport?"

This was an odd request, but Denton had been doing this for a long time and I knew better than to second-guess him.

"Sure, Denton, go ahead and bring her in. What's your ETA?"

"About 5. I'll probably start a line, just to be safe."

"Fine," I told him. Lori had walked up beside me and heard this conversation. She got my attention and held up three fingers.

"And room 3 when you get here, Denton," I added.

A few minutes later, the ambulance doors opened and Denton Roberts and his partner brought their stretcher into the ER with the young woman.

"Room 3?" he confirmed with Lori as they reached the nurses' station.

"Right," she answered, making some notes on the chart in front of her. "I'll be just a second."

As they passed, the young woman looked up at me. She seemed alert enough, but there was something dull and remote about her gaze. I could see what had troubled Denton. Then from behind her there was a small commotion as another young woman tried to squeeze through the closing mechanical doors. She was able to pry them open enough to barely make it through.

Lori looked up from her charting and said, "Can I help you, miss?"

The woman standing just inside the ambulance entrance was probably in her mid-twenties, dressed in blue jeans and a loose-fitting T-shirt and wearing flip-flops. Her hair was a dirty blonde and probably hadn't met a comb in a few days.

"I'm with her," she answered, pointing to the stretcher disappearing into room 3.

Lori stepped over to the woman and motioned to the triage entrance. "You'll need to have a seat in the waiting room," she gently directed her. "We'll let you know something as soon as we can."

"But, she—"

"Come on, I'll show you." Lori cut off her protestations and led her out to waiting.

Wanda Bennett was the name of the young woman who had just been taken to room 3. I motioned for Katie to follow me. We stepped into the cubicle, pulling the curtain closed behind us. Denton and his partner had transferred Wanda to our bed and were preparing to push their stretcher out of the room.

"Everything's still stable," Denton told me. "Blood pressure is 115 over 70 and her pulse is 72 and regular. Pulse ox is 97 percent." He shrugged and shook his head. "If anything, she may be a little more confused, or something."

"Thanks, Denton," I told him, stepping back out of his way. "I'll let you know what turns up."

He left the room, and Lori continued to work with our new patient. She attached the leads for the cardiac monitor and hung her IV fluid bag on the stand by the head of the bed.

"Oxygen?" she asked me.

The oxygen saturation of her blood was normal. She certainly wasn't in any distress. "No, we'll hold off on that," I told her, stepping closer to the stretcher.

I glanced down at the clipboard Lori had set on the counter, noting her name.

"Wanda?" I said, touching her lightly on her shoulder. "I'm Dr. Lesslie. What can we do for you today?"

She had absently been watching Lori and now turned to face me. Wanda was of a heavy build, used a little too much makeup, and had black hair of medium length.

"Who?" she asked, the word drawn out more than it should have been.

"I'm Dr. Lesslie," I repeated, a little louder this time. "What's the problem today?"

"Oh, Dr. Wesley, I…I…who brought me here?"

She seemed confused now and began to look around the room. Lori immediately stepped close and took her hand. "It's okay, Wanda. You're in the hospital. We're here to help you."

This seemed to confuse her even more, and she became a little agitated. She looked at Lori and asked, "The hospital? What's the matter?"

I tried to get some coherent information from her, but without success. She repeated my questions, but never answered them. Leaning closer, I tried to detect the odor of alcohol on her breath. Nothing there. A brief exam did not turn up anything unusual, and I was in a quandary as to what might be causing her decreased level of consciousness. She certainly wasn't helping, so we would need to use a broad, shotgun approach.

Katie and I walked back to the nurses' station, and she asked, "What do you think her problem is? She seems pretty out of it right now, doesn't she?"

She did seem out of it, and the problem was that it had appeared to be getting worse while we were in the room with her.

"I'm not sure at this point, Katie. We'll need to look at a bunch of things and see if something turns up. We'll need some blood work and probably a scan of her head." I paused and thought for a moment. "She told Lori she didn't take any medication, and Denton didn't report seeing any in her apartment. But you can't trust what she's telling us."

"What about her friend?" she asked. "What about that other woman who came in with her?"

Now there was a good thought. "Great idea, Katie. I'll ask Lori to bring her back and see if she can shed any light on this."

A few minutes later, Lori walked up to the nurses' station with the woman we assumed was Wanda Bennett's friend.

"Dr. Lesslie, this is Amanda Davis," Lori introduced her. "She's Wanda's roommate."

Amanda was nervously looking around the department, trying to locate her friend.

"Miss Davis," I said to her. "I need some information about Wanda."

"Okay, I'll be glad to help," she answered. But her eyes never met mine.

"When did she start getting like this? This confusion?" I asked her.

"She, uh, she was fine last night. I guess it started just a little while ago, right before I called 9-1-1."

"Was she complaining about anything when you called, any pain or headache? Anything unusual?"

"No, nothin' like that. She just wasn't acting right. Started talking funny, I guess. And didn't make much sense." She was becoming a little nervous for some reason. "Is she alright?"

"She's okay right now," I tried to assure her. "We're trying to figure out why she's acting this way. Is she taking any medication or using any drugs?"

I watched closely for any telltale change in her body language, any hint that what she might tell me was not the truth.

At this point she looked in my eyes and slowly shook her head. "Nope. She doesn't take any medicine and doesn't use any drugs or stuff like that. She doesn't even drink."

I continued to study her face, and asked again, "Are you sure? No prescription meds or anything? Sleeping pills? Something for her nerves?"

"No, she doesn't take anything." She looked away after saying this, and asked, "Can I see her now?"

"Dr. Lesslie, can you come over here?"

It was Lori, standing in the doorway of room 3 and motioning for me to hurry over.

Amy Connors had been listening to this exchange and had heard Lori. She stepped around the nurses' counter and took Amanda by the elbow.

"Miss Davis, if you'll follow me, I'll take you back to the waiting room," she instructed her. Amy was polite, but left no room for questioning.

"But..." Amanda murmured, yet followed Amy obediently toward the triage entrance.

When I went into the room, one of our lab techs was drawing blood, adjusting the tourniquet on Wanda's right arm. Lori was standing at the head of the stretcher and pointed to the cardiac monitor as I pulled the curtain closed.

"Maybe she seems a little more confused, Dr. Lesslie," she explained. "But this is what has me worried."

My eyes followed hers to the monitor screen. There was a steady beep-beep-beep, nice and regular, but now the rate had fallen to 58.

"Her blood pressure is okay," she told me, anticipating my next question. "But her rate is slowing, and every once in a while she has what looks like a PVC. Look—right there," she said, pointing again to the monitor.

I had seen it as well. It looked like a PVC, an extra heartbeat, sometimes normal, but also at times associated with some underlying heart problem or irritability. There had only been one, and then it was gone.

"Let's get an EKG and see what it looks like," I instructed Lori. "And could we get those labs back as quickly as possible?" I asked the tech. She had finished drawing blood and was pressing a Band-aid over the puncture site.

"Should only be a few minutes." She hurried out of the room.

Wanda Bennett's EKG was troubling. I was sitting at the nurses' station, studying the tracing and trying to unravel this mystery. Somewhere in this multitude of undulating ink lines might be the answer, waiting to be discovered.

She continued to have a slow yet nearly normal pattern. But every few beats there was a slight lengthening of the whole electrical complex, and then it would tighten up again. That was strange and didn't make much sense. I wasn't sure I had seen it before.

Katie was standing behind me, looking over my shoulder. I pointed out the unusual finding on Wanda's EKG.

"What could cause something like that?" she asked. "She's too young for a heart attack, isn't she?"

She actually wasn't, but these findings didn't go along with a heart attack. Something else was happening here.

"I don't know, Katie," I answered honestly. "Maybe some toxin, or something like that. Something that's affecting her heart's electrical conducting system. Sometimes carbon monoxide poisoning can cause strange heart problems, but it's summer, and people probably aren't using space heaters now."

"Dr. Lesslie." It was Lori again. This time she stood in the doorway of room 3 and once she caught my eye, she stepped back into the room without another word.

We walked quickly around the counter and into the cubicle.

Wanda was relaxed on the stretcher, seemingly asleep. Her left arm hung limply over the side of the stretcher, and her mouth was open. She was quietly snoring.

"She won't respond now," Lori told me. "BP is about 60, and her heart rate is 40 to 50."

I looked at the monitor and immediately pressed the button that allowed a rhythm strip to print continuously. Her rate was 48, and now every complex was widened—and seemed to be getting wider as we watched.

I rubbed Wanda's sternum and loudly called her name in her ear. No response. Then I turned to Lori and asked her to give several medications in an attempt to speed up her heart and reverse this down-ward spiral.

"I'm going to find Amanda Davis and have another talk with her," I said, turning toward the door. "And I'll send Jeff in to help."

Amy Connors led Amanda into the department once more and toward the nurses' station. Room 5 was empty, and I motioned for her to follow me there. Once Amanda was in the room, I pulled the curtain closed behind us and asked her to have a seat.

"Miss Davis, this is very important. Your friend, Wanda, is not doing well. She's unresponsive. I can't wake her up now. And something's going on with her heart." I paused, letting these words sink in. "Is there anything you can tell me about her, about what she's been doing over the past few days? Is she taking any medication? Any recreational drugs?"

She looked down at the floor when I said this.

"Amanda, listen, I'm not the police. And nothing you say to me will be reported to the police. I'm trying to help Wanda. And if you know anything, anything that could be of use…" I pleaded. And then more sternly, "I need your help."

She turned her face up to me and was about to say something. There was a conflicted look in her eyes, but they hardened again and she looked down at the floor.

"No, I don't know of anything," she persisted.

She knew something, or I thought she did. And I was starting to get angry.

"Let me say this once more, Amanda," I said to her, my voice firm yet as measured as I could make it. "Wanda is in trouble. Real trouble. She may die. Do you hear me? If we don't determine what's causing this, she may very well—"

"Code blue, room 3!"

Jeff Ryan's voice spoke urgently over the department intercom.

"Code blue, room 3!" he repeated.

Wanda Bennett had crashed, and I sprang for the door, but not before nailing Amanda with a look of anger and disgust and accusation.

I threw the curtain aside and saw several people heading to room 3. Then from behind me I heard, "Dr. Lesslie! Please, Dr. Lesslie!"

It was Amanda Davis, and she was following me as fast as she could. I stopped and turned, facing her.

"What do you want?" I asked her, knowing I needed to get to Wanda Bennett, but also wondering if Amanda had something of value to tell me.

She was crying now and wringing her hands. Then she blurted out, "Dr. Lesslie, she made me promise not to tell. She made me promise! That's why I didn't…before…I couldn't—"

"What is it, Amanda?" I demanded.

"She took her daddy's pills. A bunch of them. Last night and again this morning. Said she was tired of livin' and puttin' up with everything. I didn't think she was really serious, 'cause that's all she took. She's talked about this before, but—"

"Amanda!" I snapped, getting her attention. "What did she take?"

"That's just it, nothin' serious. That's why I thought…She just took some of her daddy's blood-pressure medicine, that's all. That shouldn't really hurt her, should it?" she asked innocently.

My mind was sorting through the various classes of blood-pressure medications, searching for the answer that would fit this woman's problems. It was forming in my mind, but it was not quite there yet.

"What was the name of it? What was on the bottle?"

A puzzled look came over her face, and I gave up, turning toward room 3.

"Dalozam, or diltozam. Something like that," she mumbled.

The answer flashed like lightning across my brain. She had taken a huge overdose of a calcium-channel blocker, a commonly used blood-pressure medication. It blocked the movements of certain chemicals in various parts of the heart, slowing the heart rate and easing the force of contractions. It was obvious what too much of that drug could do.

I turned to Amy and said, "Take her to the waiting room." And then I hurried into room 3.

There was a flurry of activity around the stretcher, controlled chaos. Lori had set out the emergency airway tray and in less than a minute we had secured Wanda's breathing.

"She just stopped breathing and then went flatline," Lori told me, a little out of breath. Jeff was doing chest compressions. Just then the lab tech came into the room and handed me Wanda's lab reports. Everything was completely normal. I searched for the calcium level and it was normal too. But then it should be. She had plenty of calcium on board—it just wasn't able to do its job because of the medication. The only thing to do was give her *more* calcium, in the hopes of overcoming the blockade.

"Give her two amps of calcium," I told Lori.

"Two amps?" Jeff questioned. "Do you want to try some epi first?" He was only trying to help, following what should be standard protocol.

"No, Jeff. We're going to give her calcium, and a lot of it. We're going to need more amps from the main crash cart," I told one of the techs. Then I explained to Jeff and Lori what I had learned.

It all made sense now. The sleepiness, then the worsening confusion. And then the widening of her electrical complexes. It was all logical and explainable. And if I had known from the beginning, or had just had a clue…Why hadn't she told me? And why hadn't Amanda Davis seen the danger to her friend and told me from the outset?

"Nothing here," Lori told me, feeling for a carotid pulse. And there was no electrical activity on the monitor.

We continued our efforts for another 45 minutes, pumping Wanda full of calcium and other emergency medications. She didn't respond to anything.

Finally, I knew we had to stop. She was dead. We weren't going to change that.

Lori noted the time of death on her chart while everyone else filed out of the room. Everyone except Katie. I had forgotten she had been standing behind me the whole time, never uttering a word. There was a troubled look on her face as she stared down at the lifeless body of Wanda Bennett.

"Come on, Katie," I said to her, putting my hand lightly on her shoulder. "Let's go outside for a minute."

We stood together under the portico of the ambulance entrance, shielded from the afternoon sun.

"That was—really tough, Katie." I spoke, then became silent, wanting her to express her thoughts.

"I don't understand, Dr. Lesslie," she shook her head. "I don't understand a couple of things. I didn't know something simple like blood-pressure medicine could do something like that to you. And I wonder if she knew it." She thought for a moment. Then, "Do you think she had any idea this might happen? And I wonder if she really wanted to kill herself? What if—"

"That's something we'll never know, Katie. There's no way you can know the mind of another person, much less their heart. I don't have any idea what she was thinking, or what she was trying to do. It doesn't matter now," I told her. "I only wish…"

We were silent for a moment, and then Katie continued my thought. "Do you think it would have made any difference if you had known right away what she had taken? Do you think it could have been reversed or something?"

I had been struggling with the same question. My head told me that she must have taken a massive overdose of this medicine, and that by the time she'd come to the ER, there was nothing anyone could do to reverse its actions. It had all happened so quickly.

But my heart told me something different. I wasn't used to being in this position, and feeling helpless. And I found I was angry with Wanda. But I wasn't going to voice that to this young nurse. I wasn't the one lying on the stretcher in room 3, a sheet drawn over my face.

"No, Katie. I think she sealed her fate when she took all those pills. There was no going back."

"It just seems like such a waste. What makes someone want to die like this? What would make her want to kill herself?" she asked, not expecting an answer. Maybe not wanting one. "She's only a few years older than me, you know."

We didn't talk any further. And I thought of Sally Carlton.

Now choose life,
so that you and your children may live
and that you may love the Lord your God,
listen to his voice,
and hold fast to him.

DEUTERONOMY 30:19-20

All That Glitters…

Judgment comes from experience,
and great judgment comes from bad experience.

SAYING

Beware lest you lose the substance
by grasping at the shadow.

AESOP

Tuesday, 9:45 a.m. Amy Connors dropped the pen she was holding and stared in amazement over my left shoulder. "Good Lord," she murmured. "Would you look at that?"

I was standing at the nurses' station and turned around to see a young man behind me, not more than five feet away. He was staring straight at me, his arms hanging limply by his side, his knees slightly bent as if ready to pounce. The look on his face got my attention. There was a mixture of fear and pleading, and something else. His eyes were wild, and I began to wonder if he was dangerous.

He was barefoot, and his worn jeans were tattered at the edges. He wasn't wearing a shirt and I noticed the tattoo of a multicolored, robed wizard over his heart.

"Doc," he whispered in a shaky voice, "I need some help."

Lori Davidson, our triage nurse this morning, had walked up behind him.

"Sir," she said, reaching out and lightly tapping his shoulder.

Then his arms stiffened and his eyes widened in what looked like abject terror. His legs straightened and his arms went out zombie-like. His head twitched for just a second and he began to arch backward, first his head, and then his upper torso. He did this very fluidly, as if having practiced it over and over. His long hair dangled behind him, and when he finally stopped, he was almost nose to nose with Lori. Her eyes widened in surprise, and she seemed frozen on the spot. As for this young man, he looked like a pretzel. I was impressed with his flexibility.

Suddenly he let out a terrible and unnerving scream. "Aghh!" And that did it. The chart in Lori's hand flew ten feet into the air and we all jumped, seeking a safe distance from him. I reached for the countertop, trying to find something solid to hold on to. And then without warning he snapped back to his original position, arms hanging by his side, knees slightly bent. His eyes were once again fixed on mine.

"Doc, I need some help. I can't stop doing this. Do something," he pleaded.

"What in the world…" Amy muttered behind me.

Jeff Ryan was on duty today and was walking up the hall. He stopped beside me, intently studying our young patient.

"What's going on?" he whispered to me.

"I don't know," I answered him honestly. "This guy just walked in, and—"

Suddenly it started again. This young man's arms stiffened, his legs straightened, he began arching backward, and Lori moved further away. When his torso was parallel with the floor, he let out another scream and his body whipped forward, hair flying in all directions. This time I was prepared and didn't react with the same surprise. Jeff watched these startling contortions but seemed unfazed. After a brief assessment, he suspected mischief.

"This guy's wacko, Doc," he said. "I'm gonna take him to room 5 and get him to calm down. Look," he added, gesturing down the hallway at several patients and visitors who were peeking out from behind their curtains and watching this spectacle.

"Good idea, Jeff," I agreed. "But I'm not sure about this guy. This is pretty strange."

Jeff nodded his head. Then he addressed our new patient. "Why don't you come with me…uh…what's your name?"

"Jimmy Blake," the man answered, happy that someone was finally going to help him.

Jeff headed to room 5, with Jimmy obediently following behind him. Suddenly he stopped, still in the hallway, and the gyration began again. He immediately stiffened and then began slowly arching backward. Jeff didn't know his patient had stopped, and he continued on to room 5, talking. When there was no answer, he turned around just as Jimmy was snapping his body forward and screaming.

This time even Jeff jumped. "Come on in here," he told him, shaking his head and holding the curtain open. "Have a seat on the stretcher."

When Jeff had gotten Jimmy undressed and in a gown, he walked out of room 5 and over to where I stood. He handed me his chart, and said, "He's all yours. He did that goofy thing twice more while I was trying to get his vital signs. The blood pressure is probably pretty close, but I don't know. Anyway, it's the best I can do."

He walked toward the medicine room to wash his hands.

I looked over Jimmy Blake's chart. Twenty-three years old. Vital signs were normal. No medications and no allergies. "Denies alcohol or illicit drugs," Jeff had written. Not much to go on here.

Virginia Granger had walked up behind me and was glancing at the record.

"Better take a close look at this one," she said to me, slowly nodding her head. Then she turned and walked down the hall.

Jimmy was standing in the middle of the room as I entered. "Have a seat, Mr. Blake," I told him, pointing to the stretcher. "I'm Dr. Lesslie, and I'm here to help you."

I was hoping that having him off his feet and on the stretcher would distract him from his contortions. If he was malingering, maybe that would take his mind off it long enough to confirm to me that this was a voluntary thing. But if he *was* malingering, pretending to have these wild movements, what was in it for him? What did he stand to gain? This was really bizarre.

Jimmy followed my instructions and hopped up on the stretcher. But just as he settled onto the thin mattress, he jumped back down on the floor and began his strange dance. Once again it ended with a loud scream and his hair flying in my face.

"I'm sorry, Doc, I can't help it. Please help me stop!" he pleaded. Without being asked, he got back up on the stretcher.

While I was examining Jimmy, I asked him about any trauma, any medical problems, and especially about any medication.

"No, I don't take any medicine," he insisted.

"And what about any other types of drugs? Something without a prescription?" I questioned him, pressing a little.

"No nothing like that," he answered, shaking his head but shrugging his right shoulder at the same time. He was sending a mixed signal, and might not be telling the whole truth.

"Jimmy, this is important for me to know, if you want me to help you," I pushed.

"Well…I'll smoke a joint every once in a while, Doc," he finally admitted. "And maybe drink a couple of beers. But nothing hard, you know. No crack or anything like that."

Then he jumped down, and it started all over again. After the final jerking of his head, he looked up at me with frustration and a growing fatigue in his eyes. "Doc, please, do something!"

The consistency of each episode was worrisome. If he was faking this, it would be difficult for him to duplicate each "dance," but that was what was happening. It was the same every time. No—there was something else here.

"Alright, Jimmy," I continued, a little more sternly this time. "I have to know if you've taken anything unusual today, smoked anything, popped any pills, anything like that."

He looked me squarely in the face and began to shake his head. "No, nothing." But as he said this, some new realization seemed to dawn on him, and his eyes widened.

"Wait a minute, Doc," he said with a little excitement. "There *was* something I took last night. Yeah, maybe that's it! My girlfriend gave me one of her brother's pills—Haldol, I think it was. Yeah, it was a Haldol tablet. A little white pill. He's pretty messed up and I shouldn't have been takin' his medicine. I guess I should have known better. Made me feel pretty strange, and I thought I slept it off. Actually, Doc...it was three of them," he added sheepishly. "Could that be—"

"Are you sure it was Haldol?" I interrupted. "This is important, Jimmy."

"Yeah, I'm sure, Doc. I read it on the bottle. Do you think—"

I stepped to the curtain and pulled it aside. "Jeff, we need to start a line here, normal saline. And we need some IV Benadryl."

From across the nurses' station, Jeff acknowledged my request with a wave of his hand.

Turning to Jimmy, I began to explain the cause of his strange gyrations and how we were going to stop them.

The Haldol he had taken was a strong antipsychotic medication. It acts on several important areas of the brain, and even at normal doses it can cause involuntary muscle movements and cramps. Some of these can be really painful and very disturbing. At high doses, which was apparently where we were with Jimmy, all of these symptoms can be amplified.

Fortunately, the side effects of Haldol can be easily and quickly reversed with Benadryl, a simple and commonly used antihistamine medication.

"You're going to be okay, Jimmy," I assured him.

He hadn't been malingering after all. If we had followed our initial assumptions, things could have turned out much worse. There was a lesson here for Jimmy, and maybe for me. And once again, I was reminded to pay attention to Virginia.

I signed Mr. Blake's chart and tossed it into the discharge rack. Just as I did this, the curtain of room 1 opened. Blair Higgins stepped out. He pulled the curtain closed behind him and walked over in our direction, stopping right beside me.

Blair was a thirty-two-year-old internal-medicine specialist. He had only recently finished his training, having completed a fellowship in some specialty I couldn't remember at the moment. He was a very bright guy, and personable enough. But he exemplified the term "flea" as it was frequently applied to specialists in the field of internal medicine.

Years ago I had mentioned "flea" in Lori Davidson's presence, and she had asked me what it meant.

"Well, you see Lori," I began to explain. "The field of internal medicine requires a certain mind-set if you're going to be good at it. It's all about attention to detail, and following every possible lead until you run a problem to ground. When every other physician has scratched their heads about a patient and finally walked away, the internal medicine doc is the last to leave. Just like a flea is the last to leave a dying dog. Hence the term 'flea.'"

"Is that a good thing or a bad thing?" she had asked me.

"Well, if you're sick, really sick, I'd think you'd want a 'flea' taking care of you, wouldn't you?"

She thought for a moment, "Yeah, I think I would."

The problem with Blair Higgins was that he had not yet had enough practical experience to temper his extensive medical knowledge.

As we stood at the nurses' station, he began to write on the chart of the patient in room 1.

"What was all that commotion out here?" he asked me, not looking up from his writing. "What's with all that screaming? I could barely hear myself think."

"Just another interesting case," I answered, winking at Amy. "Everything's under control."

"Well, that's good," he said. And then, "Speaking of interesting, here—take a look at this, Robert, and tell me what you think."

He slid the chart of room 1 across the counter, right in front of me. He stood up straight and looked at me over the top of his glasses, adjusting them with the long finger of his right hand. For a split second I was transported back to my intern days, making rounds with one of the staff physicians and being quizzed on every minor detail of a patient. It didn't matter how much you knew about your patient or about his or her condition. The "attending" would continue questioning until you were finally stumped on some trivial finding, no matter how obscure. The goal seemed to be to remind you of your place in the pecking order of things, and how little you actually knew. I didn't like the feeling.

"Okay, let's see here, Blair," I responded, willing to play his game and focusing on the medical record before me.

The patient was a twenty-three-year-old male, presenting with complaints of nausea, vomiting, and diarrhea. It had started yesterday, and the triage nurse had noted that he "was unable to keep anything down."

His vital signs were stable, with only a slightly elevated pulse of 102. His temp was 99.8. Not really elevated. He was on no medications and listed no history of asthma, diabetes, or heart disease. He didn't smoke.

"His exam?" I turned to Blair and asked.

"Completely benign," he declared. "Maybe a little dryness of mouth, nothing more."

I glanced down again at the chart, looking for some hidden clue or some subtle piece of information. It seemed pretty straightforward to me.

"Well, it looks to me—" I began, but was interrupted.

"Take a look at this," he said knowingly. "Maybe this will give you a clue."

He placed a lab slip on top of the chart, patting it for effect.

It was the CBC report of this young man. I picked up the piece of paper and glanced through the multiple numbers on it.

His white count was elevated, a little over 18,000, and consistent with an infection of some kind. His hemoglobin was fine, no evidence of anemia. And his platelet count was normal, no obvious evidence of any bone-marrow problem.

"Okay, is this all you have? Any other lab studies?" I asked him, trying to figure where he was going with this.

"No, this is all. Just this CBC. That's all I need," he answered. Then he impatiently started drumming his fingers on the countertop. "Well, what do you think now?"

I looked at the chart again, and then at the lab slip. I must have been missing something here. It seemed pretty simple.

"Well?" he persisted. "What do you think?"

"Okay, I would say he has a mild to moderate case of gastroenteritis," I answered him. "Probably a viral infection. We've seen a bunch this week, and a few already today."

Out of the corner of my eye I could see Amy nodding in agreement.

"He might be getting dehydrated," I continued. "So I would consider giving him some IV fluids while he's here. Then I'd treat him symptomatically. That would be the extent of it," I said, sliding the chart back over to him.

"Hmm…well, that's not what I think." Blair placed his palm on the chart. "This young man has leukemia."

Amy looked up at this pronouncement and rolled her eyes.

"Leukemia?" I responded. "What makes you think that?"

At some point during this conversation, Jeff had walked over to the nurses' station. When he heard this proclamation, he had sidled a little closer, trying to get a peek at the chart. Something interesting was going on here.

Dr. Higgins sighed with obvious impatience. "Well, for one thing, this young man has some vague symptoms, some that are not easily explained. But the most important thing is his white count. It's entirely too elevated for a simple and benign process."

"Blair," I tried to reason with him, "I've seen white counts in the 20,000s with viral gastroenteritis. They come down in a couple of days and don't mean anything. I've pretty much stopped getting them in this scenario. It just confuses things."

Just like this time.

"Nope, I don't believe that's the case here," he said, obviously not listening to me. He began to stroke his chin thoughtfully and then said, "I'm going around to the lab and order some more tests. Maybe a bone-marrow analysis. This young man will need to be admitted to the hospital and worked up."

"But Blair—" I tried once more.

"Thanks anyway, Robert," he dismissed me. "I'll let you know what turns up."

He spun around and started down the hallway. Suddenly he stopped, then slowly turned and once more placed his hand to his chin, stroking it professorially.

"You know, Robert, the key here is observation," he spoke with great gravity. "That's right—observation. You...uh...*we* need to pay attention to every detail, look under every rock, *observe* every possible thing about our patient. That way, we won't be led astray."

Allowing no opportunity for a response, he turned and walked off, leaving me standing there with Jeff and Amy, all of us wondering what was to happen with the young man in room 1.

"Doc," Amy interrupted my thoughts, "that is a classic example of too much head sense and not enough common sense."

Then Jeff looked up at me and said, "Yeah, and that's a case of bein' a real jerk. Does he think he's some kind of a professor?"

That part of it didn't bother me. I had come to expect such remarks from Blair. But a few years earlier, fresh out of residency, I would probably have bowed my neck.

Then Jeff said, almost apologetically, "What if he's right? What if that guy has leukemia? What about the white count?"

"The white count doesn't bother me at all," I told him. "It's just a red herring."

"A what?" He looked confused.

"A red herring," I repeated, realizing I would need to explain the remark. "A red herring," I began, "is something that leads you away— away from the main point or object. It's a distraction. You know, something that takes you down the wrong path."

"You mean this guy's white count would be a distraction, and lead Dr. Higgins in the wrong direction?"

Jeff understood. "Yes, that's right. He's intent on chasing that lab value when it's really not the problem at all."

"Okay then, why do they call it a red herring?" he asked.

Another good question. Fortunately I was ready for this one. I made it a habit to look up the origin of obscure sayings and metaphors, especially the ones I used from time to time. "One fell swoop." "Wet your whistle." "Son of a gun" (now *there's* an interesting one).

"Well, that's a good story," I began to explain. "It seems that if you cook a herring by smoking it, the fish will turn a reddish color. Now apparently, several hundreds of years ago, there were animal lovers in England who didn't particularly like the idea and the cruelty of a fox-hunt. They would sabotage these hunts by tying a smoked herring to a string and then dragging it on the ground across the fox's trail. This confused the hounds and led them off in the wrong direction. Much as Dr. Higgins is being led in the wrong direction right now."

Amy Connors cleared her throat and skeptically asked, "Dr. Lesslie, is that true? Or have *you* been smokin' somethin' other than herring?"

"Of course it's true!" I insisted. "It makes sense, doesn't it?"

"Well, sort of..." Jeff said, feigning allegiance with Amy. "But then again, it does seem a little far-fetched."

"Okay then," I countered. "Just what is the origin of the term 'far-fetched'?"

"Oh Lord, here we go," Amy said, giving up. "This could go on all day."

Jeff chuckled, and I picked up the chart of the next patient to be seen.

She was a thirty-two-year-old woman, with a "laceration of left index finger." Apparently she had cut it on a broken glass in her kitchen sink.

"Well, that doesn't change the fact that Dr. Higgins is a jerk," Jeff stated again flatly.

I put the chart back down on the counter, a thought having come to my mind. "Well, you know, he *did* mention something about observation, didn't he?" I asked. Amy looked up from the ER registration ledger, nodding her head.

"Yeah, he did," Jeff answered. "But I didn't pay much attention."

"Well, let me tell you something that happened when I was in medical school."

Amy settled back in her chair, and Jeff turned to face me.

"There was a pathology professor, a Dr. Black," I began. "He was one of our favorites, a real character, and I'll never forget a lesson he taught us one morning. It had to do with developing this essential skill of observation."

We had been sitting in our main lecture hall, about a hundred and twenty of us. It was our first year of medical school—we were all pretty green. This was one of our first pathology classes, and the instructor, Dr. Black, was going to lecture on diabetes. I can still see him now, walking across the stage, his lab coat barely covering a pretty good-sized belly. And then he stopped right in front of us and held up a beaker of yellow liquid.

"Young men and ladies," he had addressed us. "Tell me how you would make a diagnosis of diabetes in a middle-aged man."

He waited for a response from some brave soul. There were in fact a few murmurs of "get a blood sugar" or "what are his symptoms?" but nothing very assertive. He feigned being hard of hearing, cupping his hand to his ear and leaning toward his audience.

"No thoughts, eh? Well, here we have the urine of a person with diabetes," he said, holding up the beaker of liquid. "And what can you tell me about this?"

There was a painful silence in the large auditorium as he scanned the group for some willing volunteer. That person not forthcoming, he pointed to an unfortunate student on the front row and motioned for him to come up on the stage.

As the student approached, Dr. Black continued. "You can tell a lot about a person's health from a thorough examination of his urine. Specific gravity, pH, chemistries. But what can you tell me by inspection of this specimen?" he asked the student, now standing by his side.

Dr. Black held the beaker in the young man's puzzled face and swirled it a little. "I, uh…it…it looks like urine to me," he stammered.

"That's very good," Dr. Black congratulated him, and we all nervously chuckled, glad we were still in our seats.

"You see," he went on, "with diabetes, your blood sugar is elevated, sometimes to very high levels, and the sugar spills into your urine. If you are at the bedside of a patient and don't have access to a laboratory, you can perform a simple test to check for the presence of sugar in a urine specimen, such as this."

With that, he held the beaker out in front of him, stuck his finger deep into the urine, swirled it around a little, and then put it into his mouth.

"Hmm…definitely sweet," he stated. "This man's blood sugar is probably two or three hundred. Maybe more."

He then held the beaker out in front of the student. "Tell me what you think," he instructed him. There was a collective moan from those of us sitting in the room, which Dr. Black quickly silenced with a stern glance.

The student's eyes widened, and like a deer frozen by the headlights of a car, he dutifully held out his hand, stuck a finger into the beaker, and then into his mouth.

"Ugh!" he couldn't help but uttering.

We all moaned again, and this time Dr. Black only chuckled and nodded at us. "Any comments, young man? he asked.

The student just grimaced, wiped his mouth with the back of his hand, and shook his head.

"And how about you?" he asked, turning to those of us in the auditorium. No one said a word.

"Hmm…we have some work to do here. Go have a seat, young man," he instructed his reluctant assistant.

Dr. Black walked over to the podium and placed the beaker on a small table standing beside it.

"This is an important lesson for you," he told us. "And I want you to remember it. *Observation*. That's one of the essential requirements of being a good physician. Listening, seeing, touching, smelling, maybe even tasting. But mainly close and focused observation. If this young man had been watching closely, if he had been paying close attention and *observing*, he would have noticed something very important."

At this juncture he held out his hands, an imaginary beaker in one, and the index finger of his other pointing straight at the ceiling.

"You see, when I tested the urine specimen, I dipped my index finger into the beaker," he said while elaborately demonstrating this maneuver, twirling his finger in mid-air. "And then I stuck my long finger into my mouth"—again showing us what had actually happened.

"I of course would never taste a person's urine specimen."

There was a moment of silence as this revelation had its effect on us. And then there was hesitant laughing and a nodding of heads. No one had caught this sleight of hand, certainly not his student assistant, who had now jumped up from his seat and was heading for a water fountain in the back of the room.

"Observation!" Dr. Black intoned. "Don't take anything for granted— and always, always pay attention to detail!"

Jeff chuckled. "That's great," he said. "I bet if Dr. Higgins had been there, he would have been the one up on that stage."

"Maybe so," I agreed. "I'm just glad it wasn't me." I knew I would have done the same thing.

The next morning, I asked Amy to call upstairs and check on the status of the young man who had been in room 1, Dr. Higgins's patient. He had been admitted to the fourth floor and placed in isolation.

"Yeah, that's him," she said into the telephone, nodding her head at me. Then after a moment she said, "Okay—thanks, Sally. Talk to you later."

She hung up the phone and then looked at me. "They gave him some fluids overnight and repeated his white count this morning. Completely normal. He's up and walking around, and being released as we speak. 'Viral gastroenteritis' is his discharge diagnosis."

It is not good to have zeal without knowledge,
nor to be hasty and miss the way.

PROVERBS 19:2

4

Dogged Perseverance

*It ain't what you don't know
that gets you into trouble.
It's what you know for sure
that just ain't so.*

Mark Twain

It's remarkable how quickly a moment of relative calm in the ER can be shattered. And sometimes it happens in the strangest of ways...

Sunday afternoon, 4:45. The department was under control, an unusual thing for this time on a Sunday. I was sitting behind the nurses' station, talking with Jeff about nothing in particular.

The doors of the ambulance entrance suddenly burst open, pushed aggressively inward by the backside of a tall, slender, middle-aged woman. She was dressed in a nurse's uniform and was pulling an antiquated stretcher behind her.

As soon as she had cleared the doorway, she yelled out, "Hey, ya'll! We need some help!"

The volume of her voice didn't match her slender frame, and it got our attention.

Jeff had jumped up from his chair and was already around the corner of the counter.

"What's going on?" he asked the woman.

When she turned to face him, I recognized her as one of the clinical staff at Peaceful Acres, a local retirement center. She frequently came to the ER with some of their clients, usually after a fall or some minor mishap. *Modine.* I seemed to remember that was her name.

She was flushed and out of breath, obviously upset by whatever circumstances had brought her to the ER. I walked up behind Jeff and noted her nametag. I was right. "Modine." Then I noticed the stretcher behind her. It had just now cleared the doors.

It required a moment to take in the full picture. There, on a rickety gurney that listed dangerously from side to side, was an elderly gentleman, easily upwards of eighty years old. He was on his back, arms strapped to the side of the stretcher. Straddled across his abdomen, barely supported by this conveyance, was a *healthy* young woman, actively performing chest compressions. She weighed at least three hundred pounds, and with each chest compression the stretcher lurched precariously, creaking loudly, as if calling out for help. Sweat was dripping down her forehead and onto the helpless old man beneath her.

"Liza Sue, keep up them compressions! And make sure his chest is goin' in enough!" Modine directed the young woman on the stretcher.

Jeff tapped Modine on the shoulder and repeated his question. "Modine, what's going on here? What happened to this man?"

Then he stepped around her to get to the side of the patient.

By this time, the entire group had made it through the entrance and had now stopped in front of the nurses' station. Amy was standing up behind the counter, her eyes wide as she studied the action before her.

I had stepped around to the other side of the stretcher and was trying to examine this unfortunate individual. It was difficult, with Liza Sue's elbows flying in my face after each compression and her sweat flinging itself in all directions. I took a chance, and after a particularly aggressive chest compression, I wedged myself against the stretcher and reached out to check for a pulse. The man's color was surprisingly good, and his skin was warm and dry—all good signs.

"He had a card-yac arrest," Modine explained to Jeff. "We found him flat out on the floor in the hallway, and he wasn't breathin' or nothin'. Liza's certified in BCL…or BCS…or…anyway, she knew what to do and what to check for. He was done gone, and she called for help."

She caught her breath and nodded in the direction of Liza Sue. "She was doin' CPR when I came runnin' up. And we've been doing it for the last twenty, maybe thirty minutes, switchin' off and takin' turns."

Jeff had positioned himself at the head of the stretcher and was shining a light into the man's pupils.

"They're still reactive," he told me. "But I can't tell if he's trying to breathe."

My fingers had found a strong, regular carotid pulse on the right side of his neck that seemed to be in rhythm with Liza Sue's compressions. I watched closely, but saw no respiratory effort.

"Like I said," Modine continued, "he was completely unresponsive, so after we started to get him stabilized, I called for a stretcher and told the staff to get our ambulance ready."

Peaceful Acres was the oldest retirement home in the county. As evidence of that fact, they still kept an ancient ambulance on the premises and used it from time to time. It might have seen its earlier years as a hearse. In my experience, they had used it only to transport minor problems, never anything as serious as a cardiac arrest. I was a little confused as to what made this case different, and why they hadn't called EMS.

"Modine, what—" I was about to ask her about this, but she silenced me with a wave of her hand, seeming to anticipate my question.

"We didn't have time to call for the EMS. Mr. Wood was in real trouble, and we just did what we thought was best. Somebody pushed the stretcher down the hall. Then Liza Sue threw him on it and kept on doin' CPR. Never missed a beat." She paused here and looked over at her assistant. "Liza, you're doin' good, honey! Real good!"

Liza Sue tried to blow some errant hair out of her face and only succeeded in blowing sweat in mine. "Sure thing," she answered.

"Do you need anything, Dr. Lesslie?" Amy called out from behind the nurses' station. "X-ray or lab? An EKG?"

We were going to need all of these, but first I needed to get a better handle on the patient's status.

"Yeah, Amy. Get them all coming, and we'll head to the cardiac room."

Jeff had grasped the end of the stretcher, gently moving Modine to one side. He began to carefully lead the group into cardiac. Liza Sue kept doing chest compressions, balancing as best she could on top of her patient.

"What did you say his name was, Modine?" I asked her. "Mr. Wood?"

"Yeah, Mr. Wood. Wesley Wood," she answered. "And he's a fine gentleman. One of our favorites. Never has a harsh word for anyone." She paused, shaking her head. "Hmm, hmm. This is a real shame."

Once we were in cardiac, I motioned for Jeff to help me move Mr. Wood to our bed. Jeff's eyes widened a little, and he glanced in the direction of Liza Sue. She wasn't about to stop what she was doing. I shared Jeff's concern, but it was time to get the woman off this poor man. Something didn't add up here.

I laid my hand on Liza Sue's shoulder and firmly said, "Hold on a minute here, Liza. Let's check Mr. Wood and see what we've got."

She stopped her chest compressions and sat up straight, blowing out a long breath of air. She had been working hard.

I leaned down, my face close to Wesley Wood's.

"Mr. Wood, can you hear me?" My fingers remained on his carotid artery, and I could still feel a strong, regular pulse, this time without Liza's chest compressions. But other than that, there was no response. Something was peculiar here, and I—

Liza Sue had been watching closely, and when she could see no apparent sign of life, she leaned forward, straightened her arms, and before I could stop her, she applied a vigorous compression to the middle of Wesley's chest.

Then she was at it again.

"One-one-thousand, two-one-thousand—"

"Hold it!" I demanded. "Just stop everything!"

Reluctantly, Liza Sue complied.

I searched Mr. Wood's face for any response and for any evidence of a respiratory effort. There was none. And then suddenly, his mouth seemed to move. He appeared to be trying to form some word, but I heard nothing. I leaned closer, my ear inches from his mouth.

There was a lot of noise in the room, and I raised my hand for quiet. And I listened.

Then, there it was.

"Get her off me."

It was only a whisper, and I wasn't exactly sure what he had said.

"What did you say, Mr. Wood?" I asked him. His words had been so quiet that no one else in the room could possibly have heard them.

And there it was again.

"Get…her…off…me."

It was no louder this time, but he was emphatic. And I understood him clearly.

I straightened and looked at Liza Sue. "Let's hold off on any chest compressions for a minute, Liza. We need to check him over."

She had a puzzled look on her face, but she understood, and once again sat up straight and placed her hands on her hips.

We all looked down into the face of Wesley Wood. For a split second there was nothing, and I wondered if I had imagined hearing his request.

Then his eyelids flickered—and suddenly he took a deep breath. He exhaled loudly and began looking around the room.

"Have mercy! Praise the Lord and thank you, Jesus!"

The exclamation came from right behind me and caused me to jump. It was Modine, and she began clapping her hands in my ear.

"Liza Sue, you done saved his life! Look, he's breathin'! You done it!"

Mr. Wood's eyes were now wide open. He continued to look around the room and tried to free his arms, which were still strapped down and pinned beneath Liza's knees.

She sat up even straighter, surprise and amazement clearly written on her face. She wasn't sure what to do or say. None of us were.

Modine kept clapping and shouting, "You done it! You saved his life, Liza!"

Wesley Wood looked up at me again. This time his eyebrows were furrowed in determination. "Get her off me!" he whispered with a newfound strength in his voice.

"Jeff," I said. "Let's help get Liza Sue down off the stretcher and then get Mr. Wood over to our bed. We need to check him out, make sure he's okay. And good work, Liza Sue," I added.

"You sure he's alright?" she asked me. "I don't want him to stop breathin' again…" She clasped her hands together as if to resume her CPR.

"No, no, he's fine," I assured her, waving her back.

"Here, be careful," Jeff said, helping her get off the stretcher. There was a precarious moment as she shifted her weight to one side. The rickety contraption almost went over, but then she was off and standing on the floor. Wesley Wood was lying flat on his back, somehow looking even smaller than when Liza was straddling him. But there was a look of relief on his face.

"Why don't you two go out to the nurses' station and fill out your report?" I motioned with my head to Jeff. He nodded and began to herd them toward the door.

"Way to go, Liza!" exclaimed Modine once more. They gave each other a high five as they left the cardiac room. Jeff closed the door behind them and walked over beside the bed. He began to check Mr. Wood's blood pressure and pulse, and then his oxygen saturation.

Wesley's shirt had been torn open during the episode, Liza Sue wanting to expose his chest for CPR. He was gently rubbing his sternal area, and I could see reddish-blue discoloration over most of his chest. He was going to have some bruises, at the very least.

"110 over 80," Jeff told me. "Pulse is 92 and regular, and his pulse ox is 98 percent."

"How do you feel, Mr. Wood?" I asked. His vital signs were fine.

He looked up at me and shook his head.

"How do you think I feel?" he answered, his voice stronger now, no longer a whisper. "Did you see the size of that woman? My chest is killing me. I think she busted my ribs."

"Here, let me take a look," I said, reaching out and gently beginning to examine his bruised thorax. "Do you remember what happened?"

"Remember? Doc, it was a nightmare. A complete nightmare." He glanced over his head toward the door. "They gone?" he asked.

Jeff nodded his head, and I said, "Yeah, they're out of the room, Wesley. It's just us."

"Okay—well, here's what happened."

We couldn't wait to hear this, and out of the corner of my eye I saw Jeff cock his head.

"It's Sunday, you know, and we always have a big dinner. Families come over, and there's a lot of visiting. I usually eat with one of my friends, Neal Wingate. He doesn't have any family either, so we are usually alone. And he needs some help now, 'cause he seems to be getting a little forgetful...and, well...none of us are getting any younger."

"I understand," I told him, and then waited for him to continue.

"Well, after that, we sat around in the sunroom for a while, and then I walked him down the hall to his room. He wanted to watch some baseball. Heck, it's not even baseball season. Anyway, I got him situated and then I headed for my room. Gonna do some reading. Well, I was walking down the hall, and I thought I was being careful. Always watch out for stuff on the floor, electrical cords and stuff like that. But I guess I didn't see the water. Somebody must have spilled some in the hallway. I stepped in it and—wham! There I was on the floor, flat on my back. It happened really fast, and I didn't have time to catch myself or anything. One minute I was standing up, walking, and the next minute I was flat on my back. I must have bumped the back of my head when I fell, 'cause I was seeing stars."

He paused here, and began rubbing his head. "You know, it's really true, Doc. You really *do* see stars when you bang your head."

"Do you think you were knocked out?" I asked him. "Do you remember everything?

"Oh, no. I wasn't knocked out. Just startled, I guess. I thought about that too, but I was clear as a bell. My butt hurt a little, and then the stars, but that passed pretty quickly. And then I remember thinking to myself, *Did I break anything?* So I started moving everything, my arms and legs, and I moved my head from side to side. Everything was working, and nothing really hurt. And I remember feeling relieved. Then I decided it would be best if I just rested on the floor for a few minutes, sorta collecting myself, you know? So I relaxed and closed my eyes. In a minute or two I was going to get up, and everything would be fine. And then it happened."

A troubled look came over his face, and he began rubbing his chest again. He tried to turn his head so he could see the door.

"They're still gone," Jeff told him. "It's just us."

He sat back and continued his story.

"Like I said, I was just lying there, collecting myself. First thing I know, I start to feel the floor shakin'. It got stronger and stronger. Then I heard this stomping sound and a blowin' and a pantin'… and I opened my eyes…and there she was—'Big Liza'—standing over me, blocking out the light, and then she started screaming and her arms were flailin' everywhere. And I remember thinkin', *Lord, take me quick!* Well, she gets right in my face and starts yelling my name. But I was so surprised I couldn't say nothin'. And then she jumped on top of me and started mashing on my chest. Hurt like the dickens, let me tell you! And I couldn't say a word. She was knocking the wind out of me. Tried to get her to stop, to tell her I was okay, but I couldn't make a sound."

Wesley shook his head and took a deep breath, wincing a little from the effort, but grateful to be able to do so.

"And then the other one comes along, and she starts in. 'Faster—faster, Liza Sue!' she yelled at the big one. Well, I didn't need to hear that, 'cause she was already beating on me pretty good. But she kept pressing on my chest faster and harder. I knew I was done for."

Jeff chuckled quietly at this. Wesley heard him and cut a sharp glance in his direction. Jeff cleared his throat and backed out of Mr. Wood's vision.

"Then, Doc, they somehow got me on the stretcher, and Liza Sue jumped on top. She's been pounding on my chest all the way to the hospital and up till just now. I want you to know, you saved my life. I mean it. I don't know how much longer I could have lasted."

Jeff had pursed his lips and was nodding his head. With great difficulty, I maintained a straight face.

"Well, Mr. Wood, I know they were doing what they thought was the right thing. They were only trying to help you," I told him.

"Help me? Heck, they almost killed me!" He folded his arms in anger across his chest, his chin set resolutely. "And keep them crazy women away from me! I ain't going back to that place. No sir."

"Let's see what's going on before we talk about that, Wesley. We'll need to get some X-rays to make sure you haven't cracked any ribs."

"*I* didn't crack my ribs!" he interrupted. "If they're busted it's 'cause of that big girl, Liza Sue."

"Okay, okay." I tried to calm him. "You've been through a lot, Mr. Wood. The main thing is to check out your ribs and make sure your heart is alright." The crunching I noted as I had examined his chest told me he would have a few broken ribs, maybe a bunch. And I needed to be sure his heart had not been bruised by Liza Sue's compressions.

"Okay, Doc, but I'm not going back to that place. Not ever."

"We're probably going to need to keep you overnight at least, Mr. Wood. And then we'll figure things out."

"I'm telling you, I'm not going back—"

"Jeff, let's get an EKG, and then we'll get him around to X-ray. And Mr. Wood," I said, patting him on his shoulder. "I just want you to relax now and let us take care of you."

"Fine, fine," he muttered. "But I ain't goin' back there."

I nodded at Jeff and headed toward the door. As it closed behind me, I glanced over to the nurses' station. Amy looked up from her desk, shook her head, and pointed in the direction of the ambulance entrance.

The doors were open, and Liza Sue and Modine were getting ready to walk through. Something made Liza turn and look in my direction. She took Modine by the arm and they walked toward me.

When they came up to where I stood, Liza Sue was the first to speak.

"Dr. Lesslie, I was just thinkin'…Maybe we should just check on Mr. Wood once more, make sure he's alright."

"Yeah," added Modine. "We at least got to tell him good night."

The imp on my shoulder said, *Go ahead, Robert…let them go back into cardiac and visit Wesley. And then just watch his reaction.* Hmm. Now that would be interesting.

But I knew better.

"Liza Sue, Modine—Mr. Wood needs some rest now. He'll never forget what you've done to, uh, for him today," I told them.

They stood there a moment and then nodded their heads.

"You're right," Modine said. "He needs to get some rest. I guess we'll be goin'. Come on, Liza Sue."

They turned and walked out of the department.

The difference between perseverance and obstinacy
is that one comes from a strong will
and the other from a strong won't.
HENRY WARD BEECHER (1813–1887)

The Face of Evil

Be very careful, then...
because the days are evil.

EPHESIANS 5:15

I t was the darkest night I can remember.

6:15 p.m. Sergeant Joe Walters stood beside me at the nurses' station. He was investigating a routine fender bender. The driver of one of the cars had been brought in by ambulance. He had only minor injuries and would be released in a few minutes.

"Always happens around this time of day, doesn't it, Doc?" he said to me. "Around dusk, the light gets bad, people get tired, and they don't pay attention. Good thing for this guy he was only going twenty miles an hour. Ran right up the back of a big pickup."

I was going to say something but was interrupted by Joe's radio. There were a couple of loud beeps and then some scratchy voice asking for his location. He put the receiver close to his ear, and I didn't hear anything else.

Amy Connors, sitting across from me at her secretary's station, slid a clipboard across the laminated countertop.

"Here's the chart of the belly pain in room 2," she informed me. "All his labs have been ordered."

As I reached for the chart, I heard Joe Walters utter, "A signal what?"

He dropped the paperwork in his hand and pressed the receiver closer to his ear. We couldn't hear anything, but the tone of Joe's voice and the sudden change in his demeanor told us something was going on.

"10-4," he hastily told the person on the other end. "Got it, and I'm about seven or eight minutes away."

He jammed the radio back into its holster and headed for the ambulance doors.

"Whatcha got?" Amy called out after him.

Joe was almost running, but he turned to her and said something I couldn't make out. A signal "something." And then he was gone through the doors.

Amy had heard him and had reached into one of her drawers for a laminated sheet of paper. It contained an extensive list of all of the official codes used by the police and fire departments. A "10-50" was an auto accident. But that was about all I knew.

"What did he say?" I asked. It was unusual for Joe Walters, a seasoned police officer, to act like this.

"I heard him, but I don't recognize the signal," she said, sliding her index finger carefully down the long list of numbers. "Here it is—10… Holy smoke!" she exclaimed.

"What is it?" I asked, now very curious.

"It's a…multiple homicide…"

Jeff Ryan listened closely to the police dispatcher. We were able to pick up police transmissions in the ER, and used them to prepare ourselves for what was happening out on the street. Sometimes we listened for entertainment, but not tonight.

For the previous thirty minutes, the airwaves had been alive with chatter. Several police units had been dispatched to the scene of an apparent double murder, and we were now hearing the voice of Joe Walters as he passed on information and asked for assistance. No one was alive at the scene. When an EMS unit arrived, they weren't needed and were turned away.

This kind of violence was unusual for Rock Hill, though we had our share of stabbings and shootings.

"I wonder what's goin' on," Amy stated. "Joe still sounds pretty upset on the radio."

I had noticed the edge in Joe's voice as well. Something was obviously getting to him.

It wasn't long before we found out what that something was.

Denton Roberts's EMS unit had responded to the initial call. They had only been told "multiple gunshots," nothing more. When Denton and his partner arrived at the scene, there were police cars everywhere.

"I've never seen anything like it," he told us. "Marked and unmarked cars all over the place. And there was yellow tape already going up around the whole house and yard. We could barely get down the drive, and then Joe Walters came out and told us what happened and that we wouldn't be needed." Denton stopped and shook his head. "It must have been awful."

It was indeed a murder scene, and in one of the nicer parts of Rock Hill. Denton told us what he knew.

Joe Walters said the perpetrator had smashed the glass beside the front door and then reached in and unlocked it. The noise he made must have alarmed the two owners, James and Joy Easterling. They were in their sixties, husband and wife. She had been the first the shooter had seen, and he had killed her instantly with the blast of a 12-gauge shotgun. When James had come down the hallway, the killer had turned the shotgun on him and fired twice. Neither of them had a chance.

"No apparent motive," Denton told us. "Maybe robbery, but it seems to be a random act. Just doesn't make sense. I knew the Easterlings, and they were good people."

"Any idea who did it?" Amy asked.

"Turns out a neighbor heard the shotgun blasts and got a look at the pickup truck in the front yard. Managed to get the license number too. Pretty quick thinking. Anyway, the police are on that now, and there's a county-wide search going on."

"Hope they catch that lowlife…" Amy muttered.

Just then, the police scanner got our attention. The dispatcher was notifying everyone in the vicinity of a little-traveled crossroads in the western part of the county to be on alert. The suspect's pickup truck had been spotted and was heading in that direction at a high speed.

"Maybe he'll run off the road and hit a tree and save everyone a lot of trouble," Amy remarked coolly.

"Humph," Jeff muttered, having just walked up to join us. "They'd better get him now before he gets loose on those back-country roads. It'll be the devil to find him then."

We didn't have to worry about the devil, at least not just yet. We listened as one of the county sheriff's units reported sighting the truck and forcing him off the road and into a hay field. The driver of the truck was quickly apprehended, uninjured. On the front seat of the pickup was a 12-gauge shotgun along with a half-empty box of shells.

After that, things in the ER returned to normal, and there was no more squawking of the police scanner. EMS was bringing in three individuals from a 10-50. A young man with a fishhook in his eyelid was being led to minor trauma. And the waiting room was filling up. Normal.

10:15 p.m. The nurses' station was a flurry of barely controlled activity, and I was finishing up the chart of the last of the auto-accident victims. It had been almost two hours since we had heard anything about the murders. That was when the ambulance doors burst open and it all changed.

Two police officers strode into the department, grim-faced and all business. I recognized them but couldn't recall their names. They were followed by a quickly moving group of more officers, one menacingly holding a police shotgun. In the middle of this cluster, only occasionally being glimpsed within this blue-clad moving mass, was a young man dressed in standard prisoner's garb. He had on a tan short-sleeved shirt and matching tan trousers. He wore brown flip-flops and shuffled awkwardly along, trying to keep up with the officers. It was then I noticed the cuffs on his ankles and hands. And the bloody bandages on his wrists.

The group made its way to the nurses' station and stopped. Joe Walters appeared from behind and walked up to Jeff Ryan and me.

"Is minor trauma open?" he asked us.

I looked at Jeff, who quickly glanced at the patient ID board.

"Minor trauma C and D are open," he told Joe. "What you got here?"

"This guy," he said, pointing to the man in the midst of his officers. Then he walked up close to me and quietly said, "This is the guy who killed the Easterlings. We need to take care of him in a hurry and get him out of here. Don't want any one to know he's in the ER. There are a lot of really upset people in town right now."

"What happened to him, Joe?" I asked, trying to get a glimpse of the man.

Jeff grabbed the clipboards of minor trauma C and D and motioned to the officers to follow him down the hall with their prisoner.

"Doc, I don't know how he did it," Joe began to explain. "When we caught him out on 324, his truck was pretty busted up, but he didn't seem hurt. Actually, he was trying to run. We got him without any trouble, but he must have grabbed a piece of broken glass from the wreck and stuck it in his pants. Anyway, we took him straight downtown and booked him. Then we put him in a cell—and before I knew it, one of the guards was hollerin' that he had cut himself. He had managed to sneak that glass into his cell, and as soon as the guard's back was turned, he did a number on his wrists. I mean, we're talkin' about some deep cuts. It's a wonder he hasn't bled to death."

"It's a wonder he didn't use that glass on the guard."

"You're right about that, Doc," Joe agreed. "I thought of that myself. This is one bad actor. That's why we need to get him fixed up and out of here as quick as you can."

"What's his name?" I asked.

He looked around the room, as if to make sure we were alone, which of course we weren't. Then he leaned close and whispered, "Frankie Sifford." Standing a little straighter and speaking a little louder, he added, "We don't want that to get out yet. Like I said, there are a lot of upset

people out there. The Easterlings had a lot of friends and if they knew…
Well, we just need to keep it under wraps for the time being. Anyway,
if you could help us here, Doc, I'd really appreciate it."

"I'll do everything I can," I assured him. I understood his position.
And considering the disruption that had already occurred in the department, I would also be happy to get this man out of the ER as quickly
as possible.

Jeff had wisely pulled the curtains closed for both C and D. They
could be arranged to form one large cubicle, and by pushing the
stretcher in room D against the wall, he had created some needed floor
space. It had quickly been filled by the dozen or so officers who accompanied Frankie Sifford.

"When beds A and B are discharged," he whispered to me, referring to the two other patients in the room, "I'll make sure nobody uses
those beds until we're done."

"Good idea, Jeff. Thanks," I told him. "What does this look like?"

Jeff had on a bloody pair of examining gloves. He took them off
and tossed them into a nearby trash can. "Pretty good lacerations,"
he told me. "You're going to be here a while. I can't imagine how, but
I don't think he cut any tendons." He paused, then shook his head.
"He was serious about this, though. This is the worst I've ever seen
for self-inflicted cuts. It's almost as if he couldn't feel himself doing
it. You'll see."

He stepped around to the supply cabinet and began taking down
the material necessary to repair this man's wounds. And I stepped over
to the stretcher of bed C and the young man lying on it.

The officers surrounding the bed parted a little as I approached,
allowing me access to Frankie Sifford. My attention should have been
drawn to the gaping wounds on both of his wrists. But instead, my
gaze fastened on his eyes—and I couldn't look away.

These were terrible eyes, and they seemed to bore right through
me. And yet there was nothing there. They were hollow, vacant, and
completely without any feeling. There was no hatred, or anger, or fear.
Nothing. And as I stood staring at him, a smile slowly spread across his

face. No, it was more of a leer, or something worse. He seemed to know me, to know something about me…but I had never seen him before.

"What's up, Doc?" he quipped in a flat voice. There was no emotion in his words, nothing, just like his eyes.

I tore myself away from his gaze and focused my attention on the task before me.

"Mr. Sifford," I addressed him. "Let's take a look at those wrists."

"Call me Frankie, Doc," he answered. "Just Frankie."

One of the police officers standing behind him looked down scowling and shook his head. There was a lot of bad tension in this room.

"Okay, Frankie, let me see what's going on here," I repeated.

He was handcuffed, and his leg cuffs were attached to the stretcher. He wasn't going anywhere. I turned to one of the officers and said, "We'll need to take his handcuffs off, or at least loosen them. I'll need to examine these wounds."

They apparently hadn't thought about this and were obviously reluctant to take him out of the cuffs. They whispered together for a moment, and then one of them took a key out of his shirt pocket and unlocked the cuff on Frankie's left wrist. I was standing by his left side and when the officer removed the cuff, he pulled it across Frankie's chest and then quickly snapped it around the rail on his right side. They weren't going to take any chances.

While they were doing this, I studied the man lying before me. He was in his early twenties, slight of build. His hair was light brown, uncombed, and hung to his shoulders. There was nothing really remarkable about him—other than his eyes, and the fact he had just murdered two people in cold blood.

Jeff positioned Frankie's left arm and wrist on a board that slid under the mattress of the stretcher. He had draped it in sterile cloth. I sat down on a rolling stool, slid it toward the stretcher, and began to examine Frankie's wrist.

It was a mess. He had three long, deep gashes running perpendicularly across his anterior wrist and lower forearm. They were gaping open, and I could easily see exposed tendons. There was not much bleeding, just a slow ooze, indicating that he had probably not severed any major blood vessels. But he had been serious about this. These were big cuts, and must have hurt.

Then I noticed something strange. There were no hesitation marks. Usually when a person is trying to harm themselves with a blade, or piece of glass, or some other sharp object, they will be unable to do so with one clean incision. It hurts, and there will be evidence of one or more initial efforts, usually just superficial scratches. Sometimes that's all we see, these hesitation marks. They ultimately couldn't go through with it.

But not this time. These were clean, deep, and almost surgical. He had never hesitated.

Something made me look up. Frankie was staring at me with the same leering smile on his face. He didn't say a word.

Usually at this point, I'm looking for an opportunity to ask the patient about why they tried to hurt themselves. I would be trying to assess the risk of another suicide attempt. I didn't have to worry about that this time. It didn't matter, since Frankie Sifford would be locked up in jail, probably for the rest of his life, however long that might be.

Then I began to wonder why he would do this. And I thought I might know the answer. Not infrequently, incarcerated individuals will feign an injury or illness in order to be taken out of the jail and to the hospital. It might be just to have a change of scenery, or it might be in the hope of escaping. It had happened before. Once, an inmate had faked having abdominal pain and was so convincing that two officers had to bring him to the ER. As soon as the police car had pulled up to the ambulance entrance and the door was opened, he bolted, straight for some nearby woods. He made it as far as the corner McDonald's before he was apprehended.

I was pretty certain that was the case here. Frankie Sifford was not trying to kill himself. Rather, he was looking for an opportunity to escape. And he knew his injury would need to be something serious.

As if reading my mind, he said, "Pretty bad, isn't it, Doc?"

I looked up at those dead eyes once again and answered, "Well, we've seen worse." Some primitive part of me wanted to be sure he didn't receive any satisfaction from this. "We're going to put these lacerations back together and send you back to the jail with these officers. It shouldn't take too long."

And there it was. Just the tiniest flinch of his eyelids. That had bothered him. He was hoping to be admitted to the hospital with these wounds, maybe even have surgery. That would give him time and opportunity to find a way to escape.

He didn't say a word, and his eyes returned to their vacant stare. And that crooked smile remained on his face.

When I took a closer look at his wounds, I hoped I hadn't misspoken. These were bad cuts. I knew it was going to take awhile to repair them. But there were no major structures injured, and it was only going to be a matter of carefully sewing them up.

I looked at his right wrist, moving his bandages around the handcuff. There were three lacerations there as well, almost identical to those on the left. Deep, long, and down to his tendons. And like the other wounds, there were no significant structures injured.

Curious. There was really no difference in the wounds.

"Are you right- or left-handed?" I asked him.

"Amphibious," he smirked.

I didn't look up, and certainly didn't smile.

The policeman standing at the head of the stretcher popped him on the shoulder with the back of his hand.

"Don't get smart," he said. "Answer the doctor."

"That's okay, officer," I told him. "It doesn't matter."

Jeff looked over at me, and I nodded. He began setting up a suture tray and getting some packs of suture material out of the cabinet. He had a half dozen of these in his hand and said to me, "I'll get some more when you need them."

This was going to take awhile.

Joe Walters walked up behind me as I began to work.

He leaned closed to me and asked, "Whatcha think, Doc? How long?"

Normally, this question would be a little aggravating. But this was a different circumstance.

"Probably about an hour on this side, and the same on the other," I estimated.

"Hmm. Okay," he muttered. "We're just gonna stay right here. Let me know if anyone gets in the way."

I was pretty accurate with my guess. Two hours and fifteen minutes later, Jeff was finishing up with the bandaging of Frankie Sifford's wrists. His cuffs were put back on, and he was ready to go.

"Thanks, Doc," Joe Walters said. "We'll be getting him out of here now."

A few minutes later, Frankie Sifford and his entourage were walking toward the ambulance entrance. He was looking down at his shackled feet. But when he reached the nurses' station, he looked up and directly into my eyes. Someone has said that the eyes are the portal to the soul. If that's true, then Frankie's soul was a dark and forbidding place.

Outside, the darkness was thick and somehow threatening, and a cold wind was beginning to blow. A gust found its way into the department, and Amy Connors shivered.

It took me a while to write up Frankie Sifford's chart. I described the wounds and the repair that was required. And then I slid the chart over to Amy.

"We can file that," I told her. "But you'd better make a few copies." We would probably all be testifying about this at some point in the near future.

I stood at the nurses' station, and suddenly realized how tired I was. Putting Frankie's wounds back together had not been physically taxing. It was the whole picture. Who he was, what he had just done. And while I was sewing him up, I couldn't help but think that those very hands, only a few hours before, had taken the lives of two innocent and unsuspecting people. And I thought about their family, and what must be going on with them at that very moment. Those are the things that wear you down.

Forty-five minutes later I stepped out of room 4 and walked across the hallway. Jeff was on the phone and motioned for me to come over.

"Thanks, officer," he was speaking into the receiver. "We'll be expecting you. And he'll be in the same room, just like before."

He hung up the phone and looked at me, shaking his head.

"What is it?" I was beginning to have a hunch, and it was troubling.

"Frankie Sifford," Jeff said. Amy turned in her chair to listen. "He's on his way back in," he continued. "Seems that when they got him back to the jail, they strip-searched him and found another piece of broken glass. Nothing else, so they locked him up. The officer on duty was supposed to be watching him closely, and perhaps he was. Anyway, Frankie apparently turned on his side away from the door and somehow started chewing on his bandages. He got them off, and then he started chewing on his sutures. Took every last one of them out. The officer said the place is a mess, and they're on the way over right now. I guess you heard me tell them to take him back to minor trauma."

I had heard that part and had glanced at the patient ID board. The room was still empty.

"That's fine, Jeff," I told him. "But what in the world..." I just stood there and didn't say anything else.

It was Amy Connors who spoke. "That's one crazy dude," she said with contempt. "They're gonna have to put him in a straitjacket."

That might not be a bad idea, if anyone still had one of those.

I sat down wearily behind the counter and waited.

The group that led Frankie into the department looked exactly as they had a few hours earlier. A mass of blue seemed to glide down the hallway and into the minor trauma room. Jeff and I followed close behind them.

They put him on the same stretcher, in the back right corner of the room, and again cuffed him to the rails.

Joe Walters was with him, and he stepped over to Jeff and me.

"Do what you need to do," he said, shaking his head. "And I can promise you this won't happen again."

From the steely determination in his voice, I knew it wouldn't, whatever that would take.

"Frankie, I'm going to need to take a look at those wrists again," I told him, stepping beside his stretcher. His face remained an impenetrable mask, but I thought I detected a hint of desperation in his eyes. He didn't say anything.

Jeff was removing his bandages, leaving the handcuffs in place. When I looked down at his wounds, I felt my face flush with anger. I had spent a couple of hours putting him back together, and he had undone that work in only a few minutes.

Every single one of the stitches was gone. I don't know how, but he had managed to rip them out with his teeth. There were tears along some of the edges of the lacerations where he had pulled the sutures through his skin. He had obviously been determined.

"Frankie," I said, unable to restrain myself. "Just why did you do this?"

He just stared at me, with that same smile on his face, and remained silent.

That was enough. I wasn't going to play any more of his games.

I turned to Joe. "There are a couple of ways to deal with this. These wounds need to be cleaned really well. And in some instances, I would probably suture them again. They'll heal more quickly and be easier to take of. However, that's not what we're going to do."

I stopped and looked down at Frankie. Then I turned again to Joe.

"He would probably find another way to screw things up, and I don't want to waste your time or mine. We're going to clean him up and bandage these again and let you go. The jail nurse can check on him tomorrow and redress him every day. It'll take longer to heal, and he'll have some bigger scars, but that will work."

"That sounds like a plan to me," Joe said. "I don't think he's gonna be worried about any scars. And like I said, this is the last time you're gonna see him for this."

The two officers closest to Frankie Sifford nodded their heads.

Jeff cleaned up the open wounds, scrubbing them with saline and Betadine. Frankie showed no emotion during this, and never flinched. He either had an unbelievable pain threshold or a stony determination to show no weakness in our presence. Whichever the reality was, it was all pretty spooky.

It didn't take long to have him redressed and on his way back to the jail. As he and his entourage slowly made their way down the hallway, Joe Walters told me more about the murder scene and about what had happened. It was a gruesome story, and was obviously the work of a sick and twisted individual.

"I would have thought there would be drugs or alcohol involved, Doc," Joe said to me. "But this guy is stone-cold sober. Nothing. He's just mean. No, he's more than that. I've never seen anyone quite like him."

As Joe was saying this, Frankie Sifford was passing by the nurses' station. He looked over in my direction and once again fixed his eyes on me. He wasn't a big man, and didn't have an impressive or threatening physical presence. In fact, he almost looked like a boy among those police officers. Yet there was something about him—something dark and ominous, something that disquieted my spirit. I was glad when he turned his head and looked away.

"Okay, Doc, I guess that's it for tonight," Joe said. "Thanks again for your help and—"

There was a sudden outburst of shouting at the ambulance entrance and the blue mass of police officers become a scrambled, moving mound of arms and legs. Several of them seemed to collapse on the floor and we heard, "Get that gun!" and "Quick! Put him down!"

Joe ran over to help his men.

As they had reached the automatic doors, Frankie had twisted his body to one side and had managed to grab the pistol from the holster of the officer walking nearest him. It had been careless on the part of the policeman, and Frankie had taken the opportunity. The only thing that saved us was that his wrists were cuffed together, and any coordinated movement was going to be awkward. Still, he managed to get the gun loose and jerked it up and away from the officer. As he did this, he struck the officer across his face, splitting open his left eyebrow.

Two other officers had immediately grabbed Frankie's arms and then thrown him to the floor, knocking the gun loose and away from him. Thankfully, no shot was fired, and no officer was seriously injured. Frankie Sifford left the department with a few more bruises than he had come in with.

The officer with the busted eyebrow stayed behind, and I closed it with about ten stitches. It would leave only a small scar. But it would forever remind him of what had happened here tonight.

When the excitement was over, Jeff and I sat at the nurses' station and were silent, each deep in our own thoughts. Then he said, "I've never seen anything quite like that. And I don't think I've ever seen anyone as...I guess, as just plain evil as that guy."

I didn't say anything, but was having the same thoughts.

"I guess he'll be meeting Ole Sparky in the not-too-distant future," he added.

Ole Sparky was the state's electric chair, located in Columbia. And it wasn't long before he and Frankie did meet.

But Frankie Sifford had sadly and permanently torn the fabric of our community, and more tragically, that of one of our families. The lives of a lot of people were forever changed that night.

> *In every man's heart there is a devil,*
> *but we do not know the man as bad*
> *until the devil is roused.*
>
> JAMES OLIVER CURWOOD,
> "THE CASE OF BEAUVAIS"

6

Walking the Walk

Greater love has no one than this,
that he lay down his life
for his friends.

John 15:13

Tuesday, 5:26 p.m. "Rock Hill ER, this is Medic 2, do you read me?"

Amy Connors rolled her chair toward the ambulance radio, getting to it just before Lori Davidson. She picked up the receiver, smiled at Lori, and said, "This is the ER, Medic 2. Go ahead."

Then she pushed the hands-free button and replaced the phone in its cradle.

"ER, this is paramedic Roberts," the familiar voice informed us. We could all hear now, and Lori had picked up a notepad, prepared to record Denton Roberts's information. I stood on the other side of the counter, listening.

"We're on the way in with a fifty-three-year-old man, complaining of shortness of breath and chest pain. Also with pain and swelling in his legs…" Denton's voice trailed off, and he added, "It's Jimmy Bostick."

"Oh my word," Amy muttered as she rolled her eyes, slamming her pen on the countertop and turning away.

A cloud seemed to pass over Lori's face for a moment, and then it was gone. She was all business. "Vital signs stable?" she asked.

"BP is 150 over 100, and his pulse is 92 and regular," Denton responded. "Looks okay."

"Room 3 on arrival," Lori told him. "And what's your ETA?"

"10 to 12. And roger, room 3 on arrival."

Lori pushed the bottom on the receiver, terminating the call.

"Jimmy Bostick," Amy said with obvious contempt. "I don't under-stand it sometimes how we see young people, good people, just all of a sudden fall over dead, or get killed in an auto accident, or whatever. And somebody like Jimmy Bostick just keeps hangin' in there. He must be too mean, or too evil to die. It's a mystery, and just not right."

"Now Amy—" Lori began.

"Lori, now you hold on," Amy interrupted. "You feel the same way about him, you know you do. You know what he did to his brother. You were here the night Dan came in and coded. Don't tell me you've forgotten that."

Lori didn't say anything, but just kept writing on the notepad. I remembered.

November, five years earlier. The atmosphere in the cardiac room was tense and electric, but controlled. A forty-eight-year-old man had stumbled into the ER, clutched his chest, and then promptly col-lapsed on the floor in front of the nurses' station. He wasn't breathing when Jeff got to him, and he didn't have a pulse.

One of his "friends" told us he had OD'd on cocaine. He had been smoking it most of the day and then "just seemed to start comin' loose, you know."

We had seen him in the ER on previous occasions, enough to know he had a significant substance-abuse problem. Tonight might be the end of that.

We worked with him for over an hour, getting a pulse back minutes after his arrival, but unable to get much of a blood pressure.

And then he began to respond.

"Seems to be making some respiratory efforts on his own," Jeff told me. He had been bagging him for most of this time, checking for vol-untary breathing every few minutes.

"80 over 60," Katie told me. His blood pressure was starting to improve. We had been pumping him full of fluids and potent medications, hoping for such a response. But he had gone a long time without a decent blood pressure, and perfusion to his vital organs would be the big question. If he woke up and was clear, then his brain would probably be all right. His kidneys might be another matter. A prolonged time of diminished blood flow to the kidneys could do severe damage, sometimes irreversible. But you wouldn't know that right away. Sometimes it took hours or days for kidney failure to declare itself.

"100 over 72," Katie informed us, making a notation on the code record. "Getting better, and he's starting to move around some."

I had noticed the same thing. First his legs began to move, and then he began to reach up for the endotracheal tube taped to the corner of his mouth.

"Better restrain his arms," I told Katie. "I don't want him grabbing that tube."

Over the next twenty minutes, Jimmy Bostick continued to improve. His blood pressure stabilized and he became a little more responsive. He ultimately required sedation in order for us to keep him calm and quiet. When he was transferred to the ICU, his vital signs were stable, his pupils were reactive, and his breathing was controlled. All good things.

A few days later, we learned that he had left the hospital AMA (against medical advice). He had improved to the point where they were able to take him off the ventilator and move him out of the ICU to a step-down unit. He required close monitoring but was making steady progress. And then he decided it was time to leave.

When one of the nurses went in to his room, she found the IV line hanging from the pole beside his bed, the remaining fluids having run out over the floor. And his hospital gown was gone.

Jeff and I were talking with her as we all stood in the ER hallway.

"Probably got some attention when he walked into McDonald's wearing that thing," she had told us. "And he left the IV needle in his arm. Must have taped over it, knowing he could use it to shoot up with. You guys might be seeing him later on tonight."

Jeff shook his head and muttered, "Jimmy Bostick. Hmm, hmm. Doesn't surprise me that he jumped AMA. He's done that before."

"A couple of times," the nurse responded. "But don't worry, if you don't see him tonight, it won't be too long before he shows up again."

"What makes you say that?" I asked her. She seemed to know something more about Mr. Bostick.

"Well, Dr. Shaw's been following his labs, and this morning he was pretty worried. Jimmy might feel okay now, but his kidneys are dead."

Eight days later—1:30 a.m. Jimmy Bostick followed the triage nurse into the department. He was shuffling along, his hair unkempt, his color gray, and his face bloated. He looked like death. This was a big change from the last time I had seen him.

The nurse took him to room 4, then stepped out and pulled the curtain closed behind her. She walked over to where I stood.

"He's in pretty bad shape, Dr. Lesslie," she said, handing me his chart. "Fever, short of breath, you name it. And he looks terrible."

She headed back out to triage, and I studied the ER ledger in my hands.

"Was that Jimmy Bostick?" Amy asked me. "I just caught a glimpse as he walked by, but…if it is, somethin' bad's goin' on."

It *was* Jimmy Bostick, and something bad *was* going on. His work-up told us he was in kidney failure. His blood pressure was sky-high, almost every one of his lab studies was abnormal, and his heart was enlarged. He was a train wreck. No slipping out AMA tonight.

I talked with the kidney specialist on call for the ER and we arranged for Jimmy to have emergency dialysis. He was again admitted to the ICU.

While he was still in the ER, his family members came to the hospital to check on him. His mother and father were there, as were his younger sister, Susan, and older brother, Dan. It was a little bit of a shock for us when they came back into the department. We had known Jimmy for years as a druggie—no job, always dirty, always abusive when he was high on something. But his family was just the opposite. His parents were quiet-spoken, well-dressed, and very courteous. His brother and sister were the same, though Susan, out of Jimmy's hearing, was outspoken about the grief he had caused all those who cared about him.

"He's going to be the death of Mother and Dad," she had told Lori. "I don't know how much more of this they can take."

Dan told us they had tried everything: counseling, rehab hospitals, even involuntary commitment. Nothing worked. It was always the same. He would straighten out just long enough to be released, then disappear again. And in a few weeks or months, he would surface in the ER, in trouble.

Tonight he was in big trouble, and I tried to explain his condition to them.

"Jimmy is in renal failure, complete shutdown. No kidney function at all, and he probably won't get any back. We think it started the last time he was in the hospital, after the cocaine overdose."

"That's when he left against medical advice," Susan said, looking over at her parents.

"That's right," I told them. "And I don't know if it would have made any difference in his condition, but we are where we are. Jimmy's going to have dialysis tonight, and we'll see how that goes. The problem is that when the kidneys go, everything else gets out of kilter, and things go downhill. Sometimes pretty quickly, like we're seeing with Jimmy."

"Is he going to die?" his father asked.

That was a real possibility, and they needed to know the truth.

"Your son is a very sick man, Mr. Bostick," I answered him. "And yes, he may die. If the dialysis helps, the kidney doctors may be able to turn things around for a while. But he'll need to be on regular dialysis, maybe three or four times a week. And then there's his heart, and his—"

"What about a kidney transplant?" his mother asked hopefully. "Wouldn't that help him? Wouldn't that fix things?"

"That's putting the cart before the horse," I gently told her. "We need to take one day at a time and try to get your son better. Then we can talk about what might come next."

"I'm sure the transplant waiting list for drug abusers is a short one," his sister said cynically.

"Now Susan, he's your brother," Mrs. Bostick chided. "And if it would save him…"

It turned out that a transplant was going to be the only thing that would save the life of Jimmy Bostick. Initially, dialysis had seemed to be helping. But then he developed an infection, and his labs started getting worse. He spent six weeks in the ICU and his doctors weren't holding out much hope. And they weren't being very optimistic about a kidney transplant. Susan was right about that waiting list.

That's when Dan Bostick walked up to one of Jimmy's doctors one day and asked about donating a kidney to his brother. There were discussions about studies for compatibility, inherent dangers to both parties, and then questions about Dan's overall health status.

It turned out that Dan had mild high blood pressure and had been on medication for over ten years. It was under good control now, but Jimmy's doctors were leery about pursuing this. They didn't want to take any chances with Dan's health, even though people live long and full lives with only one kidney.

And Dan's family was opposed to the idea. His mother didn't want to lose both of her sons, but it was Susan who was especially vocal.

"You're only putting yourself at risk," she told him. "And if Jimmy gets better, he's just going back to doing the things he's always done. And do you think for one minute that if things were reversed, he'd give you one of his kidneys?"

"I don't know the answer to that," Dan said. "But if I don't give Jimmy one of my kidneys, what chance does he have of living?" He had asked this of the doctors in the presence of Susan and his parents.

"Well, to be honest, none," one of them replied. "He has a month, maybe two."

"Then that's the answer," Dan had said resolutely. "When do we do it?"

And so Jimmy received one of Dan's kidneys. The operation went well, and Dan was out of the hospital in a few days, doing great. Jimmy's hospital course was miraculous. He seemed to turn on a dime, and within a few weeks, his blood pressure was good, his labs normal, and his heart was returning to normal size. He was released from the hospital and instructed to follow up with the kidney doctors in a few days. He was on some powerful antirejection medicines and would need to be closely monitored. A big concern was the risk of him getting a serious infection.

He didn't make it to that appointment, or the next. Jimmy Bostick just seemed to disappear—again.

Though he left the hospital feeling great, things didn't go so well for Dan Bostick. One month after the transplant, his doctor found some protein in his urine, and his blood pressure was beginning to creep up. Then he began to develop some swelling in his legs.

His cardiologist told him the difficult truth—his remaining kidney was being overworked. And while it was not in danger of failing, it was not able to keep up with the demands placed upon it. Apparently, his long-standing elevated blood pressure, though mild, had taken its toll. And in spite of aggressive medical management, Dan's overall health was being negatively impacted. His cholesterol began to rise, and he developed evidence of vascular disease.

Three years after the transplant, Dan Bostick had a heart attack. He didn't die, but he came very close. When he got to the ER, his blood pressure was dangerously low and his initial labs indicated extensive heart damage. He was improving with some pain medication and careful IV fluid replacement.

Then suddenly he coded. That was what Amy was reminding Lori of. One minute he was sitting up and talking with us, and the next he was unconscious, his heart fibrillating like a quivering mass of jelly. Lori was the first to see the monitor and had quickly charged up the paddles and shocked him. Fortunately, he had quickly returned to a regular and effective rhythm.

We had stabilized him in the cardiac room and were waiting to send him around to the cath lab when his family arrived. His mother and father were there, as was his wife and Susan, his sister. But not Jimmy. I didn't ask.

Dan was in the hospital for a week, and then in an aggressive rehab program. His doctors were able to keep his blood pressure under control, but his heart catheterization had revealed blockages in a lot of vessels, some of which couldn't be fixed. It would be a day-to-day thing for Dan, and hoping for the best.

And so, here we were, waiting on Jimmy Bostick to arrive in the ER. I wondered what his story would be this time.

A few minutes later, the ambulance doors opened and the Medic 2 team came into the department with their patient. Denton rolled the stretcher into room 3, and Lori headed in that direction. I had looked down at Jimmy as he rolled by, and he managed to give me a slight nod. Once again, he looked awful.

I gave Lori a few minutes to get him settled. Then I walked around the counter toward his room. Denton was backing his stretcher into the hallway, and he pulled me aside.

"Dr. Lesslie, he looks terrible this time," he told me. "Worse than I can remember."

"Where did you pick him up?" I asked. "I didn't know he was back in town."

"Over on Wisteria Drive. You know, down by the old bus station."

That was one of the worst parts of town, a place that generated a lot of business for the ER. That would usually be gunshots, and stabbings, and overdoses. It was a tough street.

"I recognized a few of the guys he was staying with," he continued. "Some of the usual characters, or maybe usual suspects. The place was filthy."

"Did he say when he got back in town? I wonder if his folks know he's here."

"Says he's been in Atlanta for the past few years," Denton told me. "And just came in yesterday on the bus. Hooked up with some of his old buddies, and they called us when he kept complaining of feeling bad. You heard my report, I guess. Shortness of breath, swollen legs. Looks like he might be in heart failure. And he's got these nasty-looking places on his neck and elbows. All red and draining. Like I said, Doc, he's a mess."

"Hmm. I wonder if he's started using drugs again," I mused.

"Come on, Doc, what do you think?" Denton shook his head. "Needle tracks up and down his arms. Even on his ankles. And he's staying with Bubba Burns, the biggest dealer in the county."

"Oh man," I sighed. "After all he's been through. And after all he's put his family through."

"Some folks just don't learn," Denton said. "And Jimmy Bostick is one of them."

He was right.

Jimmy later told me he had been living in Atlanta ever since the kidney transplant. He had done well for a while and felt good. And then he had stopped taking all of his medicines. Too expensive, and he didn't want to go to the trouble of registering with one of the free clinics down there.

His family had tried to find him, but he didn't want anything to do with them. Dan had somehow figured out where he was staying and had showed up one morning. Jimmy threw him out, threatening to hurt him if he ever came back. And that was the last contact he'd had with any of them.

"I guess you know about Dan," I said to him.

"Dan? No, is something the matter? He looked fine when I saw him in Atlanta."

I thought it best to wait for a while before I told him about his brother and his health problems. But then, he might not even care. So I changed the subject and asked him about any recent substance abuse.

He did admit to falling back into his old drug habits. He could hardly tell me otherwise, with the evidence screaming from the ruined veins of his arms.

And that's when he told me about his HIV. He and his friends shared needles—and girlfriends. When he learned that one of his buddies had advanced AIDS, he decided it was time to be tested, to make sure he was clean.

The day he was tested he was put in the hospital. His white count was dangerously low, and he had pneumonia. On top of that, Dan's kidney was failing. Without the antirejection medication, Jimmy's body was destroying the very organ that stood between him and his own death. It was a perfect storm. His defense systems were compromised, he had multi-organ system problems, and the AIDS virus was rapidly replicating. There were not many options open to him or his doctors.

He had refused dialysis in Atlanta, and after several courses of high-powered medicines, he had once again left the hospital AMA.

"I just decided to see what was gonna happen," he told me. "One day at a time, just see where all this takes me."

And the bus had brought him back to Rock Hill. I found that part interesting. He could have stayed in Atlanta with his "friends," but he'd chosen to come home. But what was there here for him? He had driven away his family by turning his back on his parents and threatening Dan.

I asked him about that, and why he had come to Rock Hill.

"Look at me, Doc," he said holding his hands out as if showcasing his decimated body. "I don't have much time, do I? You know that."

He was right. His blood work indicated he had little if any kidney function, and a chest X-ray showed his heart was once again enlarged. Worst of all, he had a bad-looking pneumonia. That's what usually kills people in this situation. And usually pretty fast.

"You're right, Jimmy," I agreed. "You've got some serious problems. Do you want me to get in touch with your family? I'll be glad to call—"

"No! I don't want them to know I'm here," he said emphatically. "Just do what you need to do, and don't bother them. I've been enough of a burden...about fifty years of heartache, I'd say. They can find out when this...when it's over."

His eyes were vacant as he said this. I was looking at the shell of a man, and it was impossible for me to know what he was thinking. But I knew I needed to honor his request. I didn't want to think how his mother and father might react if they saw their son like this.

"Okay, Jimmy. But if you change your mind, just let me know."

"Thanks," he said heavily, and I walked out of the room.

Standing at the nursing station, talking with Lori Davidson, was Dan Bostick. How did he know his brother was here?

Lori looked over at me and raised her eyebrows. Dan followed her glance, turned, and walked toward me.

"Dr. Lesslie, how's Jimmy?" he asked, grabbing my hand and shaking it. But his grip had no strength, and his skin was cool and damp. "One of my friends with EMS called and told me he had been brought in. Can I see him?"

I immediately thought of Jimmy threatening to physically hurt him in Atlanta, and of his request that his family not be notified of his presence here. While Jimmy was not in any condition to do much resisting, this could turn into a pretty ugly scene. And yet, he was dying, and here was his brother.

"He's over in room 3," I told him, pointing to the cubicle. "And he's pretty sick."

Then I quickly added, "Actually, Dan, he's very sick. He's not going to make it this time. I don't know how long he has, but—"

"I understand, Doctor," he interrupted. "I knew this was coming. I'm just glad he's home, and that he's here."

Dan walked over to room 3, pulled the curtain open, and stepped inside. I looked at Lori and she just shook her head.

We didn't know what to expect. I waited about fifteen minutes and then went to check on the two brothers. As I approached, I didn't hear any voices from within and felt a little nervous. I pulled the curtain back and was about to step into the room. But I stopped abruptly in the doorway.

The head of the stretcher had been raised to a sitting position, and Jimmy was leaning back against it. His head was resting comfortably and his eyes were closed. His breathing was regular and unlabored. Dan was sitting on the edge of the bed with his arm around his brother's shoulders. His head hung down on his chest.

Neither of them looked up at me, and I left them alone.

7

Just Plain Stubborn

An obstinate man does not hold opinions,
but they hold him.

SAMUEL BUTLER (1835–1902)

I don't know what I said or what I did, but when Amy Connors remarked, "Dr. Lesslie, you're starting to act like Dr. Candler," I stopped what I was doing and stared at her.

"What do you mean by that?" I asked, bothered by the comparison.

"You know what I mean," she said. "You're being stubborn here."

Jeff Ryan was standing nearby and he chuckled.

"Might be starting to look like him too," he quipped.

I glared at him and then turned again to Amy. "Wait just a minute, Ms. Connors. You need to explain yourself."

"Now don't get all riled up." She smiled. "I'm just kiddin'…though you *were* pretty rough on that lab tech."

"Rough?" I exclaimed, trying to think of what I might have said that could have triggered this. "I was only telling her how to run the tests on the knee fluid from the guy back in ortho. She wanted to do it her way, and—"

"See, there you go. And you wanted to do it *your* way. She was just doin' it the way her supervisor told her to. You almost had her in tears."

I hadn't noticed that, and I looked around to see if she was still in the department.

"Don't worry about it, Doc," Amy said. "She'll be okay. And you're not quite as bad as Dr. Candler…not yet, anyway."

"Yeah," Jeff added. "We still have our phone."

He was referring to an episode that had occurred in the ER a few months ago. It was late at night, and Dr. Ray Candler had been called in to see a trauma patient. Ray was a neurosurgeon, well-trained and very capable. But he had a short fuse, and we had learned to stay clear of him when certain warning signals were present. The most obvious was a flushed face—and then, when he rolled up his shirtsleeves, we knew someone was in for it. That someone turned out to be the nursing supervisor on that particular evening.

The patient he had been called in to examine would need to be taken to the operating room for a head injury. Amy Connors had called the nursing supervisor to get the OR crew organized. Apparently, the response and the time frame she was given didn't satisfy Dr. Candler.

"Here, give me that phone," he brusquely ordered Amy after she had told him it would be at least forty-five minutes before things would be ready.

"Who is this?" he demanded of the person on the other end of the line. There was a pause and then some expletives, and then his face went from bright red to scarlet and finally to a dangerous maroon.

And then the phone came off the wall. Actually, it flew off the wall as he hurled it down the hallway. Wires went everywhere and plaster showered onto the counter at the nurses' station as he stomped down the hall. If you look closely, you can still see the repair job where the new phone has been attached.

"Well, maybe I need to go around to the lab and apologize," I suggested, not knowing what to do. I didn't want to hurt the tech's feelings. But I knew how I wanted things done.

"No, she'll be fine," Amy answered. "It wasn't a big deal."

I needed to think about this one. There was a fine line sometimes between insisting on what was right and insisting on having your way. Or maybe it wasn't so fine.

"Do you remember the night you called Dr. Candler about the young Webb boy?" Amy said, interrupting my thoughts. "Jason Webb, remember?"

"Yeah," I said, chuckling, happy for the release from my thoughts. "Now that was something."

Wednesday, 3:00 a.m. This was not a call I had wanted to make, but it had to be done.

"Dr. Lesslie," Amy said, shaking her head, "it's Dr. Candler."

She handed the receiver across the countertop to me, but at the last minute covered the mouthpiece with her hand and whispered, "Doesn't sound like he's in a very good mood."

I didn't expect him to be. After all, it was the middle of the night, and it was Dr. Ray Candler, not the happiest of guys even in the middle of the day.

Amy took her hand from the receiver and I grabbed it, placing it to my ear.

"Ray, this is Robert."

"Hmm" was the response from the other end.

"Sorry to bother you this time of the morning," I apologized. "But I've got a twenty-year-old here with a neck injury. Moped accident, out on a dirt road. Apparently he ran off the trail and hit a tree. No helmet on, but no obvious injuries except for some neck pain. He's completely awake and alert, and complaining of numbness and weakness in his right arm and leg."

I paused, wanting to be sure my colleague was still awake and listening. There was no response.

"Ray?" I said, checking.

"What!" The response was not really a question, but more of a statement. He obviously was not very interested in what I was telling him.

"Anyway, he does have some weakness on that right side, and his cervical X-rays look like a fracture and maybe a jumped facet." This was a potentially unstable injury, and one that would need surgery. Especially the "jumped facet" part. That meant the spine was no longer normally fitting together, but was out of place. Making matters worse was the fact that the hospital's one CT scanner was down for repairs. We would have to make do with these plain X-rays.

I waited for his response, and after what seemed like a long time, he mumbled, "Are you sure about that?"

"Sure about what?" I asked him, getting a little aggravated now.

"About the X-rays," he said. "Are you sure they're abnormal?"

I took a deep breath before I answered. "Ray, I'm not a radiologist, but I can tell if a neck is broken or not. And this one is broken."

Amy looked up at this, her eyes wide with surprise. And she just shook her head again.

Then he said something I will never forget. In fact, it was so bizarre I had to ask him to repeat his request.

"Robert, go get those films and hold them up to the phone," he told me.

What? He sounded like he was awake, but—

"You want me to do what?" I asked incredulously.

This got Amy's attention. She looked at me questioningly. I leaned across the counter and cocked the phone away from my face, allowing her to hear Dr. Candler.

"Go get those X-rays and hold them up to the phone," he repeated. "I want to take a look for myself."

Amy almost burst out laughing, and had to cover her mouth with both hands. She rolled away from the counter, putting distance between herself and the phone. She was snorting loudly.

"Ray, do you really want me to do that?" I asked him patiently, hoping he was only partially awake. I couldn't look at Amy or I would start laughing myself. "Do you really want me to hold the X-rays up to the phone? Don't you think you need to come in and see the kid and look at the X-rays yourself?"

"I…uh…what?" he muttered, apparently trying to collect himself. "Of course, I'll…I'll come over. Be there in a minute. But it sounds like a waste of time."

There was a loud click as he slammed his phone down.

Amy laughed out loud as we both remembered this episode. "I would never believe that if I hadn't heard it myself!" she declared. "Not in a hundred years! He must have been out cold—sleepwalkin' or sleep-talkin' or something!" She kept laughing and shaking her head. "Sometimes that man can be just plain…well, just plain stubborn as a mule. I guess that best describes it. And even when he knows he's wrong. I don't know what makes a person do that, but boy, he can really dig in his heels. As if he has something to prove."

She paused, suddenly thinking of something. "About the only person I've ever known to be more pigheaded was Maggie Reynolds. Remember that woman?" she asked me, a mischievous look on her face.

"Maggie Reynolds," I repeated thoughtfully. And then it came to me. "Yeah, I remember Maggie! And I bet I remember the night you're talking about. It happened right over there," I said pointing to room 3.

"Yep, you're absolutely right," Amy confirmed. "It was right over there."

Maggie Reynolds was a fifty-year-old nurse, sent to the emergency department from a temp agency. Why in the world the hospital administration would send us someone with little or no ER experience was beyond us, but there she was. Lori Davidson had been the charge nurse that day, and she decided to give Maggie a limited assignment. She would be covering only rooms 3 and 4, and hopefully wouldn't get into too much trouble.

From the moment she arrived in the ER, Maggie began asserting herself.

"Why do you people put this paperwork over here?" she had asked Amy. The questions went on. Why don't you do this? Why don't you do that?

Amy Connors would have committed manslaughter had we not been so busy that morning. And that was a good thing for Maggie Reynolds.

Lori had instructed our triage nurse to send the serious patients to beds other than rooms 3 and 4, and to use those only if absolutely necessary. Throughout the morning, she had been able to give Maggie simple sore throats and a few coughs. Nothing serious or complicated.

And then Michael Beck came into the department.

To be fair to our triage nurse, Michael had been less than forthcoming about his reason for being in the ER. He told her he wanted to be checked by the doctor, but reported nothing specific. His vital signs were completely stable, and he looked fine. She brought him on back without any real concerns.

Michael was a veteran of the Vietnam War. He had been moving around a lot, working various jobs and trying to find his space. He had settled down in Rock Hill for the past few years and had been working as a technician with a local telecommunications company. He had been in Special Forces and was still in great physical condition.

I looked up as he came by the nurses' station with the triage nurse. He was neatly dressed and his hair was close-cropped, betraying his military background. His eyes held mine with an intensity that was anything but threatening. He was obviously intelligent, and there was a gentle spirit behind that rough and tough façade. He was an interesting man. I noted he was being taken into room 3.

Maggie noticed this as well and quickly headed into the cubicle.

I was writing up the record of a patient in the cardiac room and was standing within earshot of room 3. I heard the entire exchange between Maggie and Mr. Beck.

"Mr. Beck," Maggie began. "I will be your nurse today, and I'm here to help you. And my name is Maggie Reynolds. Do you understand me?"

With a half-perplexed, half-humorous look on his face, Michael replied, "Yes, Ms. Reynolds. I understand you."

"Good. Now, what is the problem this morning?" she asked him, busying herself around the room, straightening the countertop, and rearranging our supplies.

"I've been stabbed," he said matter-of-factly.

Maggie stopped what she was doing and turned to stare at him. I thought I had heard the word "stabbed" as well. I looked over in his direction. Everything seemed calm, and he still looked fine. Then Amy Connors handed me the phone and said, "Here's Dr. Shaw. He's on for cardiology and he's returning your call about the heart attack in cardiac."

"You what?" Maggie asked Mr. Beck, now beginning to lose her patience.

"I've been stabbed," he repeated calmly.

"What in the—" she mumbled. "Now see here, Mr. Beck. We've no time to spend with any tomfoolery. If you think I'm going to—"

"Ms. Reynolds, I'm telling you, I've been stabbed in the back with a pair of scissors," Michael explained, still surprisingly calm. "I was in the elevator of our building, and these two guys tried to mug me. One grabbed my arms and I felt the other one punch me in the back. Then I saw he had a pair of scissors in his hand, and I knew I was in trouble. That's when I knew he had stabbed me."

"What…you say he…" she muttered incoherently, totally taken off guard by what he had just said.

"I've handled much worse, and I left the two of them on their butts in the elevator—you'll probably be seeing them soon enough—and then I went back upstairs to our lounge. I remember seeing some Saran wrap in one of the cabinets, and I found it and wrapped it around myself and came straight over here."

Maggie Reynolds was trying desperately to collect herself and regain control of this situation.

"Are you telling me you've been stabbed in the back?" she asked.

Michael shook his head, showing the first sign of frustration. "That's what I've been telling you, Maggie."

"It's Mrs. Reynolds, young man," she asserted herself. "Now, about this stabbing—"

"Here, take a look," Michael said, taking off his shirt.

He was not wearing an undershirt, and his chest was completely encircled with several layers of Saran wrap. It extended from just below his armpits to his mid-abdomen.

He twisted around on the stretcher and tried to point to his right mid-back. "Here, this is where I think he got me."

Maggie glanced at his back and saw the pooled blood beneath the Saran wrap. Her eyes widened as she began to realize Michael might be telling her the truth.

His training in the Special Forces had prepared him for the possibility of such an injury. He knew that a stab wound of the chest was serious business and could rapidly prove fatal. If the stab penetrated the chest cavity and lung, you could develop a tension pneumothorax— where the cavity quickly fills with air from the outside, creating a pressure that forces the collapsed lung against the heart. Finally, the blood flow from your heart is compromised and you no longer are able to move air in and out of your chest. And then you die. Something adherent and waterproof like Saran wrap will close off the stab hole and prevent air from entering your chest. It will buy time until you can get help. Michael had saved his own life.

What happened next was a blur. I was trying to tell Dr. Shaw about the patient in the cardiac room, and at the same time it was beginning to dawn on me that I had a real problem in room 3. And Maggie was at the center of it.

"Let me take a look at that," Maggie said, stepping over to the stretcher.

"Just be sure not to remove that dressing," Michael warned her. "If you—"

"Now don't tell me my business," she clucked. "I know what I'm doing."

"Just be sure you don't—"

I heard the concern in our patient's voice and looked over at room 3 again. Maggie had not yet pulled the curtain closed, and I could easily see what was happening.

Michael was sitting sideways on the stretcher, his legs dangling over one edge. Maggie had walked around behind him, where he couldn't see what she was doing. It was a strange sight, this gentleman sitting on our bed with Saran wrap tightly encircling his chest. And then it happened. Before I could call out and stop her, Maggie took a pair of scissors out of her pocket and deftly and completely cut through the plastic wrap on Michael's back. It fell away as if it were the peel from an onion.

"No!" he yelled, turning and facing her. But it was too late. He tried to hold his breath, knowing it could prove fatal. But he couldn't, and with a sudden gasp, there was a terrible sucking sound, and the wound in his back began to bubble. Without saying another word into the phone, I dropped the receiver on the counter and slid it across to Amy. Then I raced toward room 3.

I reached the room and pushed Maggie out of the way, just as Michael Beck collapsed, almost falling off the stretcher. His color was a dusky blue, and he wasn't breathing.

"Get me an 18-gauge angiocath on a 50cc syringe!" I called behind me to Jeff. "And then I'll need a chest tube tray."

"What do you want me to do?" Maggie asked, still very assured and apparently unaware of what she had just done.

"I want you to step out into the hall," I told her, not looking up. "And stay there."

There was a rush of air when I punctured Michael's chest with the needle, buying us the time we needed to insert a larger tube between his ribs. Its purpose was to keep draining the leaking air from the wound in his lung until it had time to seal off and heal.

Half an hour later, he was stabilized, breathing, and talking. As I explained to him that he was to be admitted to the ICU for a few days, he kept looking over my shoulder and around me, searching for something—or someone.

I smiled briefly. "Don't worry, Michael. She's not here. And she won't be back."

"Now that was one pigheaded woman," Amy said. "And you know, the more I think about it, you can be pretty pigheaded too, Dr. Lesslie," Amy added with conviction.

I sighed, shook my head, and waited.

"Jeff," she said, glancing in his direction. He was sitting behind the nurses' station, drinking a cup of coffee. "Do you remember Kevin Mayer?" she asked him, but she was looking at me with eyebrows raised.

"Boy, do I," Jeff answered, smiling. He knew where this was going.

"Wait a minute!" I interjected. "That's not fair. I was only trying to give the guy a chance."

"Sure you were," Amy said. "And the rest of us were trying to tell you the guy needed to go. We were the ones having to work with him, not you. And we were the ones seeing what was going on."

"I know, I know," I muttered. "But he never hurt anybody, or at least no one you guys ever told me about."

"No, it was just that…well…he was just a screwball," Jeff tried to explain. "Something just didn't add up with him. In fact, some of us even wondered if he was really a doctor."

Kevin Mayer was in fact a doctor, having trained in several well-respected medical centers. He came to our ER with little experience, but an excellent resumé and references. We scheduled him for the weekday daytime shifts, since they were the quietest and most normal shifts we had. As if anything in the ER was normal.

From the outset, the nursing staff and Amy Connors were concerned about his performance. There was nothing concrete, as Jeff had said—just some vague misgivings about his medical judgment and experience.

"Give the guy a chance," I had vigorously responded on many occasions. "If you have something specific, let me know, and I'll address it. But remember—we all had to start somewhere."

I should have been suspicious when our most objective and reasonable nurses complained, especially Lori Davidson. She hadn't wanted to raise the issue, but she was concerned as well. Yet, there was nothing specific, nothing I could concretely address. Not until Madeline Waters came into the ER in congestive heart failure.

Madeline was in trouble. Her blood pressure was low. Her lungs were backing up with fluid from her failure. She had been in for this before, and we all knew her. But this was the worst Lori could remember seeing her.

Kevin Mayer was on duty, and with Lori's help, he made the right diagnosis. Then he slipped out of the department and hurriedly went around to our office. Unbeknownst to the staff or to me, when he came across something he didn't recognize or wasn't sure of, he would quietly retire to our office and consult our medical texts. That was fine, and I encouraged such activity. The problem this morning was that Kevin was looking at an internal-medicine book circa 1945. We had kept it in the office as a kind of interesting artifact. It provided some fascinating reading during slow times. Of course, there was no mention of pharmaceutical interventions or advanced monitoring techniques. Instead, the recommended treatment for congestive heart failure, referred to in this text as "dropsy," was rather primitive and of questionable effectiveness.

Kevin came back to the department armed with this newfound information and his treatment plan.

"We need to get some rotating tourniquets going," he ordered with authority. This was an interesting concept, incorporating the placement of tourniquets on both arms and both legs. The idea was that if you inflated one or two of the tourniquets, you would remove a significant portion of the blood volume from circulation, allowing the failing heart to beat more effectively. After a few minutes, you would let down the pressure in that tourniquet and inflate another one—hence the term "rotating." (I did say "primitive," didn't I? There hadn't been this kind of equipment in the hospital for twenty years.)

But it got worse.

"And…we need to draw off about a liter or two of blood." It was the old "cupping" idea. If you removed blood from the circulation, you would ease the work of the heart. It made sense, in a peculiar way. But we didn't have a "cupping" device in the department. And we probably didn't have any leeches, either.

"And we need to do it in a hurry!" he added.

Lori Davidson had stood in front of him and stared, her mouth open and eyes wide.

"Let's get going!" he ordered.

"But, Dr. Mayer—" Lori objected.

"I've got an idea how to do this," he mused, not paying her any attention. "Quick, get a big IV going, and we'll connect it to wall suction. That's it! And turn the suction on wide open. That should get it done. We'll take out about two liters of blood."

He was confident now, having determined his plan and now setting it in motion.

Or so he thought. When Lori realized he was dead-set on this, she slipped away to the nurses' station and called my home number.

I had worked the night before and was sound asleep. It took a moment for me to clear my head and for this strange tale to sink in.

"I'll be right there," I told her.

"Yep, he was stubborn and crazy—*and* a screwball!" Amy declared with a twinkle in her eye. "I'll never forget how you looked when you came through those doors. Hadn't even tucked in your shirttail or combed your hair. But you were bug-eyed and wide awake. And the next thing we know, there goes Dr. Mayer out the ambulance doors. Never did see him again either."

I was silent, letting Amy enjoy this moment of satisfaction.

She just sat there and smiled up at me. Then I turned and headed down the hallway.

"And where are *you* going?" she called after me.

"Where do you think I'm going?" I answered her over my shoulder.

When I reached the end of the hall, I turned and headed toward the lab. There was a certain tech who deserved an apology.

> *There are few, very few,*
> *that will own themselves in a mistake.*
>
> JONATHAN SWIFT (1667–1745)

8

Foolish Pride

Human pride is not worthwhile;
there is always something
lying in wait
to take the wind out of it.

Mark Twain

When you think you're pretty good at what you do, when you think you can handle anything that comes through those ER doors, there it is, lying in wait. And that *something* is waiting to knock the wind right out of you.

Friday, 9:15 p.m. Bill Thatcher was forty-eight years old. At least that was what his chart said. To me he looked a good bit older, maybe in his sixties. He had walked into the ER complaining of mid-to-upper back pain. "Nagging" was how the triage nurse had described it on his record.

He was at least fifty pounds overweight. I surmised that his two-pack-a-day cigarette habit was probably the cause of his premature aging. His skin had the sallow look of a veteran smoker, and he had a slight but audible wheeze as he walked down the hallway.

Once he had been settled into room 4, I picked up his clipboard and headed in his direction.

"Mr. Thatcher," I said to him. "I'm Dr. Lesslie. What can we do for you tonight?"

He had been struggling with his hospital gown and looked up as I spoke.

"First of all, Doc, have I got this thing on right?" he replied, gesturing to the light-blue gown.

I glanced at the garment, noted that he was wearing it correctly, and that he had already tied the strings in a series of knots that could only be undone with scissors. Then I noticed the hospital emblem on the front of the gown. It was from a facility a hundred miles distant, and fleetingly I wondered about the journeys of this particular cotton robe.

"You're fine," I assured him. "Just right."

Over the next few minutes, I asked him about his complaints of back pain—when it started, how bad it was, what made it better or worse. It seemed like a straightforward muscular complaint, maybe just a simple strain. It had started yesterday and had gotten worse over the past few hours.

His vital signs looked okay, other than a heart rate of 96. That wasn't dangerous, but it was a little bit of a red flag. It should have been around 70, but everyone is a little different. His pain might be causing it to go up. He described it as "maybe 5 on a scale of 10." Or it could be due to the recent strenuous activity of tying all those knots.

Still, something had brought him to the ER, something that had him worried. We needed to check this out and make sure nothing bad was going on.

His exam was unremarkable, eliciting no worrisome physical findings. His lungs sounded fine, his heart regular and strong, and his abdomen was completely soft. I considered the possibility of early shingles, but his back was clear of any skin lesions, and there was no pain when I palpated the area where he was hurting.

"Let's check a few things," I told him, picking up his chart from the counter beside his stretcher. "We'll start with a urine specimen and check that for blood or any sign of infection. Do you need anything for pain right now?" I asked.

"No, I'm okay," he answered. "Well, maybe a couple of Tylenols, if you've got some. That might be good."

"Sure, we can do that," I said, heading out of the room. "One of the nurses will be right back with that, and we'll get that urine."

At the nurses' station, I asked Lori to give Mr. Thatcher his Tylenol tablets, and I wrote some orders on his record. "Urinalysis." I was about to hand the chart to the unit secretary when I stopped and put it back down. Maybe we needed a CBC, just to check his white count and hemoglobin. His symptoms were vague. This might either help confirm that nothing bothersome was going on, or lead me in another direction. I would probably bet on the former—but I had thought about it, so I needed to do it. That was a lesson that had been drilled into my head by my earliest instructors. "If you *think* about doing something, you'd better do it." I had never had reason to doubt that wisdom.

I wrote "CBC" on his chart, slid it across the counter to the secretary, and picked up the record of the next patient to be seen.

Twenty minutes later, the urinalysis report was attached to Mr. Thatcher's chart, but the blood-work report was not yet back.

He had a small amount of blood in his urine, but nothing else. No abnormal chemicals or protein, no sugar, and no evidence of infection. The blood could go along with a kidney stone, but he didn't seem to be in that kind of pain. Usually people with stones would declare themselves by their inability to sit still. They would be pacing the floor, constantly moving around, unable to find any relief by lying or sitting. Bill Thatcher was doing none of that. Curious.

I stepped back into his room to see how he was feeling, and was struck by the change that had taken place over the past few minutes. He was sitting upright on his stretcher, staring straight in front of him, and actively inhaling-exhaling like a woman in labor. His color was good, but there was sweat on his forehead.

"How are you feeling?" I asked him, moving quickly to his side and checking his pulse. It was still regular, but now easily more than 100. "What's the problem?"

He looked up at me with a strained smile, not altering his forced breathing pattern. "I don't know," he stammered between breaths. "The pain is gone, but I just got a little short of breath."

I listened again to his heart and lungs. Nothing unusual there. No wheezes or abnormal sounds that would indicate asthma or pneumonia or heart failure. His skin was damp but warm, and while I was listening, his breathing seemed to return to normal.

He sighed loudly and sat back against the head of the raised stretcher, visibly relaxing.

"Boy, that was scary," he said, looking up at me. "Better now, though."

It *was* scary, and I wasn't exactly sure what to make of this. The thought of a pulmonary embolus crossed my mind—blood clots that would have originated in his legs, broken free, and traveled to his lungs. But he didn't have any risk factors for this, and he hadn't complained of any leg pain or previous shortness of breath. I examined his calves again, just to be sure there was no tenderness or swelling. Normal.

"What are you thinkin', Doc?" he asked.

There were several things flying through my brain, none of which were yet concrete.

"I don't know, Mr. Thatcher. You've got me a little worried here. I'm going to check on your blood work. But we'll need to do some more testing. I don't like your having trouble breathing, and I need to find out why that happened," I told him. "Any pain now, anything new?"

"No, no pain. I actually feel a little better, just weak, I guess," he answered.

"Okay, just let me know if something changes. I'm going to get some things going."

Lori was standing at the nurses' station, and I asked her to put Mr. Thatcher on a cardiac monitor.

"He'll need an IV going too, normal saline, just 100 cc's an hour right now. And we'll need to keep a close watch on him."

She nodded her understanding and headed to room 4.

"Amy," I addressed our unit secretary that day, Amy Connors. "We'll need an EKG, portable chest ray, and some blood work on Mr. Thatcher in 4. And a blood gas." I needed to check the oxygen content of his blood. A low level might indicate the presence of a blood clot. That might explain his unusual findings.

She had already begun filling out the necessary order slips, and she picked up the phone before I finishing speaking.

"Anything else?" she asked, looking up at me.

I thought for a moment. "Not yet. Let's see what turns up."

One of our lab techs had walked up the hall carrying her metal mesh basket. It contained an assortment of multicolored stoppered vials, syringes, needles, alcohol swabs, and Band-aids. When she reached the nurses' station, Amy slid an order form across the counter to her and said, "Room 4, Suzie."

Suzie had Mr. Thatcher's CBC report in one hand and exchanged it for Amy's order slip. "Thanks," she said, picking up the lab orders and noting what needed to be done. She turned and stepped toward Mr. Thatcher's room.

I picked up the CBC report and quickly scanned the automated results. His hemoglobin was normal, no obvious evidence of any excessive bleeding. And his platelet count was a little low, just borderline. But what was troubling was his white count...18,000. That was high, and indicated some infectious or stressful process going on. It still didn't make much sense, and I was having a hard time putting things together. I hoped that his X-ray was going to give me some clue, or maybe his EKG.

It was then that Richard Sanders walked out of the cardiac room and over to where I stood. Richard was one of the cardiologists on staff and had come in to see one of our patients. I had asked him to examine the elderly woman in the cardiac room. She was in congestive heart failure and would need to be admitted to the hospital.

"You're right about Mrs. Chambers," he said to me, gesturing with a nod of his head to the cardiac room. "She's in failure and will have to come in. Any family members with her?"

I told him her husband was in the waiting room and that a daughter was on her way in.

"Good," he responded. "I'll need to speak to them as soon as they're all here." He walked around the counter and sat down, beginning to write on Mrs. Chambers's chart.

"Richard, if you've got a minute, let me tell you about the guy I have in room 4."

I proceeded to run the strange case of Mr. Thatcher by him, hoping he might be able to shed some light on this enigma. As I was finishing, Lori walked out of room 4 with his EKG, followed by Suzie, the lab tech. She had collected several tubes of blood and was on her way back to the lab.

Lori handed me the EKG, and said, "You might want to check on him in a few minutes. He seems stable, just maybe a little confused. He's starting to repeat things."

I studied the heart tracing, relieved that it was completely normal, other than an elevated rate of 110. There was no evidence of a heart attack, and no evidence of any unusual strain. I slid it across the counter to Richard Sanders.

"Looks normal to me, Robert," he confirmed. "Puzzling, isn't it? And what's this about confusion? You think he might have early meningitis, with his elevated white count and all?"

That was a reasonable thought, but he had no fever and his neck had been completely supple. But things can change quickly, and I needed to re-examine him.

As I was about to enter room 4, the department's portable X-ray machine was being pushed out of the cubicle by the radiology tech.

"I'll be back in just a minute with the film, Dr. Lesslie," she told me.

"Fine, Carol. Just make sure I see it as soon as you come back."

Stepping into the room again, I immediately noticed a subtle change in Mr. Thatcher's behavior. His color was still good, and his breathing was normal, not labored. But he was nervously glancing around the room, seemingly unable to focus on any one object. He looked up at me as I walked toward him, and then he looked away.

"Bill, how are you feeling now?" I asked him, placing my hand on his shoulder.

He seemed to calm a bit, and said, "Doc, I…I…somethin's just not right. I…don't know what, but…somethin'…"

He stopped talking and just stared up into my face, slowly shaking his head.

I felt the side of his neck with the back of my hand. There was no obvious fever, but I would need to have his temperature rechecked. And then I grasped his head in my hands, moving it up and down, and then side to side. His neck was completely supple; no evidence of meningitis.

"Are you hurting anywhere, Bill?" I asked him.

"No, I'm not havin' any pain," he answered, again shaking his head. "Somethin's just not right."

"Dr. Lesslie." The voice came from behind me. It was Carol, having just returned from the radiology department. "Your X-ray is hanging on the view box."

"Thanks, Carol," I told her. And then turning again to Mr. Thatcher I said, "Bill, I'm going to look at your chest X-ray and then I'll be right back."

"Somethin's just not right," he repeated, once again glancing around the cubicle.

I stepped out of the room and over to the view box. Richard Sanders was already there, intently studying the chest X-ray.

"This is interesting," he mused, stroking his chin while he looked at the film.

I walked up behind him and looked closely at the size and shape of Bill Thatcher's heart, and then I examined his lung fields.

"Interesting?" I asked him. "This looks completely normal to me."

"That's what I mean, Robert," he said, nodding his head. "It *is* completely normal. That's what makes it interesting. There's no help for you here."

He turned and walked back to the nurses' station.

Richard was right. There was no help for me here. I continued to stare at the X-ray, hoping that something would appear, hoping that some answer to this man's problem would be forthcoming. But there was nothing.

"His labs are back," Amy called out, sliding several slips of paper toward me on the countertop. Lori was standing there, making some notes on Bill Thatcher's chart.

"Lori, would you repeat his temp and check his blood pressure again?" I asked her.

"Sure," she answered, and immediately turned toward his room.

I thumbed through the multiple lab studies that had just been returned. Glucose, electrolytes, liver studies, cardiac enzymes, blood gases—all normal. Nothing in all of his studies was out of line. I shook my head and attached the slips to his chart.

Richard Sanders looked up at me and was about to say something, when Lori suddenly called out from the doorway of room 4. "Dr. Lesslie, come quick!"

I immediately stepped across the corridor and into the room. Richard was right behind me.

Lori was now beside the stretcher, lowering its head and placing Mr. Thatcher flat on his back. He was staring blankly at the ceiling—and was barely breathing.

"I took his temperature—99," she told me over her shoulder. "And then while I was starting to take his blood pressure, he just mumbled something and stopped breathing."

Richard was feeling for a pulse and I moved to the head of the stretcher.

"Were you able to get a blood pressure?" I asked her.

"Just barely. I think I heard something at 60. Not any higher than that."

That was a dangerously low reading, indicating that something bad was happening. He was crashing right before our eyes.

"I've barely got a pulse here," Richard called out. "What do you want me to do?"

"Just hang in here a second, Richard," I told him, glad he was in the room. "Lori, get me the airway tray, and call respiratory therapy when you get a chance."

She had already anticipated this and was opening the tray behind me, spreading out the contents on a movable metal stand.

"Mr. Thatcher!" I spoke loudly in his ear. "Can you hear me?"

There was no response, and now he wasn't making any respiratory effort. He was turning a dusky blue.

"Richard, can you bag him for a minute while I get ready to intubate him?" I handed my colleague the ambu bag and face mask, not waiting for a response.

"Sure," he said, stepping around me and positioning himself by Bill Thatcher's head.

Within less than a minute, I had his airway secured with a tube in his windpipe. Richard was rhythmically inflating the ambu bag, watching the patient's chest rise and fall with his efforts. Bill was getting good air exchange, but his color was not improving.

"Any pulse?" I asked Lori while I instinctively felt for the carotid artery with my fingertips. Maybe there was a weak one, but I couldn't be sure.

"No pulse here," Lori said, her hand on his femoral artery.

Richard and I both glanced at the cardiac monitor. It showed a slow but regular cardiac rhythm, around 70 beats a minute. And it was a good, tight complex. But it wasn't doing anything. There was little if any blood moving.

The door to the room opened and two respiratory therapists walked in.

"Anything we can do?" one asked us. He was tall and muscular, and Richard and I spoke almost at the same time. "Yeah, we need to start chest compressions here."

The therapist quickly stepped over to the side of the stretcher, methodically noted the appropriate landmarks on Bill's breastbone, placed his palms in the correct position, and started depressing his chest. Richard timed his ventilations with the compressions. It was all textbook, perfectly orchestrated and carried off without a hitch. We began giving all the appropriate emergency medications through his IV line, following all the standard protocols. But nothing was working.

"Still no pulse," Lori told us. "Maybe a faint one with the compressions."

The respiratory therapist may have taken this as a challenge, and seemed to intensify his downward thrusts.

Yet there was no improvement in Mr. Thatcher's color. I glanced again at the cardiac monitor. It still showed a regular, tight complex, but now it was slowing—55 to 60 beats a minute.

"Any thoughts?" I asked Richard.

"I don't know, Robert," he answered, looking down at Mr. Thatcher's unresponsive face. "I guess he could have had a huge pulmonary embolus, or a stroke, or a tear in his aorta. But you checked all that out…and anyway, you're not going to save him if something like that's going on."

Save him? In the suddenness of Bill's collapse, my attention had been focused on the immediate things that needed to be done. Your training takes over—airway, breathing, circulation. And then you try to stabilize things as quickly as possible. Now, having done those things, and with the initial adrenaline rush beginning to fade, I had a moment to reflect. But "save him"? I hadn't had time to really consider that. He had been talking to me only moments ago. And though I knew he was in trouble, it had never occurred to me that I might *lose* him.

I immediately rattled off more orders, repeating doses of medications that might, just *might,* help him. And I again ran through a list of possible diagnoses that would fit this circumstance. Nothing new came to mind.

We continued working the code for another twenty minutes. His cardiac monitor showed a slowing electrical activity, and then a widening and more bizarre complex. His heart was dying. There was no response to anything we were doing. And when Richard stopped bagging him, there was no respiratory effort. He was dead.

I didn't want to stop. I didn't want to give up trying to save this man.

"Robert." It was Richard who finally spoke. "We need to stop. He's gone."

Lori Davidson had stepped behind me and lightly put a hand on my shoulder.

"10:58," she spoke quietly, noting the time on her wristwatch, noting the official time of Bill Thatcher's death.

And with that, all activity ceased, and people began to file out of the room.

"I'll see if there are any family members in the waiting room," Lori said, heading for the nurses' station, leaving Richard Sanders and me alone, standing by the stretcher and the lifeless body of Bill Thatcher.

We were quiet for a moment, and then he spoke. "I know how you feel, Robert. It's tough…when you do everything you know to do and it just doesn't work. But it happens. We can't save everyone, and some people are beyond saving. Whatever was going on with this man was going to take his life, no matter what you or any of us did."

I understood what he was saying. But it didn't make this moment any easier.

"I hear you, Richard. But I don't even know what killed him. I still don't have a clue."

I stared down at the body before me and shook my head. "I'm supposed to figure these things out. That's what I do, or—"

"Wait a minute, Robert," Richard interrupted. "Did you hear what I just said? Sometimes, hopefully not very often, we're all going to lose people, no matter what we do. Our patients are going to die. But we're not failing them when we do everything that can be done."

He paused for a moment, thinking. Then he nodded his head and quietly said, "Maybe that's it. Maybe it's all wrapped up in our not being able to handle failure, or what we *think* is failure. We fear it because it threatens our sense of invulnerability, our being able to handle every patient and every circumstance that comes our way. We think we're somehow invincible and all-knowing. But that's a dangerous place to be. That's when we find ourselves in trouble. We even think that life and death is in our hands. It's really not, is it?"

He paused, as if waiting for my response. Then he said, "I'm glad it's that way."

I listened to what he was saying, and I knew he was speaking the truth. Yet, I was having a hard time letting this thing go. Maybe it *was* my pride, but there was a heavy weight on my shoulders, and I couldn't shake it loose.

"Richard," I said, looking him squarely in the eyes and placing my hand on Bill Thatcher's motionless chest. "This man is dead. He walked into my ER, looked me in the face, talked with me—and now he's dead. Why is that not my failure?"

Nothing he could say at this point was going to change my mind. It was a hollow, painful feeling, and it struck to the core of who I thought I was as a doctor. There was no safe place to hide from this.

"You can call it what you want," Richard said. "But to my mind, this isn't your failure. It's tough, it's something terrible—but in the end, it was out of your hands."

He shifted his weight, placing both hands on the rails of the stretcher.

"Let me tell you something that one of my residency attendings told me years ago. He was a thoracic surgeon and did a lot of teaching with the cardiology residents. I'll never forget what he said and when he said it. Another resident and I were riding in an elevator with him, and he started talking about fear and about failure. Apparently one of his thoracic residents had freaked out during a chest case that had gone bad. I think a thoracic aneurysm had burst and the poor guy didn't know what to do. Anyway, the attending started telling us about this, and about how fear and the fear of failure can paralyze you. It can stop you in your tracks, and then you're no use to anyone. 'If you're afraid to fail,' he told us, 'You'd better find another profession.'"

Richard paused. "He was right, you know, Robert. That's especially true for you here in the ER. This is a tough place to work, and if you're going to be good at this, if you're going to help the people who need you, you can't be afraid. But you're not. I've never seen you paralyzed, never even close. You need to think through this, and you'll work it out."

He stepped to the door and turned around. "I'm going to check on our lady in the cardiac room. We *can* do something to help her tonight."

And then he was gone, leaving me alone with Bill Thatcher, and with my thoughts.

A week later I got a copy of the autopsy report. After reading it, I walked to the pathology department, confused by the findings. I wanted to talk with John Dial, the pathologist who had performed the autopsy.

"Yeah, Robert, this was a strange one," he said, scratching his head. "Absolutely nothing. No stroke, heart attack, blot clot, nothing. Your IV lines and endotracheal tube were all in the right places. There was just no obvious cause of death, nothing I could find to explain this. Happens sometimes. Sometimes we just don't know. I guess it was just his time."

I stood there for a moment thinking, trying to put all of this together.

This knowledge was of little consolation. It didn't change anything for me. And it didn't change anything for Bill Thatcher.

I thanked John, and headed back to the ER.

Perhaps God brings us to the end of our resources
so we can discover the vastness of His.

Dr. Neil T. Anderson

9

Idle Hands

Idleness is the devil's workshop.
GERMAN SAYING

Wednesday, 2:35 p.m. "You can tell the guy in 3 he's ready to go," I told Lori, tossing his chart into the discharge basket. He was the only patient in the ER, which was very unusual for this time of day.

Amy Connors, our unit secretary this afternoon, was sitting at the nurses' station, going through the daily log. She was doing some statistical work for Virginia Granger.

I looked across the counter at her, and I guess that's when it happened. It was the evil imp on my shoulder. And I couldn't muster the will to resist him.

For the past month, one of the area grocery-store chains had been advertising a promotional campaign. They were randomly drawing names each week and giving away hundred-dollar certificates for free groceries. Since they were the most frequently shopped grocery stores in town, almost everyone had filled out a form for the drawing. One of Amy's friends, an OR tech, had won two weeks ago, and I knew that Amy herself had filled out more than a dozen of the forms and kept her fingers crossed.

I walked down the hallway to our office as nonchalantly as possible. Alone in the room, I picked up the phone, got an outside line, and called the ER. This was in the days prior to caller ID, so I was anonymous.

The phone rang twice, and then, "This is the Rock Hill ER, Amy Connors speaking. How can I help you?"

I lowered my voice and affected an exaggerated Southern accent.

"Ms. Connors?" I paused and waited for a response.

"Yes, this is the ER. Can I help you? Is this an emergency?"

I searched her voice for some evidence of recognition, but detected none. So far, so good.

"No, no emergency," I told her. "My name is Rob Alexander and I've got some good news for you."

I waited for her response, and again for any sign that she might know it was me.

"Who did you say you were?" she asked, her tone completely unsuspecting.

"I'm Rob Alexander," I repeated, this time with more excitement in my voice. "The manager of the Giant Apple grocery store on Cherry Road. And like I said, I've got some good news for you."

"Uh…what is it, Mr. Alexander?" she asked. From the tone of her voice, I knew she was hooked and on the line. Now I was going to reel her in.

"Well, Ms. Connors, you registered for our grocery giveaway, I believe."

"I sure did, Mr. …What was your name again?" she asked, speaking a little faster now.

"Mr. Alexander. Rob Alexander. And I'm happy to tell you that you've won the one-hundred-dollar giveaway this week."

I waited again. I heard her say something, but it was muffled. She had apparently covered the phone with her hand and was speaking to someone at the nurses' station.

Then—"You say I won?" Still no hint of doubt in her voice, only a growing excitement.

"You most certainly have, Ms. Connors. And congratulations!"

"I—" she began, but I quickly interrupted. It was time to close the deal.

"Now, you understand you have to come by the store within the next thirty minutes in order to claim your prize?" I said.

"What…thirty minutes?" she seemed puzzled.

"Yes, that's the rule, you know. So we'll see you at the Cherry Road store. Just ask for Rob Alexander. And again, congratulations!"

I hung up the phone, not wanting to risk betraying my identity.

A sudden wave of guilt washed over me. Surely she was not taken in. But what if she was? What if she took off for the store? What if she got there and asked for Mr. Alexander and they said, "Who?" But that would be too good. Anyway, Amy was smart, and she wouldn't fall for something like this. Or would she?

The wave of guilt quickly passed.

I walked out of the office and up the hallway. And at once I knew I was in trouble.

Standing behind the nurses' station, hands on her hips, staring at me over the top of her horn-rimmed glasses, was Virginia Granger. I thought for a moment I saw smoke rising from the top of her nurse's cap.

And then I noticed that Amy Connors' chair was empty.

Lori Davidson glanced at me, shook her head, and gave me the palm of her hand in farewell. Then she walked quickly into the medicine room. She knew when to head for cover.

"Dr. Lesslie," Virginia said, her voice threatening. "I need to have a word with you."

How could she know?

"In my office," she added emphatically. Then she turned and walked around the nurses' station.

I followed her like an obedient puppy, my tail between my legs. But how did she know?

"Close the door," she told me, sitting down behind her desk.

I obeyed her without question and stood before her, not being brave or presumptive enough to sit down.

"Now," she began. "Tell me about Amy Connors and her winning the grocery giveaway," she asked.

How…?

"Well, I…she…did she win something?" I responded, not very convincingly.

"Dr. Lesslie, she's on her way there now. I couldn't stop her. She said she had to be there within thirty minutes." She was studying me intently as she said this.

I felt my face flush and knew I was cooked.

"Well…I…that's great! I'm glad she won," I stammered.

"Dr. Lesslie," she intoned, and then just waited.

I studied the tops of my shoes, and then the clock on the wall. Finally I looked at her. My shoulders slumped and my chin fell to my chest.

"Virginia, I…well…" And then I heaved a great sigh.

"She's going to want to kill you when she gets back," she said matter-of-factly. "And I think I just might let her."

I stood there, my hand in the cookie jar. I didn't know what to say. Then I mustered the strength to whimper, "I'll have to tell her I'm sorry, and that I won't do it again."

"Well, that might work, if you get down on your knees and plead for forgiveness. But she's going to be very hot."

"Maybe you could sort of cool her off," I suggested. "You know, maybe…"

"I'll do what I can," she answered, shuffling some papers on her desk. "But you know, Dr. Lesslie, this is not the first time you've done something like this."

She looked at me knowingly, and I knew what she was talking about.

A night in mid-February, 1:15 a.m. Dr. Johnny Gee. Now there was a piece of work. Johnny was an ER doc who lived in Charleston, about a three-hour drive from Rock Hill. He had worked with us for more than ten years and was a favorite of the nursing staff. More importantly, he was a good doctor and took care of his patients. And he was an animal when it came to picking up uncovered shifts. He would frequently make the trip to Rock Hill on a moment's notice, never seemed to need much sleep, and was always pleasant and cheerful. He was genuinely fun to have around.

This particular night, he had worked the 3 p.m. to 11 p.m. shift. He had left a couple of hours ago, heading across town to the Sleep EZ Inn. He was scheduled to relieve me at 7 a.m., and was going to get some rest.

"Now Robert, call me if you need me," he had told me as he was leaving. "You know I usually don't sleep much when I'm up here."

"We'll be fine," I told him. "Go and get some sleep, and I'll see you in the morning."

Jeff walked out of triage and over to the nurses' station. "We've cleared out the waiting room," he announced. "It's completely empty out there."

He walked around the counter and sat down heavily as I handed Lori Davidson the chart of our last patient.

"Here's his prescription," I told her. "And he needs to follow up with the orthopedist sometime next week."

She took the clipboard and headed to room 3 and the waiting patient.

I walked around the counter and sat down beside Jeff.

Amy Connors looked up and said, "Pretty quiet for a Friday night. Maybe it'll stay this way."

For the next hour, it did. Nobody checked in at the reception desk. Nobody called 9-1-1 for EMS transport. It was unusual, but we appreciated the calm.

"Do you think Johnny Gee really caught that marlin he was telling us about?" Jeff asked. He was referring to a fishing tale told earlier in the evening, one that sounded pretty tall to most of us.

"Maybe, but I doubt it," I answered.

"You know good and well he didn't catch any such fish," Amy flatly stated. "He wouldn't know a blue marlin if it bit him on the...well... you know."

"Might have, though," Jeff mused, nodding his head. "You never know with the G-man."

I guess that's when the idea began to form somewhere in the deep recesses of my mind. Maybe in a place that should be kept locked.

"Slide that phone over to me," I asked Amy. "I've got an idea."

As she did so, she saw the glint in my eye and pulled the phone back toward her. "And just what are you up to?"

"You'll see," I answered. "Just give me that phone and listen. Oh, and would you hand me the phone book?"

I looked up the number of the Sleep EZ Inn and called the front desk. The young girl who answered seemed a little skeptical, but when I told her who I was and that it was important that I get in touch with Dr. Gee, she gave me his room number and the number to dial to get his phone. I thanked her and hung up.

"You're not going to—" Amy began.

"Shhh!" Jeff hushed her. "Just listen."

Jeff knew me pretty well, and he had a mischievous streak that might have exceeded my own.

I dialed the number the clerk had given me, leaned back in my chair, and smiled at Amy. Jeff leaned close, trying to get his ear near the receiver. Amy couldn't help herself and did the same.

The phone rang once, twice, three times, and then, "Heeelooo." It was Johnny, and he sounded asleep.

"Is this Mr. Gee?" I asked, trying to disguise my voice. I doubted that in his sleep-drugged state he would be able to recognize me.

"Yes…this is Mr…. Dr. Gee. Who is this?" he asked, still sounding asleep.

"This is Sergeant Pepper with the Rock Hill Police Department," I told him in an official tone. Amy put her hand over her mouth, trying to suppress a chuckle.

"Sergeant Pepp…Who did you say you were?" He was beginning to wake up a little.

"Sergeant Pepper. And I want you to listen to me. First of all, do not leave your room. Do you hear me? Do *not* leave your room, under any circumstance."

There was silence on the other end, and then Johnny muttered, "Don't leave my…What's going on, officer? Is there a problem?"

"As I said, Mr. Gee, do not leave your room. Do you understand?" I repeated.

"Yes, yes…I mean no, I won't leave my room. What's the—"

"There's been a drug bust in the parking lot of the Sleep EZ Inn, right outside your door, room 112." I paused here for effect, letting this sink in.

"A what?" he asked.

"A drug bust. And the suspects stashed some bags of cocaine in a dark blue Volvo station wagon. Has a dented back fender."

"That's my car!" he exclaimed, and Jeff slapped his hands on the counter and squinted his eyes in devilish glee.

"I've got to go out there! There's been some kind of mistake. I don't know any—"

"I told you to stay where you are," I warned him again. "Don't go out in the parking lot. It's dangerous. Just let us handle this. I just wanted to let you know what was going on, in case you heard something. And if you hear gunshots—"

"What! Gunshots! Listen, officer—" he began, now obviously wide awake.

"Stay put!" I ordered him once more and hung up the receiver.

Amy let out a loud whoop and clapped her hands together.

Lori Davidson had been standing on the other side of the counter and just shook her head. "I'm not having any part of this." She walked off down the hallway.

"Now what?" Jeff asked. "What's next?"

I really hadn't thought about that. But it immediately came to my mind what the next call was going to be.

"We'll wait a few minutes," I told them. "And then we'll see."

"Do you think he's out in the parking lot?" Amy asked. "I bet he is. I bet he couldn't help himself and went outside to see what's going on."

"Well, we're just going to have to find out," I told her, and smiled. "You're going to make the next call, and here's what you need to say."

I told her what she should do, and after she stopped laughing, I dialed Johnny Gee's number again. Then I handed the phone to Amy, and Jeff and I leaned close.

This time, the phone only rang once.

"Hello?" There was no sleepiness in his voice now.

"Mr. Gee," Amy said, drawing out his name for effect.

"Yes, who is this?"

"This is…Nancy at the front desk." Amy had struggled for a split second to come up with a bogus name, and I hoped Johnny hadn't picked up on that.

"Nancy? What's the problem?"

He didn't seem to have a clue as to her true identity.

"Well, we've had a complaint. And it's about you," she told him, covering her mouth and squinting hard.

"A complaint? What kind of complaint?" he asked her, incredulous. "What's the problem?"

Amy quickly composed herself and went on, "Mr. Gee, someone called this desk and complained you were out in the parking lot in your underwear, walking around your car."

This was the gamble. We were taking the chance that he had not obeyed Sergeant Pepper and that his curiosity had overcome his good sense. It might be dangerous in the parking lot, but yet…

We were also gambling that he hadn't taken the time to get dressed but had bolted out of bed and out the door. The three of us leaned forward in our chairs, tense and hopeful.

"Well…" he stammered.

It was the pause that told us. He *had* been in the parking lot *and* in his underwear. That was all Amy needed.

"Mr. Gee, I don't know what you were up to or what's going on in your room, but it has to come to a stop. Do you hear me?" she reprimanded him.

"But…you see, there was a drug bust…and Sergeant Pepper…" he tried to explain.

"A drug bust?" she questioned dubiously. "Now listen here, Mr. Gee. You're not the only guest in our motel, and there are people here who need to get some sleep tonight. And it might surprise you to know there are people who don't necessarily care to see you running around in your underwear."

"But you don't—" he tried to inject.

"Don't you interrupt me," Amy hammered him. She was really enjoying this, but it was time to get off the line. I drew my index finger across my throat and she quickly nodded her understanding. Jeff leaned back in his chair and gave her a thumbs-up.

"Now as I said," she told him with finality, "just stay in your room and don't come out again."

Before Johnny could respond, she hung up the receiver, beaming.

"I bet he's going crazy," Amy proudly announced. "He didn't have a clue."

"Didn't sound like it," Jeff agreed.

I didn't say anything but reached for the phone.

"You're not…" Amy asked, a smile breaking across her face.

"Just need to bring this thing to closure," I said, dialing Johnny's number one last time.

"Hello," he answered. He must have been wondering what was coming next.

"Mr. Gee, this is Sergeant Pepper again."

I waited, but there was no response.

"Mr. Gee, I've talked with the front desk."

I waited again, letting this sink in.

"Listen, Sergeant, I—"

"It's okay, Mr. Gee. I understand your concern. But you've got to stay in your room. And just so you know, we found three kilos of cocaine in the back of your car."

"You what!" he exclaimed. "Cocaine!"

"Calm down, Mr. Gee," I told him. "We know you didn't have anything to do with this, but since it was in your car—well, you know. There will have to be an investigation."

"An investigation?" he asked helplessly. "But I didn't—"

"Where will you be tomorrow?" I interrupted. "We need to handle this quickly."

"I'll…I'll be in the ER, at Rock Hill General. I go in at seven o'clock in the morning. You could find me there."

"That'll be fine, Mr. Gee. We'll come over some time in the morning and get this straightened out," I told him. "Now you get some sleep."

That would be doubtful.

I hung up the phone and looked at Amy and Jeff.

"You're a devil," Amy said, shaking her finger at me.

"Me?" I asked innocently. "And what about you…*Nancy*?"

"That was a good one," Jeff pronounced. "A *real* good one."

But we weren't done, not just yet.

7:02 a.m. The ambulance doors opened and Johnny Gee walked into the department. He carried his briefcase in one hand and a cup of coffee in the other. As he approached the nurses' station, he looked at Amy and said, "You won't believe what happened to me last night."

She was sitting at her station, and I was standing in front of her at the counter. Jeff, on cue, walked nonchalantly into the cardiac room.

"That so?" Amy responded, not looking up from her work. It was a good thing he couldn't see her face.

"Yeah," Johnny continued. "There was some kind of a drug bust, or something strange going on in the parking lot at the motel, and I…"

He paused, looking down at the chart I was writing on.

I had barely looked up when he came into the department, immediately resuming my writing on the record in front of me.

"Hmm," I muttered, shaking my head, obviously disturbed by the chart I was dealing with.

The top sheet was a form that we use for our cardiac arrest patients, and I had made some notes on it. At the bottom, in big, bold print, I had written:

"DOA"

As Johnny had walked up beside me, I lifted this sheet, revealing another ER record beneath it. This one was a routine encounter form, documented in Johnny's handwriting. It was the actual record of a thirty-eight-year-old man he had seen the past evening. He had complained of a simple sore throat, and his diagnosis at the bottom of the sheet read "pharyngitis."

I made sure he saw that note and his signature, then I let the "DOA" form fall back over it.

He had seen it. That's when he had stopped in mid-sentence.

"What...?" he said haltingly. "What's that, Robert? Let me take a look."

He stepped closer, putting his briefcase on the floor and his coffee cup on the counter. I slid the chart in front of him.

"This guy...did he...?" he stuttered.

"Came in just a little while ago," I explained to him. "Full arrest. Don't know exactly what happened."

Amy tucked her head down even farther and put her hand on her forehead.

"I saw him last night..." Johnny said, studying first his note and then mine. "He seemed fine, and I..."

I slid the chart away from him and said, "I read your note, and it looks fine. Vital signs were all normal, his complaint was just a sore throat. Nothing suspicious there, Johnny. Don't know what happened. Could have been his heart, a stroke—who knows?"

I picked up the clipboard, turned, and then walked toward the cardiac room.

Without prompting, Johnny followed right behind me.

"Robert, he looked fine when he left last night, and he's only thirty-eight..."

I didn't say anything.

We stepped into the room and Johnny closed the door behind us.

Jeff was standing in the corner, writing on a notepad and arranging some equipment on one of the shelves.

In the middle of the room was the cardiac stretcher. And on that stretcher was the form of a large patient, completely draped with a hospital sheet—all except for the right great toe. It was bare and was sticking out from beneath the cover. And attached to that appendage was a cotton string with a toe-tag, identifying this unfortunate individual.

Johnny stepped over to the stretcher and picked up the tag, hoping there was some mistake. The name on the tag matched that of his patient's name from last evening.

He dropped the tag and stood there, shaking his head.

"I don't know what could have happened," he said. "He seemed fine and everything. Maybe…"

He stepped to the head of the stretcher and reached down, grabbing the top of the sheet.

"Maybe there's been a mistake," he said hopefully. "Maybe this isn't the same guy, just some kinda confusion in the registration office."

Out of the corner of my eye, I saw Jeff stop what he was doing and turn to look at the stretcher.

Johnny had a firm grip on the sheet, and he pulled it back, exposing the head and shoulders of the recently deceased patient.

When the sheet came away, the man on the stretcher came back to life, bolting straight up and letting forth a blood-curdling scream that startled all of us. It was Terry Baker, one of our surgical orderlies. He was a big man, six-foot-four and weighed more than two-hundred-fifty pounds. He had been all too happy to help us with our devious plot.

As he sat up and screamed, he reached out for Johnny Gee, zombie-like. It frightened even me a little.

But it must have terrified Johnny. He jumped straight up in the air and somehow propelled himself backward, landing on top of the defibrillator. It was an amazing feat.

Then he let out a "Yow!" and tried to climb up the wall. And he may very well have wet his pants.

Jeff burst into laughter, as did Terry and I. And then Johnny figured it out. He climbed down off the defibrillator, shaking his head, his face flushed a bright red.

"You guys..." he said, straightening out his clothes.

Terry got off the stretcher and we headed out of the room. Jeff clapped Johnny on his back and said, "You're a good sport, Johnny Gee."

Johnny just shook his head, still trying to recover his composure.

Amy was looking up at us as we approached the counter. "Couldn't see anything," she said. "But I heard it all!"

"You knew about that?" Johnny asked her.

"Why of course," she answered, grinning widely.

"Well, you guys got me pretty good," he said, looking around at each of us.

Then he turned back to Amy. "This just tops off a crazy night. Like I was saying earlier, I had no more gotten to sleep last night when I get this phone call. It was a Sergeant Pepper, Rock Hill PD, and he tells me..."

Amy had startled giggling, and then she looked up in my direction.

"He...he...says..." Johnny faltered. Then he stopped. He studied Amy's face, and he then turned to me. I was trying to maintain some sort of composure, but it was too difficult. I couldn't suppress the beginning of a grin.

Johnny looked back at Amy now. She had covered her face and was shaking with laughter.

"Wha—it was you! You guys called the motel and—!"

Terry, Jeff, and I had all turned away from the nurses' station and were headed off in different directions.

"Hey, wait just a minute!" Johnny Gee called out.

"You guys come back here!"

Just Make It Go Away

Going a little farther,
He fell with his face to the ground and prayed,
"My Father, if it is possible,
may this cup be taken from me."

MATTHEW 26:39

S ometimes we can see the road ahead, and it frightens us. We want to find another path, another journey, another ending. Sometimes, no matter what we do, no matter how hard we struggle, we can't change our destination.

Monday, 11:15 a.m. You wouldn't think a little stumble would be cause for much concern. And for Phyllis Jenkins, third-grade teacher at Piedmont Elementary, it wasn't. But she had noticed it. Just an awkward sort of stagger on level and newly mown grass. But later, back in the classroom, when the other children were busily going about their math work, something else was going on. It must have been a headache, and it must have been bad.

T.J. Blackwood had his head on his desk with his eyes closed. And he was rubbing his temples.

Phyllis walked back to his seat and asked him if he was all right.

T.J. looked up and said, "I'm okay, Ms. Blackwood. I just have a headache, and…and I don't feel so good."

He promptly gagged once and then vomited on the tiled floor.

T.J.'s mother was at the school within twenty minutes, and she brought him straight to the ER. A few minutes after their arrival, his father, Cooper Blackwood, joined us in room 2.

Lori Davidson had seen the Blackwoods out in triage, and she immediately brought them back into the department. Lori's son, Garrett, was in the same Cub Scout pack with T.J., and she and Ruth Blackwood had become friends.

"Ruth, what's the matter with T.J. this morning?" she had asked his anxious mother, leading them across the hallway to room 2.

"I got a call from the school just a little while ago," she began to explain. "T.J. had a headache and then some vomiting, and his teacher was worried. I called Cooper and told him I was on the way to the ER. T.J. was so pale, and his head was hurting, and something just seemed wrong. That's why I brought him here, Lori."

She had said this right before I walked into the room, and in less than a minute Cooper arrived.

"What's the matter with T.J.?" he asked, not addressing any specific person in the room. He stepped across to the side of the stretcher and put his hand on his son's shoulder.

Lori was in the process of checking T.J.'s temperature, and when the electronic thermometer beeped three times, she looked up at me and said, "98.5."

Then she introduced me to Cooper Blackwood. "I just got here myself," I said, "and haven't had a chance to talk with your wife. So why don't we start from the beginning?"

Ruth Blackwood told me what she knew and why the nurse had called her.

"He seemed fine this morning before he went to school. He wasn't complaining of anything at all, no headache." She paused for a moment and then added, "But he did have a headache yesterday morning. Remember, Cooper? Right before we went to church, but then it was gone. I gave him some Tylenol, and it went away."

She looked at Cooper and he nodded.

It seemed like a pretty benign story. I was going to ask a few more questions, when Ruth said, "But Phyllis Jenkins told me something unusual. I don't think it means anything, but it struck her as odd. She said that during recess, she was watching T.J. for some reason and noticed him trip or stumble. He didn't fall, but it seemed like his feet just got jumbled together and he lost his balance. The playground was as smooth as glass, and she didn't see anything he might have tripped over. She just thought it was odd."

"I'm sure that doesn't mean anything," Cooper stated. "Do you think he just has a virus or something, Dr. Lesslie?"

It *did* mean something, and it bothered me.

I asked them about any previous medical problems and any medications. Had he ever been in the hospital? Any surgeries? All of the usual questions. And then I stepped over and sat down beside T.J. on the stretcher.

"T.J., tell me how you feel," I said to him.

"My head hurts, Doctor, right here." And he pointed to both of his temples.

Then I examined him. I listened to his heart and lungs and felt his belly. When I shined the flashlight in his eyes, his pupils seemed sluggish. That's a hard call, since everyone's reflexes are a little different. But there did seem to be a delay there.

I turned the room's light out, sat down on the edge of the stretcher, and examined his eyes with the ophthalmoscope. This instrument allowed me to see the back of his eye, the retina, and to examine the blood vessels there as well as the optic nerve. Instead of clean, well-defined structures, everything seemed a little blurred. And both retinas were pale. These findings indicated papillary edema, swelling in the eyes that is usually caused by an increase in the pressure within the brain.

T.J. was sick, and would soon be in trouble.

I turned the lights back on, got off the stretcher, and stood in the middle of the room.

"We're going to need to do some testing," I told the Blackwoods. "We'll need to—"

"What's wrong?" Ruth interrupted. "What's wrong with T.J.?"

"I don't know yet," I said honestly. "The history we have, and his exam indicate that…Well, we need to find out if something is going on in his brain."

Ruth Blackwood quietly gasped and sat down beside her son, taking him in her arms.

"In his brain?" Cooper repeated, looking over at the stretcher. "That's impossible, Doctor. He's a healthy kid, and this is just some simple…some routine problem. That's all. Just a headache and, heck, he only vomited once."

Lori had stepped over beside Ruth and put an arm around her shoulder. I explained my findings. Then, trying my best not to alarm them, I told them what needed to be done.

"The first thing will be to get an MRI of his head," I said. "And we'll do that right away." I glanced over at Lori, and she immediately got up and headed toward the nurses' station.

"We'll also check some routine blood work and things like that," I continued. "But I want to see what his MRI looks like. That will tell us what we need to do next."

"What do you think this could be?" Ruth asked, beginning to suspect but not yet willing to mention the possibility.

"An MRI?" Cooper questioned. "You must think he has a…" He stopped and looked at his wife.

She sat up a little straighter. "Like Dr. Lesslie said, Cooper, we need to get the MRI and see what that shows. And then we'll go from there."

He just stood there, and quietly nodded his head.

"Let me get some things going and I'll be back in a few minutes," I told them. And then I stepped out of the room and over to where Lori was standing beside Amy Connors.

"Twenty minutes?" Amy spoke into the phone. "Okay, we'll bring him right over."

She hung up the receiver and looked up at me. "MRI will be ready for him. Anything else you need?"

I told her what labs I wanted and then turned back to room 2. Lori grabbed my arm, stopping me.

"What do you think is going on?" she asked. "He looks so pale, and his head is hurting so badly." She looked down at the countertop and stared blankly at it. "You know, Garrett is the same age. They could almost be brothers."

This was the hard part. Most of us had children, and a lot of us had kids T.J.'s age. You don't want anything bad to happen to any child. And when it does, it affects everyone in the department. And you realize all over again that it can happen to any of us.

"Let's see what the MRI tells us, Lori. Just one step at a time. If there's anything to worry about, that's when we'll worry."

She nodded and walked away. And I was worried.

Forty-five minutes later, I got a call from the radiologist who was reading MRIs that day.

"Robert, can you come around to the department and look at these films with me?" Tony Sloan asked.

I stood behind Tony and leaned over his shoulder, peering at the images on the control-room screen. He was using the tip of his pen to point out T.J.'s problem.

"This is the tumor," he stated matter-of-factly. "Pretty good size, and very aggressive, by the looks of it. Probably an astrocytoma."

This was what I had feared. So many times we get scans to rule out potential problems, thinking that the likelihood of finding a significant problem will be small. Usually, we're correct. But something about T.J. didn't feel right, and I had worried we might find something this time. What we found was worse than I had imagined.

"Is he having trouble with his vision?" Tony asked me.

"He's pretty young," I told him. "And he is not really specific about his complaints. Why?"

He shifted the tip of his pen to another area and said, "He's developing some edema here. The tumor seems to be growing pretty fast, and his ventricles are starting to dilate. He's got some increased pressure that's going to have to be dealt with."

I told him of my physical findings, confirming what we were seeing on the scan.

"Have you talked with Freddie Kleitches yet?" he asked me. Freddie was one of the neurosurgeons on staff, and he specialized in pediatric problems.

"No, not yet," I answered. "But I'm going to give him a call when I get back to the ER."

"Well, good luck with this one," he said, pushing a button and bringing up someone else's scan. "That's a tough break."

It *was* tough. It was going to be difficult telling this news to T.J. and his parents.

When I turned the corner at the nurses' station, I saw the Blackwoods standing outside of room 2, talking with Lori. They looked over at me and stopped talking. Lori searched my face and then turned and walked over to the medication room.

"What did the MRI show?" Cooper asked as I approached them. "Is T.J. okay?"

His wife shushed him, glancing back into the room at her son, and then pulling Cooper closer to the nurses' station.

"Well, what did it show?" he repeated, a little more quietly.

I stood there with my hands in my pockets and took a deep breath. Then I told them the results of the MRI. I didn't mince words, but laid out the facts as I saw them.

"The next step," I told them, "will be to get one of our neurosurgeons to take a look at T.J. And we need to do that right away."

They just stood there and stared at me. Then Ruth turned to her husband and almost collapsed against him.

Cooper held her tightly. He looked at me. "Are you sure about this?"

I simply nodded my head, not knowing what else to say.

He glanced down at the floor, silent. When he looked back up, there were tears in his eyes and he was trembling. Ruth took his hand and took a deep breath. Then together they turned toward room 2.

I followed a few steps behind them and stopped at the entrance to the room. I watched as they walked over to the stretcher and sat down, one on each side of their son.

T.J. looked up at Ruth and asked, "Momma, what's wrong with me?"

She hesitated for just a moment, and he said, "Can we still go to Carowinds this Saturday?"

Saturday, 2:30 p.m. I looked up as Jeff Ryan led Curtis Mayes through the triage entrance. Curtis was one of the general surgeons on our staff. He smiled sheepishly at me, and then held up a bandaged and bloody left hand.

"What have you done to yourself?" I asked him, putting a chart down on the counter and stepping over to him.

"Just a little table-saw accident," he told me. He was sweating and appeared a little pale. Jeff was standing behind him and he shook his head.

"Let's get you back to minor trauma," I told him, stepping out of their way. "I'll be back there in just a minute."

"Okay, Robert," he said. "But it's nothing major."

They turned and headed down the hallway.

A few minutes later, I entered the room and found Jeff carefully removing the kitchen towel from Curtis's hand. One quick glance told me that this indeed *was* something major. His thumb was gone. There was a ragged and clotted stump where it should have been. It was amputated all the way back to the first joint.

He was staring at his hand and then he sighed. He looked up as I walked over to his stretcher.

"What in the world happened?" I asked him, pulling up a rolling stool and sitting down beside him.

"I was working in the shop," he began to explain. "Building a table out of knotty alder. "And as I was making a cut, I guess I didn't read the grain of the wood. Something grabbed the blade and pulled my thumb into it, and before I could do anything…Well, here it is." He held the stump up for me to see.

Curtis was an experienced and talented woodworker. I had seen some of the beautiful furniture he had made, and I frequently reminded him that this was a dangerous hobby. Saws and lathes were no friends of flesh and bone.

I looked down at his hand. There was exposed bone, and from what I could see, this was really a mess.

"How much pain are you having?" I asked him, glancing over at Jeff. He turned and reached behind him for an IV setup and fluids.

"You know, it really doesn't hurt too much," Curtis said. "But it looks like it should, doesn't it?"

It looked like it should be killing him.

"We're going to start a line and give you something for pain," I told him. "Then we'll numb up that thumb…that area, and see what we've got."

"There's not going to be much to work with," he volunteered. "It's pretty chewed up. I brought the rest of it in, just in case. But I'm not too hopeful." He reached into his pants pocket and pulled out a zip-lock baggie filled with ice. On top of the ice was a mangled piece of flesh. I took the bag and inspected what was left of his thumb.

"We'll hold on to this, just in case," I told him, knowing there was no chance of re-implanting this lost digit.

"Robert, I know better." He gave a wry grin.

We got his IV going and gave him something for pain. An X-ray demonstrated the splintered end of his first metacarpal. I held the film up in front of the overhead light, allowing him to see.

"What a mess," he sighed. "Who's on for ortho?"

I told him and explained I had already given him a call. The OR crew had been called in and would be ready in about an hour.

"Hmm…" he muttered. "Forty percent, isn't that right?"

I nodded in understanding, and then he added, "The thumb provides forty percent of the function of the hand. Good thing I'm right-handed."

Then he was silent. And I knew what he was thinking. He made his living with his brain, but also with his hands. I did too. And I wondered how I would deal with a devastating injury like this if it happened to me. I caught myself putting my hands in my pockets.

Curtis was one of the best surgeons on our staff, known for his technical skills and abilities. He was also known for his relaxed and friendly bedside manner and for his genuine compassion. When patients in the ER were informed they would need to see a surgeon, most of them wanted to know if Curtis Mayes was available.

That was going to change. This was a career-changing and life-changing event.

"It happened so fast, Robert," he said, interrupting my thoughts. "You and I both know about accidents, and how quickly they happen. We see it every day. It's just that—well, it's true. If only…" He paused, and there was obvious regret in his voice, and a quiet sadness. But his silence was brief, and he said, almost cheerfully, "Anyway, it's done, and we just need to get it taken care of."

I had sat back down on the stool when Maude Weston walked into the room. She was the OR supervisor and had come in to help with Curtis's surgery. Maude was a big woman—gruff and not known for being subtle.

She stepped over and looked down at his thumb. Jeff was getting ready to wrap it loosely in some gauze, but it was still exposed.

Maude adjusted her glasses, leaning over. "Hmm-hmm," she murmured. "You really did a number here, Dr. Mayes."

Then she stood up and patted him on his shoulder. "You know, we all have our crosses to bear. I guess this will be yours." I grimaced, wondering what she could be thinking.

She turned and walked out of the room. Jeff began wrapping the hand.

Curtis was smiling when he looked over at me. Then he said, "You know, Robert, I was about to say something to Maude, but I changed my mind. Maybe one day I will, when the time is right."

I wondered what he might have said. I had never seen him angry or heard him speak harshly to anyone. What would he have told her?

"She's wrong about that, you know," he said quietly.

"I'm sorry about that, Curtis," I said, apologizing for Maude. "Some people just don't think before they—"

"No, I mean about this being my cross to bear," he interrupted. "Now don't get me wrong, Robert. I'm not happy about this." He gestured with his head toward his wounded hand. "This is going to drastically change my life, or at least how I make a living. But Maude is referring to what Jesus said about taking up your cross daily and following him. The key word there is 'daily.' And the cross is all about dying, and about death. Jesus isn't telling me I'll have to deal with my thumb every day for the rest of my life and feel sorry for myself. He's telling me I have to *die* each day. I have to put my selfish ways to death each and every morning if I'm going to follow him. Hard stuff, isn't it? It makes this thumb seem pretty insignificant."

I just listened. Jeff was listening as well, and had stopped wrapping the gauze around Dr. Mayes's hand. When Curtis fell silent, Jeff quickly finished his bandaging and asked him if he needed anything else.

"No, I'm fine, Jeff. Thanks for all of your help."

Then he leaned back against the head of the stretcher and crossed his legs.

"You know, Robert," he said, his voice and face suddenly very serious. "There's only one real problem here."

"What's that?" I asked him, listening carefully.

"I guess now I'll need to take off one shoe when I have to count to ten."

Amazing.

Saturday 11:45 p.m. "Hold steady, Mr. Jones. We're almost finished."

I was putting the last stitch in Mr. Jones's lacerated eyebrow. He was starting to move his head around, and it was difficult to find the end of the piece of suture. He had met the business end of a pool stick an hour or so ago and had a pretty big gash over his left eye.

He mumbled something, and I was once again buffeted by his alcohol-saturated breath. But at last he became still, and I was able to tie his last suture in place.

"Bad accident out on Highway 5," Jeff Ryan spoke over my shoulder. He had just walked into minor trauma and was preparing to help Mr. Jones get his wound bandaged and on his way. "Two units are working it now."

"What's coming this way?" I asked him.

"I don't think anything," he answered, his voice becoming quieter. "Three teenagers are being flown out to the trauma center, and one is dead at the scene."

I stood up from my stool and stretched. My low back was beginning to ache, and I needed to move around.

"Any idea what happened?" I asked him.

"Head-on, is what one of the paramedics reported. From the looks of the cars, he didn't know how anybody survived."

I walked up the hallway, leaving Jeff to take care of Mr. Jones.

At the nurses' station, Amy Connor repeated this information, adding that the coroner had called and would be meeting the parents of the deceased teenager in the morgue. They would have to identify their dead child.

"I wonder if it's anybody we know," she mused, not looking up from her logbook.

I didn't want to think about that. A lot of my friends had teenage children.

Forty-five minutes later, the coroner walked through the ambulance entrance.

"Evenin', Robert," he called out to me.

"Hello, Ed," I answered, looking up and then extending my hand.

Ed Ballard had been elected the county coroner thirty years running. He knew his business, and he knew just about everybody in the county.

"This is a real tough one," he told me. "Terrible accident. Those three kids who were sent to Charlotte probably won't make it. And if they do...well, they're in bad shape." He shook his head and stared at the floor. Then he looked up at me and said, "It never gets any easier. Thirty-odd years, and it never gets any easier."

I just stood there and nodded in agreement. He was a sensitive man, but the way he was acting was a little unusual for him. He had been dealing with this kind of thing for a long time. Something else must be going on.

"You might know the parents of this girl, Bob and Sandra Caldwell," he said, breaking the silence. "Her folks are friends of ours, and we all go to the same church. Her name's Trish. Beautiful girl too. And a really good basketball player. In fact, I think she was offered a scholarship to play ball at Erskine. Isn't that where you went to school?"

I told him I had, and that I couldn't place the Caldwells.

"You'd know them if you saw them. But don't worry about that tonight. Much as I don't want to, I'll meet them at the front of the hospital and take them back to the morgue by myself."

He took a deep breath and stood up straight. "Guess I'd better head over there now. They're on their way, and I don't want them waiting by themselves. See you later."

I didn't envy him his task. Having to deal with the parents of a dead child is heartbreaking. You don't know what to say or how to say it. And to walk them back to the morgue in order for them to identify their child...

The morgue was located in the back of the hospital, away from the public's eyes and ears. And it was a cold, sterile, depressing place, even in the middle of the day. At night, like this was, it was even more depressing, if that's possible.

I tried once more to place the Caldwells in my mind, but couldn't. Then I picked up the chart of the next patient to be seen and headed for the ortho room.

Ten minutes later, after examining the patient in ortho, I stepped out into the hallway and almost ran into Ed Ballard.

"Been waiting on you, Robert," he said, looking down at my chest. Then he looked to his right. I followed his glance.

Standing behind him, with their arms around each other and their eyes reddened with fresh tears, were a man and woman. With a sinking feeling, I knew it must be the Caldwells. And I did recognize them. Our children had played in the same church basketball league over the years, and I had met them on those and other occasions.

"Robert," Ed spoke, "the Caldwells here asked if you were on duty tonight, and if you would…if you'd be willing to walk around with us to the…morgue."

Only now did Ed look up into my eyes. He knew this was a difficult thing to ask, but he knew it must be important to the Caldwells or he wouldn't be standing in front of me.

"Of course," I answered, stepping around Ed and shaking Bob's hand.

"Hi, Bob, Sandra," I quietly said to them.

It was an awkward moment, but Ed quickly put his hand on Sandra's shoulder and said, "Let's go this way. Just follow me."

Then he headed to the back corridor and turned right.

They followed him, Bob's arm around his wife's shoulder. And as I walked a few steps behind, I wondered what the proper order should be. Should I be walking beside them? Or between them? And then I wondered why I was asking myself that question. It made no sense. But then none of this made any sense. This shouldn't be happening.

As if reading my thoughts, Bob Caldwell stopped in the hallway, removed his arm from his wife's shoulder, turned to me, and said, "Robert, here—walk with us."

I stepped between them, and once again we started down the hall.

"Thanks for being willing to come with us to…to…" he stammered and then fell silent.

"That's okay," I answered, searching for the right words to say here. "I'm just sorry—"

Bob interrupted without seeming to hear me. "I'm not sure what we're supposed to do. The coroner said we need to identify the…body…"

"Our daughter," Sandra injected. "We need to identify our daughter."

She spoke as if in another place, with no emotion in her voice. These were just words to her.

"Do you think there could be a mistake?" Bob whispered to me, a desperate hope in his voice and eyes.

Ed Ballard had heard the question. He turned to me and shook his head. Then he once again silently led our group past the back elevators and into a dimly lit corridor.

This was a part of the hospital I seldom frequented. Only members of the maintenance department and those who stored supplies and equipment spent much time here. And the pathologists. The hospital lab was in the front of the building, but the morgue was back here. When they needed to perform an autopsy, this was where it was done. They didn't like this walk any better than the rest of us.

The hallway became more crowded with boxes of medical supplies and storage carts. At one point we had to walk single-file to make our way past a sad and run-down portable X-ray machine. I glanced ahead, looking for the sign on the wall that read "Morgue." It seemed a long way still, and I was happy for that. But then, too quickly, we were there.

Ed stopped in front of the morgue door and turned to the Caldwells.

"I know this is not going to be easy," he said to them, his voice low and calm. "But it's something I'm afraid I have to ask you to do. And we'll only be here a minute. I don't want you to stay down here. There'll be time later to...to spend with your daughter."

I knew what Ed was trying to say, but somehow that struck me as odd. That time had passed. It was gone.

The Caldwells were standing in front of me, and they slumped a little as Ed said this. Then he reached to the right of the door and flipped some switches. A bright and greenish light appeared behind the door, filtering through the cracks on the sides and at the bottom.

He reached to the left and pushed three digits on a small numerical pad on the wall. There was a loud mechanical click as the door's locking mechanism was released.

Bob and Sandra flinched as they heard this sound. They moved closer to each other.

Ed grasped the door handle. He paused and just stared at it. Then he turned to the Caldwells. "We'll only be a minute."

The door opened, and we all stepped into the room. It was much brighter than the hallway, and Sandra reflexively reached up to shield her eyes. It was cold, and I could detect the faint smell of formaldehyde. And there was a peculiar mixture of other odors, some of which I could identify, and others which I didn't want to.

The room itself was small, maybe only twelve by twelve. Two of the walls were entirely composed of stainless-steel doors. These were refrigerator units, built into the walls and stacked one on top of another length-wise, from floor to ceiling. There were eight of them, and each was numbered.

Ed Ballard reached into his pocket and took out a small piece of paper. He glanced at it and then at one of the refrigerator units. Then he put the paper back in his pocket and stepped over to the wall in front of him. He reached out, and with both hands, grasped the long handle of unit 6.

He turned and looked at the couple standing in the middle of the room.

"Mr. Caldwell, Mrs. Caldwell," he said.

They put their arms around each other and just stood there, silent, not moving. Maybe if they waited long enough, this would all go away.

Ed was patient, and he just looked at them. Then he glanced at me. I had been watching all of this, trying to somehow remove myself from this scene, trying to shield myself from this pain. But Ed's glance brought me back to the moment. I reached out and lightly tapped Bob Caldwell on his shoulder.

He began to slowly nod his head. Together the couple stepped toward the wall. Ed's hands tightened on the handle and he pulled hard, sliding the door open and pulling the unit out of the wall. It contained a metal tray mounted on rollers, and the whole thing glided smoothly out into the room. There was a faint sound of metal moving on metal. Then it stopped. And the room was deafeningly silent.

On the tray was the body of a woman, completely covered with a hospital sheet. Ed stepped around to the head of the tray and reached out, taking hold of the end of the sheet. He looked over at the Caldwells, who had now stepped beside the tray, looking down into it.

"I just need to know if this is…if this is Trish," he said softly.

Then he gently raised the sheet, revealing the face of this young woman.

Sandra gasped and then pressed her face against her husband's chest. Her knees began to buckle, and Bob grabbed her tightly, pulling her close to him. Then he closed his eyes. After what seemed an eternity, he slowly began to nod his head.

"Okay," Ed said, with a sadness and weariness that echoed coldly in this terrible place.

He once more grabbed the handles of the refrigerator and pushed the tray back into the wall. There was a faint clicking as the door sealed tightly.

And then there was nothing—only the cold of the room, the bright and greenish lights, and the quiet sobbing.

> *Do not fear, for I am with you;*
> *do not be dismayed, for I am your God.*
> *I will strengthen you and help you;*
> *I will uphold you with my righteous right hand.*
>
> Isaiah 41:10

Stand by Me

If one falls down,
his friend can help him up.
But pity the man who falls
and has no one to help him up!

ECCLESIASTES 4:10

Friday, 6:45 a.m. I got in the car, turned on the ignition, and the radio immediately came on. I must have forgotten to turn it off last night when I got home.

As I pulled out of the driveway and headed for the hospital, a familiar and comfortable bass riff filled the car and surrounded me.

Bum, ch-bum, bum bum bum, ch-bum, bum bum bum, ch-bum…

It was the beginning lines of "Stand by Me." Like most of us, I knew the lyrics, but for some reason this morning, I listened intently and thought about the meaning of the song.

And I began to think about the people I've leaned on for help, those who have "stood by me." Of course the list would include my family, especially my wife. And most recently, my grown children. Through the years, there have been a handful of really close friends—one in particular—and my business partner. Some have stood by me when they probably shouldn't have. But they did.

The list doesn't seem very long. And maybe it's not supposed to be. But I have always been grateful for these people, and for just knowing they were there.

The song ended as I was stopped under a red light. I turned the radio off and began to think about the people who had stood by me during my medical training and my years of practice. I thought of those who had helped me in difficult situations, and especially those who stood out as teachers of medicine. I struggled for a moment because that's a much shorter list. But as the light turned green, I thought of Bob Scoffield.

Sunday 10:45 p.m. Polly Manchester had tripped on a carpet in her living room and fallen. Her eighty-year-old bones couldn't withstand the force of the fall and she had broken her right wrist. After I gave her this news, I walked back up to the nurses' station and asked Amy Connors to get in touch with the orthopedist on call.

"It's Bob Scoffield," she told me. "I'll page him."

Good. Polly's fracture was badly angulated and needed to be reduced tonight. Bob never seemed to mind coming in, and I was glad he was on call. And then I remembered. So I walked back over to the X-ray view box and put her films back in their folder.

Less than five minutes later, Bob Scoffield walked down the hallway and over to the nurses' station, where I was standing.

"How did you get here so fast?" I asked him.

"I was just around the corner in the surgical lounge. When I'm on call on the weekends, I sometimes just hang around the hospital. It's easier than driving back and forth. You guys keep me pretty busy," he added, smiling.

I slid Polly Manchester's chart over to him.

"She's back in ortho," I told him. "Nice lady. She thinks you might have fixed her hip seven or eight years ago."

He glanced down at the name on the chart. "I know Polly. And she's right about her hip. She's been doing great. But you said she fell and fractured her wrist tonight?"

"Yeah," I responded. I was about to say something else but I stopped. I knew the routine.

"Well, let's go take a look at her," Bob said, picking up the chart and heading down the hall.

I followed him, remembering the first time I had asked him to see a patient in the ER. When I had handed him the X-rays of that patient, he had put them down on the countertop. "Let's go look at the patient first, Robert. The X-ray should be used to confirm our diagnosis, not necessarily make it."

That night he had carefully questioned the patient about the mechanism of injury, and then even more carefully examined him. As we had walked up the hallway, he told me what the X-rays would show. He was right. And he was right every time we went through this exercise. I had started doing this myself, trying to anticipate what the X-rays were going to show me, trying to make a correct diagnosis without seeing the films on the view box. I was getting better at it, but was still far removed from Bob's uncanny accuracy.

He had taught me most of the orthopedics I knew, especially most of the practical orthopedics. And he had done it in a subtle, nonthreatening fashion. He had a real passion for the care of his patients, and for some reason, he had an interest in my development as a physician. Looking back now, years later, I am grateful for that interest and for his teaching.

We walked into ortho and Bob stepped over to Polly Manchester, gently taking hold of her good hand.

"Polly, what in the world have you done tonight?" he teased her.

"Now Dr. Scoffield, don't you go giving me a hard time," she fired back.

He then asked her what had happened and how. And then he examined her swollen and tender wrist.

"Polly, we're going to take a look at those X-rays and then we'll get you taken care of. It will only be a minute."

As we walked back to the nurses' station he told me what kind of injury she had and what the X-rays would show.

He was right, of course. I had already seen her X-rays, and they confirmed his diagnosis.

As we were looking at the films, he said, "I saw Jack the other day in the dining room. He said he's spending some time with you in the ER this summer."

"Yes, he's been here a good bit," I answered. "And it's been a lot of fun. I think he's seeing some things he didn't expect to see."

"I bet," Bob mused. "Hasn't had any more pugilistic mishaps, has he?"

He was referring to something that had occurred almost ten years earlier. I just shook my head, still not believing it had happened.

"Robert, I'm on my way to the ER. With Jack."

It was my wife, Barbara, and she didn't sound very happy.

"What's the matter?" I asked her.

"It's not an emergency. I'll tell you when we get there."

She hung up the phone without saying anything else. I knew that tone of voice, and I knew she was mad about something.

Twenty minutes later, she was walking through the ambulance entrance, our twelve-year-old son in tow. I was right. She wasn't very happy.

Jack was holding his right hand and kept his eyes glued to the floor.

"Let's go over to room 1," I told them. "Nobody's in there."

The three of us walked over to the treatment room and I instructed Jack to jump up on the stretcher. He was still holding his right hand, which seemed to be pretty uncomfortable.

I was about to ask him what had happened, when Barbara gave me the whole story.

Jack was spending the week at Camp Cherokee, a campground located about forty-five minutes away. All of our children had been going there each summer for a lot of years. It seems that at some point during the previous evening, Jack had gotten into an argument with one of his fellow campers. One thing led to another, and punches were exchanged. Jack thought he had gotten the better end of it, or so it had seemed at the time.

When he had awakened this morning, however, his right hand was swollen and bruised, and very painful. When I began to examine it, I knew he had broken at least one bone, maybe more. I was worried about the other boy's face, and I asked Jack how he had hurt his hand.

"That guy really ticked me off, and I just kept punching the back of his head," he explained.

Surprised by this, I asked, "You were punching what?"

"The back of his—" Suddenly he stopped and looked down at his hand. "I guess it wasn't very smart."

"The whole thing wasn't very smart," Barbara interjected, obviously disappointed in Jack's behavior.

"I know it was stupid," he said. "I told him this morning I was sorry. And I told the camp director it wouldn't happen again. He says I can go back to camp if it's alright with you and Momma."

He looked over at his mother but didn't find any sympathy there.

I looked at Barbara, trying to get a read on her thoughts. She wasn't buying it. "The camp director had a long talk with both boys," she said. "And he says Jack can come back if it's okay with us."

"I really want to go back," Jack pleaded.

"Well, son, I think you've broken a bone in this hand, and you're going to be in a cast. That's going to make things a little difficult, don't you think?"

"There's only two more days left till we come home anyway," he begged. "Please, Dad, I can do it!"

Having a cast on his right hand would be awkward, but he was determined.

"We'll get an X-ray and see how bad it is. Then we'll talk," I told him.

The X-rays of Jack's hand revealed a mid-shaft fracture of his fifth metacarpal. It was called a "boxer's fracture," but that was a misnomer. Boxers strike with the knuckles of the long and ring fingers, not the little finger. This was more of a "slugger's fracture." And that certainly fit Jack's punching capabilities.

The three of us stood looking at the X-rays. I called out to Amy Connors, "Amy, could you get whoever's on for ortho on the phone? I need to talk with them."

It was Bob Scoffield. When he called, I explained the problem. He just chuckled and said he would be over in a few minutes.

We moved Jack to the ortho room, and one of the nurses prepared the casting material Bob was going to need. When he arrived, he walked across the room, gave Barbara a hug, and patted Jack on his shoulder.

"Well, Jack, I understand you've had a little misadventure here," he said, smiling. Jack repeated the story and then held up his injured right hand. Bob gently palpated the wounded extremity. Then he looked Jack in the eye.

"You've broken your hand, right here near the knuckle of the little finger." He pressed lightly on the area and Jack squirmed on the stretcher, but didn't make a sound.

"We may need to reduce the angle of the fracture and then put you in a hard cast."

Then Jack asked him about going back to Camp Cherokee. Bob looked first at Barbara and then at me. I shrugged, leaving the medical decision up to him.

Then he looked back at Jack and very seriously said, "We want to be sure your hand heals correctly, and it will if you take care of it. But having your right hand in a cast isn't going to be easy, even if you were at home and your mom was taking care of you. Now being at camp—"

"I can do it," Jack interrupted. "I can take care of it."

While Bob put the cast on Jack's hand, they continued to negotiate. When the cast was in place and hardening, Bob asked him once more, "Do you think you can handle it now?"

Jack circled his right hand in the air and said, "Sure, no sweat."

It was agreed. Jack was going to behave himself, take care of his new cast, and go back to camp. Bob was washing the plaster off his hands and was standing by the sink, when Jack said, "Dr. Scoffield?"

His voice was hesitant, almost timid. I glanced over at him, thinking this a little unusual when instead he should be happy with the way things had turned out. But something was troubling him. He was staring at the floor and shaking his head.

Later, I learned he had been wrestling with feelings of shame and embarrassment and fear. Mainly fear. And when he could bear it no longer, he had mustered the courage to call out to Dr. Scoffield.

Bob was drying his hands, and he turned around.

"Yes, Jack, what is it?"

Jack took a deep breath, jumped down from the stretcher, and walked over to where Bob stood.

He didn't say anything for a moment, just stood there. Then quietly he said, "What about *this* one? It really hurts too."

He raised his other hand and extended it toward Bob. It was swollen and bruised as well, right over the knuckle of the little finger. And while not as bad as his right hand, it too was obviously broken.

I looked over at his mother. Steam was coming out of her ears, and her eyes were big as saucers.

Sheepishly Jack said, "I guess I was punching his head with both hands."

I stood in front of the view box, shaking my head and glad to be on the other side of those teenage years. Bob turned to me, smiling as well, and said, "Yep, he was one tough kid. And I bet he was the first camper to go to Cherokee with both hands in casts."

"And the only one," I added.

3:15 a.m.—Special Care Nursery. I studied the X-ray on the view box. It was a small film, and it revealed the entire body of a three-pound two-week-old. It was what I had thought—and feared. This little girl had been born prematurely and with underdeveloped lungs. She had been on a ventilator since a few hours after she was born and had seemed to be getting stronger. Suddenly, about thirty minutes ago, that had changed. She was failing. Her color had turned dusky, and her blood gases were awful. Something bad had happened, and I needed to find out what that was and fix it.

The special-care nursery had sixteen beds, or more exactly, incubators. Most were occupied. Most of the children were stable and improving. It had been a quiet night, up until this little girl went south.

I was finishing up the first year of a pediatric residency and was alone in the unit. The third-year resident was upstairs in the call room, asleep. I was probably going to have to give her a call. But the thought didn't give me much reassurance. She was great in the pediatric clinic, but when it came to dealing with emergencies like this, she would rather be somewhere else.

I glanced over at Carolyn, the tiny girl in the incubator, making sure that nothing had changed in the past minute or so. Taped to her nose was the endotracheal tube that connected her to the ventilator beside her. It was this ventilator, with its rhythmical wheezing and sucking, that was keeping her alive.

As if she were directing some unseen and unheard orchestra, her minute and almost transparent hands were purposelessly floating in space above her.

I looked back at the X-ray. Once again I saw her collapsed lung. The entire left side of her chest was black, indicating that her lung had somehow punctured and contracted into a useless mass of tissue, much as a burst balloon would do.

It had to be re-inflated or she was going to die. In an adult or older child, this was not a difficult procedure. It was a matter of inserting a large tube between two ribs and connecting the tube to a suction device. With Carolyn, it would be much more difficult. Her entire chest was the size of a golf ball, and her ribs were no bigger around than a pencil lead.

I took a deep breath and was about to ask one of the nurses to get a chest-tube tray ready. But before I could say anything, a voice at my shoulder said, "Whatcha got, Robert?"

It was Bill Bowman. I knew it without turning around, and as I recognized his voice, I felt immediate relief.

Bill was the only pediatric surgeon on our staff. He was in his mid-forties and a favorite of the pediatric resident staff. In fact, he was a favorite of the entire resident staff in the hospital. Unlike a few of our surgical types, he was not in the least bit pretentious. He treated us almost as peers or even friends. Maybe that's why we always sought him out when we needed help.

He had an amazing knack, that of seeming to always know when you were getting into trouble. Or at least when you and your patient were headed to some difficult moment. And then somehow he would be there, standing behind you, ready to help. I know that was true for me. It had happened over and over again. It was uncanny, but here he was once more.

I turned to face him. "Bill, I've got this two-week old, and—well—you see her X-ray."

He stepped a little closer to the view box and adjusted his bifocals. "Yep, I see what's going on," he said, nodding his head. "She's going to need a chest tube, isn't she?"

He didn't wait for a response but called out to one of the nurses standing nearby. "We'll need a chest-tube tray and portable X-ray on the way."

Then he turned to me and said, "How many of these have you done, Robert? How many in a child this small?"

"Two, maybe three," I told him. Fortunately, we didn't have to do many of these.

"Good," he told me. "This will be your fourth."

For some reason, I had thought he might want to do this procedure. While I was still a little nervous, I was glad to hear him say this.

"Get scrubbed up and we'll get going," he added.

Bill Bowman stood at my right shoulder the entire time, not saying a word until I had made a small incision in Carolyn's chest wall and was about to insert a tiny clear tube through the opening.

"Use your blunt hemostats," he told me. "Don't use the blade anymore. You might damage the nerve or blood vessels. The hemostat is safer."

He was right, of course. I always used a hemostat at this part of the procedure with an adult. I hadn't been thinking.

"Thanks, Bill," I said over my shoulder.

"I knew you were going to use it. I was just reminding you." I could hear the smile in his voice.

Carolyn did well with the chest tube in place. Her color improved and the amount of oxygen in her blood became normal. That was the last crisis for her. Four months later she would be going home.

After we had finished and the tube was taped in place, I reached for a nearby phone and called my sleeping third-year resident. She needed to know what was going on.

I gave her my report, waited for a confirmatory grunt, and hung up the receiver. Then I turned around. Bill Bowman was gone.

Saturday afternoon, two years later. It was a busy shift in the ER. A steady rain had been falling for more than a day, and we were taking care of a bunch of auto accidents. People in the South can't drive on slick roads. And you'd better gird your loins if there was any snow on the ground. Sometimes just the forecast of snow was enough to do it.

Some of these were just routine fender benders, but some were serious. We had already sent four badly injured patients to the operating room.

We were working our way through the most recent accident victims, when the EMS radio demanded our attention.

"General, this is Medic 2," one of the paramedics on board informed us.

The charge nurse was standing near the radio and she picked up the receiver. "Go ahead, Medic 2, this is the General."

I was finishing up a chart and heard this transmission. *Here we go again—another auto accident. Will it ever stop raining?*

It wasn't the rain.

"General, we've got an eight-year-old girl—respiratory arrest."

Everyone nearby stopped what they were doing and stared at the EMS radio, waiting.

"We're still at the scene," the paramedic continued, speaking excitedly and a little out of breath. "About five minutes away. It's a birthday party at a private residence, and this girl…she was eatin' some candy and aspirated it. When we got here, her parents were doing CPR and they had tried the Heimlich, but nothing was working."

There was the sound of several people talking excitedly in the background. The paramedic said something unintelligible to them. Then he was back on the radio.

"We repeated the Heimlich…but nothing. Tried to fish out the candy but…I…I think I just pushed it further down her windpipe. She's still got a pulse of about 100 and we're trying to bag her. But we're not moving much air. Anything further?"

The charge nurse glanced up at me. I shook my head and said, "Tell him to get here as fast as they can."

She repeated this to the paramedic.

"Loading right now. Be there in four to five." And the radio went silent.

I turned again to the nurse and said, "We need to get trauma set up for an emergency trach. And find out who's on call for surgery and get them down here."

This was a long time to be without oxygen, but maybe they had been able to get some air past the piece of candy. The fact that she still had a good pulse was encouraging. But we wouldn't have much time. She needed her airway opened, and it sounded like the only way to do this was an emergency tracheotomy. I would need to make an incision just below her Adam's apple and insert a tube into her trachea, hopefully below the lodged piece of candy. If the candy was below that, if it had been sucked or pushed even further down…

I wasn't going to think about that just yet. My pulse had already quickened as I hastily walked toward trauma. The charge nurse was ahead of me. She would be opening the tracheotomy tray and getting it ready. This would be a straightforward procedure and I knew what I needed to do—but I had only helped in three of these. And those had been different. Each of those cases had been adults, and each had involved major blunt trauma to the face and chest. One I had done myself, with a surgeon standing at my elbow. It was another one of those things we just didn't do very often.

"Any word from the surgery resident?" I spoke into the intercom on the wall by the door.

"He's scrubbed in on an appendectomy," the secretary responded. "Says he'll be down in twenty minutes."

That would be too late.

I heard the ambulance doors open and a stretcher being rapidly wheeled down the hallway. I took a deep breath, and there she was.

The paramedic and his partner quickly transferred her to our trauma stretcher.

"Didn't have time for an IV," he said, his face covered with sweat. "Still not moving much air, but she's got a good pulse."

I was quickly examining the young girl as he said this. Her color was bad, but as I listened to her chest while the paramedic bagged her, I could hear the faintest of breath sounds. Or maybe I was imagining it. Her chest wasn't moving with his attempts.

Then I took a look at her airway with a laryngoscope—and there it was. I could see a shiny, red, wet piece of candy just at her vocal cords. It was too far down to be able to grab with any instrument. Her color had gotten even worse in the past minute. She would need a trach, and right now.

After I positioned her head and neck, the nurse handed me a pair of sterile gloves and I hurriedly put them on. Then I reached for some sterile gauze, soaked it in Betadine, and prepped the front of her neck. With the long finger of my left hand locating the notch just above her sternum, I held out my right hand for the scalpel.

As the nurse placed the blade in my hand, I heard a voice behind me.

"Whatcha got, Robert?"

It was Bill Bowman. How had he gotten here? How had he known what was going on?

Before I could answer, he said, "Just a little higher, toward her head. About a centimeter."

I followed his instructions, adjusting the position of the scalpel.

"Good, that's fine," he calmly said. "Go ahead."

I made a quick and steady incision and then reached for a blunt instrument to separate the tissues covering her trachea.

"There, that's where you want to go," he said, indicating the membrane between two cartilage rings.

And we were done. The trach tube slipped easily into her windpipe and we began to bag her. Bill and I watched as her chest wall moved easily up and down. Her color quickly began to improve. Within a few minutes, she was starting to take a few breaths of her own. And then she was purposely reaching up to her neck. Everyone in the room was relieved.

This time when I turned around, Bill Bowman was still standing behind me.

"Thanks, Bill," I told him. "I'm glad you happened by."

I knew that wasn't true. It was no coincidence he was here. I didn't know how, but when I needed him, when I *really* needed him, he would somehow be there, standing beside me.

"Hey, you didn't need me, Robert. You did fine."

Then he turned and walked out of the room.

God is our refuge and strength,
an ever-present help in trouble.
Therefore we will not fear, though the earth give way
and the mountains fall into the heart of the sea,
though its waters roar and foam
and the mountains quake with their surging.

Psalm 46:1-3

12

I'm Only Doing My Job

Honor and shame from no condition rise;
Act well your part: there all the honor lies.

ALEXANDER POPE (1688–1744)

I t was the middle of the afternoon. Jack had come to the ER with me today, and we had just returned to the department from lunch. Things were caught up, and we sat down behind the nurses' station with Amy Connors.

"Dad, I've been noticing something," Jack said to me. "It seems that not too many people appreciate what all of you do around here. I mean…I don't hear too many people thanking you, or anything."

That was an interesting observation. He was right, of course. I guess it was the nature of the beast. People don't come to the ER because it's something they want to do. They're usually in pain, or worried about something, or with a loved one and worried about them, or they're unconscious. Or maybe they're inebriated. It doesn't really matter, though. Our job is to take care of them. And yet…

"Well," I answered. "You're right, I suppose. But, maybe every once in a while someone thanks us."

"Yeah," Amy injected cynically. "It was *once*, and it was a while ago."

Jack chuckled, and was about to say something when Pat Jackson walked up and said, "Well, what about Sadie Abernathy?"

Jack turned around in his chair to face Pat. She was thirty and had been working in the emergency department for the past six years. Pat worked mainly during the day, and was a solid ER nurse. She was quiet,

390

unassuming, and steady. And she was always there. If you needed some help, or some equipment, Pat was standing right behind you. It was an invaluable skill and much appreciated.

"You're right, Pat," Amy said. "I guess I forgot about Sadie."

"You remember Pat, don't you?" I asked Jack.

"Sure, Ms. Jackson," he answered, standing. "It's good to see you. What's this about a Sadie Abernathy?"

"Well, that's an interesting story," Amy started. "You'd better have a seat for this one."

"Oh Amy, don't go telling *that* part again," Pat pleaded, blushing.

"You're doggone right I'm gonna tell it," Amy continued. "It's how Pat got her name—'Action Jackson,'" she said to Jack.

He looked at Pat Jackson, surprised by this revelation. He knew her to be anything but loud and intrusive. Certainly nothing that nickname would imply.

"Yes sir, Jack, this is the *real* Action Jackson," Amy said, leaning back in her chair. "And it all happened about a year and a half ago, around Thanksgiving."

Pat Jackson was doing her weekly shopping at her local grocery, picking up some odds and ends for the family's Thanksgiving meal. She was pushing her cart down the canned goods aisle when she noticed an elderly woman coming toward her. It turned out to be Sadie Abernathy, a seventy-year-old lady who Pat saw on occasion in the store. They were about thirty feet from each other when Sadie looked up and saw Pat. Sadie waved and then started pushing her grocery cart again, studying the confusing array of cans on the shelves beside her.

Suddenly she stood up straight, and with wide-opened eyes, stared at Pat. Then she clutched her chest and collapsed on the tiled floor. Pat says she will always remember the sound Sadie made as she fell. There was a gasp, and then an awful thump. And then there was a terrible grunt as the air was knocked out of her. The grocery cart careened down the aisle, veering to one side and knocking a bunch of cans to the floor, making a clattering racket.

Pat jumped around her cart and ran the short distance down the aisle. Sadie wasn't breathing, and when Pat checked for a pulse, she couldn't find one.

She looked around for some help and saw a teenage stock-boy standing at the end of the aisle, staring. He was carrying a case of soda, and when Pat yelled at him to call 9-1-1, he dropped it and ran.

"Sadie!" Pat shouted at the woman. There was no response.

She positioned Sadie flat on her back and struck her on the middle of her chest. Then she began chest compressions and mouth-to-mouth ventilations. She knew what to do.

The store manager appeared seconds later, and said, "We've called EMS, and they're on the way. Do you need any help?"

"I could use some help with these compressions," she told him, flushed and beginning to sweat from the effort.

"I...I..." he stammered, shuffling his feet.

"Never mind," Pat said. "Just try to keep these people back. Give us some room."

By this time, a dozen shoppers had gathered around, curious as to what was going on.

This was something the manager could do, and he quickly took charge.

"Everybody step back here," he directed them with his arms waving. "Give us some space."

Pat continued CPR for another five or six minutes, until the paramedics of Medic One arrived. They recognized her immediately and quickly relieved her, continuing the CPR. Pat leaned back on her heels and said, "We need to see what kind of rhythm she's in," she instructed them. "Let's take a quick look with those defibrillator paddles."

One of the paramedics quickly pressed the paddles against Sadie's chest and Pat studied the monitor. There was only chaotic electrical activity—nothing purposeful.

"Charge it up to 200," Pat directed. "And hand me those paddles."

The paramedic complied with her orders, pressing a button on the defibrillator and then handing the paddles to Pat. There was a faint buzzing sound as the machine responded, followed by a beeping, indicating it was ready to fire. Pat made sure the paddles were adequately lubricated and then said, "All clear!"

Everybody around Sadie moved back just a little, making sure they weren't in contact with her body. Then Pat pressed the paddles against Sadie's chest, glanced once more at the monitor, and fired the defibrillator.

There was a mechanical "thumb" as the electrical current passed through Sadie's chest and heart, and her body jerked uncontrollably.

"Just like on TV," someone whispered from behind Pat.

She continued to watch the monitor. The shock had caused all electrical activity in the heart to stop, and then, there it was. First a single complex, and then another, and another. Her heartbeat was speeding up, and looked reasonably normal.

"We've got a pulse!" one of the paramedics announced, his hand now on Sadie's neck.

Pat reached down and checked Sadie's femoral artery to confirm that her heart was pumping adequately. The pulse was faint, but it was there.

"We need to get her intubated," she told the paramedics. "And give me an angiocath. I'll get a line started."

She started the IV effortlessly, and continued to direct the code, ordering emergency medications and making sure Sadie was being properly ventilated.

"She's trying to breathe," one of the paramedics said.

And there it was. This elderly woman was dead a few moments ago, and now she was breathing and her heart was beating. A couple of people standing behind the store manager actually clapped.

I was in the ER when Sadie was brought in by the paramedics. She was still confused, but was relatively stable, considering what had happened to her. She was admitted to the CCU, where she stayed for five days. She continued to improve, and miraculously had a complete neurologic recovery. It was a real success story.

When she was discharged from the hospital, she insisted on being brought through the emergency department.

She was rolled up to the nurses' station in her wheelchair, and asked, "Is Pat Jackson working today?"

Pat was in triage, and Amy called her on the intercom. She came out and walked over to Sadie and they hugged. And Sadie thanked her for saving her life. Pat had blushed and patted her on the arm.

"I'm just glad I was there and that I could help," she told Sadie.

"And I'm glad you were too, honey," Sadie said. Then she left the hospital and went home.

"That's when we started calling her 'Action Jackson,'" Amy told Jack. "Just like in the movies."

Pat just shook her head, and smiled. She was still blushing.

"And tell him the rest of it," Amy told her. "Tell him the best part."

"Oh Amy, that's enough," Pat said.

"What else happened?" Jack asked her.

"Go on, Pat," Amy chided. "Tell him what happened."

"Well, Jack," Pat explained. "I was kneeling on the floor of that grocery store, doing chest compressions and trying to keep track of ventilations and everything. It wasn't easy, with no help and all."

She paused, and Jack leaned closer.

"And while I was doing that, I felt a tap on my shoulder. Just a light tap, nothing hard. I thought someone had come up to help me. Well, I turned around and there was this woman standing behind me. She was leaning over, and when I looked up at her, she cupped her hand to my ear and said, 'Would you mind handing me a jar of mayonnaise?' And then she pointed to the shelf beside me."

Jack's mouth dropped open. That was crazy, but then this was Pat Jackson, and he knew she must be telling the truth.

"What did you do?" he asked her.

"Well, I just reached down and grabbed a jar of Duke's, handed it to her, and just kept on doing CPR. Barely missed a beat."

"Like I said," Amy declared. "Action Jackson."

Later on that afternoon, Jack picked up the same conversation. We were alone, and he asked, "Does it ever bother you that not many people act thankful for what you guys do? I mean, there's Sadie Abernathy and all, but that must not be very common. Seems like most people just take it all for granted."

I thought about this for a moment.

"You know, Jack, it probably did bother me some at first. There might have been a couple of times, maybe when I just finished my residency and had started working here in Rock Hill," I answered him.

And then I thought about Andy Pettigrew, and that hot summer day fifteen years earlier.

Thursday, 3:15 p.m. "Dr. Lesslie, it's for you," the unit secretary said, handing me the receiver. "Dr. Blevins in Fort Mill. He sounds sort of upset."

I wondered what this was going to be. Dr. Blevins was an older family practitioner in a town six or seven miles away. He usually had a few people in the Rock Hill hospital, and I had gotten to know him when he came through the ER on his way to make his rounds. He was a nice guy, and his patients seemed to really like him.

Reaching over the counter, I took the phone.

"Dr. Blevins, this is Robert Lesslie," I told him.

"Robert, listen…I need your help here." He did sound upset, and out of breath.

"Sure, what—" I began to respond.

"I've got a man here in the office," he interrupted, "Andy Pettigrew, and it looks like he's having a heart attack."

I didn't say anything, and waited for him to go on.

"He's forty-two I think, maybe forty-three, and he walked into the office just a few minutes ago, complaining of weakness."

He paused, and I heard him make some unintelligible comments to someone in the background.

"Excuse me," he continued. "I just told the staff to call 9-1-1 again and to start some oxygen. Anyway, Andy came in with this weakness, and he looked terrible. He was pale, and confused, and...Well, my nurse got him in an exam room and took his blood pressure. The first one was 60 over 40, but it's gotten lower since then. And his heart rate is pretty slow, only about 55 beats a minute."

That was a dangerous blood pressure, and a dangerous heart rate. I wondered what he had done for this man. And then I wondered what he would be able to do in his office. It was a good thing he had called 9-1-1. Andy Pettigrew was going to need some help, and quickly.

"What's his pressure now?" I asked him.

"We've...we've still got a pulse, but no...blood pressure. At least I can't hear one. But he's still responding a little, and he's breathing."

"How far away is EMS?" I asked.

"They're just down the street," Dr. Blevins told me. "And...wait, I think that's them coming in the front door."

There were some muffled sounds in the background, and I heard him direct someone to the "front exam room." Then he was back on the phone.

"Good, the ambulance is here," he said with relief. "They'll be bringing him to the hospital and I was hoping you could look at him in the ER until someone from internal associates can get over there. I'll give them a call right now."

"Sure, I'll be happy to see him," I answered, my pulse quickening a little. This would be a challenge. We had some good internal-medicine specialists in town, but at that time no cardiologists. And in the four or five months I had been in the ER, I didn't know of anyone putting in a pacemaker on an emergency basis, which is what it sounded like Andy Pettigrew was going to need. "We'll be looking for him."

Dr. Blevins hung up, and I handed the phone to the secretary. We had about ten minutes to get ready.

"Sarah," I said to the charge nurse. "Do we keep a pacemaker tray in the ER?"

She stopped in the hallway and gave me a puzzled look. Then she put her finger to her lips, thought a moment, and nodded her head.

"Yes, we keep one locked up in the medicine room. Do you think you're going to need it?" she asked me.

"It sounds like it," I answered. "How about getting it out and meeting me in the cardiac room."

As she turned in the direction of the medicine room, the EMS radio squawked loudly, demanding our attention.

"Rock Hill ER, this is medic 3."

The paramedic responding to Dr. Blevins's office gave me the current condition of Andy Pettigrew. He had a pulse but no blood pressure. He was breathing on his own, but confused and barely responsive. And the EKG that Dr. Blevins's nurse had been able to get in the office showed what looked like an acute heart attack.

"It looks like a big one, Dr. Lesslie," the paramedic told me. "His S-T segments are sky-high, but his rhythm is still nice and regular. Slow, though. About 50. O₂ going and a line of normal saline. He hasn't responded to two doses of atropine. Anything else you want us to do? We'll be there in three minutes."

They were doing all the right things, and were almost to the ER.

"No, just bring him on in," I instructed him. "Let me know if something changes."

"10-4," and the radio went silent.

I walked across the hallway to the cardiac room, where Sarah was preparing the pacemaker tray.

"Have you ever done one of these?" she asked me. The question was sincere, almost helpful, and I wasn't bothered by it. Looking back now, I should have been bothered by the fact that I had only put in a half-dozen or so of these.

But that didn't matter. It sounded like Andy Pettigrew was having a major heart attack and wasn't responding to IV medications. If he was going to survive this, he would need an emergency pacemaker. And that would be me, along with Sarah's help.

"Sure," I answered her, mustering as much confidence as I could. "How about you? Have you helped with these?"

"I've helped the surgeons put these in upstairs," she answered. "But that's always been on an elective basis. Never something like this... when it's an emergency."

She studied my face for a response and drew the correct conclusion. "But we'll get this done, Dr. Lesslie. I'll be right here."

I glanced down at the tray, relieved to see familiar equipment and supplies. The pacemaker itself was one of the ones we used in Charlotte during my training.

My relief didn't last very long. I heard the ambulance doors open and the clatter of a stretcher being quickly wheeled down the hallway.

"Cardiac room!" the secretary called out.

Seconds later, Andy Pettigrew was being transferred to our cardiac bed. The paramedics gave me his latest status.

"No BP, but he's still got a regular rhythm. Slower now, though. About 40."

Andy Pettigrew looked awful. His color was dusky, almost blue. And he didn't respond when I loudly called out his name.

Sarah quickly had him on our monitor and was hooking him up for an EKG. I watched it come off the printer, and immediately turned to the pacemaker tray, pulling it near the head of the stretcher.

He was having a bad heart attack, and his EKG indicated a potentially large amount of muscle loss. His slow pulse and low blood pressure indicated a lot of damage. Andy Pettigrew was lucky to be alive.

Sarah handed me a pair of sterile gloves, and started to put some on herself.

I felt Andy's neck for the needed landmarks. He was a big man, with a short, thick neck, and it was difficult finding anything I was comfortable with. I decided to insert my needle below his right clavicle, and then thread the pacemaker through that catheter.

Sarah stood at my side, and uttered, "Good," as blood flashed back into the syringe. I was in the major vessel, and now all I needed to do was pass the pacemaker wire through that vessel and into the right side of Andy's heart. At the tip of the wire was an electrode, and if we were successful in placing it against his heart muscle, we would be able to send a current down it, stimulating his heart, and speeding up his heart rate. If everything went well, that would improve his blood pressure and the amount of blood flowing into his coronary vessels. And it would give him a chance, the only one he had.

Sarah handed me the wire, and I threaded it through the catheter, which was now protruding from below his collarbone. I noted the markings on the side of the wire, and estimated the distance it would need to be advanced before coming in contact with his ventricle. Several things could go wrong. It could coil around on itself and go nowhere. Or it could turn and go up one of the large veins in his neck. Or it could perforate a weak area of his heart and kill him. None of those things were going to happen—I hoped.

Sarah picked up the control box and made some adjustments. She set the amount of current to a medium range, knowing that we would back down to the least amount needed. And she would be prepared to set the rate of stimulation when I gave her the go-ahead.

She stood there, and waited.

I didn't feel any resistance or unusual sensations as I advanced the pacemaker wire. When it was at the depth I wanted, I stopped, looked at Sarah, and took a deep breath. It was then I noticed that the two paramedics had not left the room, but were intently watching all of this.

"Start with 70?" Sarah asked me.

I glanced over at the cardiac monitor. His rate was now 35, and he still didn't have a pulse.

"70 is good," I told her. My eyes remained fastened on the monitor.

Sarah turned the dial of the pacemaker control to a rate of 70, and we waited.

Immediately, we could see the tall, slender pacemaker spike on the monitor. The pacer was working, and its electrical current was being picked up on our monitor. But there was no capture. His heart muscle was not responding. We should be seeing a complex on the monitor, one with every blip of the pacemaker. That would indicate the pacer was working, and his heart muscle was responding with a purposeful contraction.

I waited for a few more seconds. Still nothing. Then I advanced the wire two more centimeters. And there it was! There was the spike of the pacemaker, and immediately after that was a bizarre-appearing electrical complex at a rate of 70 beats a minute, indicating that we had capture and that the tip of the pacemaker was against his heart muscle.

Now, if only…

"We've got a pulse!" one of the paramedics excitedly reported, having placed his fingers over one of Andy's femoral arteries.

And in less than a minute, we had a blood pressure. It wasn't great, only 90 over 60, but it was getting blood to his brain, and he was starting to come around.

After another fifteen minutes, one of the doctors from internal associates came into the cardiac room. His eyes widened when he realized what was going on.

I told him about Andy, and what we had done. And I was glad to turn the case over to him.

"Thanks, Sarah," I whispered as I passed by her on the way out of cardiac.

Two days later, I decided to go up to the CCU and check on Andy. We had heard he was doing much better, and was stable, at least as stable as he could be, considering everything.

I walked into the unit and searched the patient board for his name. He was in bed 2, and I headed over, pulling the curtain aside and stepping into the cubicle.

Andy Pettigrew was sitting up in bed, watching a small television suspended from the wall in front of him. There were IVs in both arms and oxygen tubing attached to his nose. Various monitors were beeping regularly, and reassuringly.

He looked up as I entered.

"Andy," I said to him. "I'm Dr. Lesslie."

A puzzled look clouded his face, and he said, "Doctor who?"

Then I realized he had no idea who I was, or why I was in his room. He had been unconscious the entire time he was in the ER.

"I…I just came by to check on you," I stammered. "Glad you're doing well."

I turned around and grabbed the curtain, closing it behind me as I left.

"Thanks for coming by," he called to my back. Then I heard him change the channel of his television.

Saturday morning, Walmart. "Dr. Lesslie?"

The voice was coming from behind me. I was in the sporting goods department, looking for some golf tees and a soccer ball, and I was a little surprised that someone was calling my name. I turned around to see who it might be.

A few feet away stood a smiling, middle-aged woman. At her side was a teenage boy. He was tall and muscular, and he was intently studying my face. I assumed he was her son.

"Dr. Lesslie," she repeated. "I'm sure you don't remember me, but I'm Mabel Strong. And this is my boy, Samuel."

He nodded his head at me, and continued his staring. It was a little unnerving.

"Good morning, Mrs. Strong," I replied. "I—"

"Like I said," she interrupted. "I'm sure you don't remember—it's been a lot of years—maybe fourteen or fifteen. But I saw you standing over here and I just wanted to come over and thank you. And I wanted Samuel to meet you."

She nudged him gently with her elbow, and he said, "Nice to meet you, Dr. Lesslie."

I'm terrible at remembering names, but pretty good with faces. Yet, I couldn't place either of them. Mabel Strong apparently read my thoughts, and tried to put me at ease.

"I know you see a lot of people in the ER," she explained. "And I know it's impossible to remember everyone you take care of, but I just wanted to thank you for what you did for Samuel here. He was about three years old, and we came to the ER early on a Sunday morning, around six o'clock, I think. He had bad asthma back then, and was wheezing up a storm. We had no sooner walked back into the ER when he collapsed on the floor."

Suddenly I remembered. How could I forget?

"Dr. Lesslie! Come quick! We need you right now!"

I had been dozing in the ENT chair, catching a few winks before the end of the shift. Debbie Latcher was the nurse on duty, and she had burst into the ENT room, startling me to sudden alertness.

She didn't say anything else, but turned and ran down the hall toward the nurses' station. I followed her as quickly as I could.

Standing in front of the counter was a young woman. She was obviously distraught, holding her head in her hands and staring at the lifeless body of a young boy lying crumpled at her feet.

"Please do something..." she cried.

Debbie knelt beside the child, checking for a pulse and any sign of life. There was none.

When I reached the boy, I snatched him up and headed into the cardiac room. Debbie was right behind me, and as we entered the room, she immediately reached for our airway tray.

I laid the child on his back and positioned his head to allow for the best air exchange. Debbie handed me an ambu bag and with one hand I pressed the mask to his face, covering his mouth and nose. With the other hand, I began squeezing the bag, forcing air into his lungs. His chest was rising and falling with my bagging, and I was satisfied that we were getting oxygen into him.

"We'll need to tube him as soon as we can," I told Debbie.

She reached for an endotracheal tube and a special light. It had a straight blade on it that would allow me to visualize his vocal cords. I would then be able to pass the tube through the cords and into his trachea, giving us a secure way to ventilate him.

Debbie checked the light and held it out to me. This was the moment of truth. I would have to stop bagging him while I attempted my intubation. I couldn't take much time, since he wouldn't be getting any air while I did this. I only had a few seconds.

I put the bag down by his side and took the light in my left hand. Placing it into his mouth, I moved his tongue out of the way and searched for his vocal cords.

There they were!

"Tube," I said to her, holding out my hand while not taking my eyes from these important landmarks.

Debbie placed the endotracheal tube in my hand and I easily passed it into his trachea. I immediately attached the end of the tube to the ambu bag and began inflating his chest. Debbie listened to each side of his chest with her stethoscope and said, "Breath sounds are equal. He's still tight, though."

The underlying problem of his asthma hadn't gone away, but now we would be able to make sure he was getting oxygen. And we would be able to deliver medication directly into his lungs, dilating his constricted airways. He must have worn himself out trying to breathe, and that's what had caused him to collapse. I was thankful this hadn't happened at home or in their car.

Debbie attached him to the cardiac monitor and I continued to bag him. His heart was young and healthy, and once we were able to breathe for him, it quickly sprang back into action.

"Heart rate is 120," she told me. That was good, and a good sign that he hadn't been without oxygen for very long. Now we only had to worry about his brain. But it would take a while before we would know about that. Maybe days.

"I'll get an IV started," Debbie told me. "And I'll call respiratory care."

It was then that I noticed the woman standing behind Debbie. It was the boy's mother, and she had pressed herself against the wall, the knuckles of both hands held tightly to her mouth.

I got Debbie's attention with my eyes, and motioned with my head toward the young woman. Debbie turned and immediately walked over to her, placing her arm around the woman's shoulders.

"Your boy's going to be alright," she assured her. "You can stay here if you want, or we can take you to the family room, if you'd be more comfortable."

"I'll stay," she sobbed, not moving.

"That'll be fine," I told her. "Debbie, why don't you pull that stool over here beside the stretcher, so she can sit down."

The boy was beginning to move his legs now, and was trying to reach up to his face and the tube now taped to his cheek.

"It looks like he's doing better," I said. "But he's still very sick, and will need to be admitted to the hospital. I'll need to know if he has a pediatrician or a family doctor?"

We made the necessary arrangements for him to be admitted to the ICU, and an hour after his collapse, he was stable and on his way upstairs. It had all happened so fast.

I didn't see him after that, but Debbie told me two days later that he was up and talking, and doing well.

How could I forget that?

"I remember that morning," I told Mrs. Strong. Then she told me that Samuel was a straight-A student and captain of the basketball team. And he was planning on going to Wofford in the fall.

"We're real proud of him," she said.

I had been looking at Samuel and thinking of what might not have been. Yet here he stood, strong and healthy, and very much alive. At that moment, I was humbled, and truly thankful to have had a part in what happened fifteen years ago. Then I glanced at his mother and there were tears in her eyes. She was looking up at me and thinking the same thing.

A moment ago, she and her boy had been complete strangers to me. And now, there was a bond, a special connection—something that words were not meant to describe.

"Mrs. Strong…" I said, my voice breaking.

"You don't have to say anything, Dr. Lesslie," she told me, smiling. "Anyway, I didn't think I'd ever get the chance to thank you for that morning," she said again. "And when I saw you, I just had to come over."

Without prompting, Samuel held out his hand.

"And I want to thank you too, Dr. Lesslie," he said.

I took his hand in mine and looked into his eyes. There was a genuine warmth there, and a deep and peaceful self-assuredness, unusual for someone his age. And his handshake was solid and firm.

"Take care of yourself, Samuel," I said to him. Then to his mother, "Thank you."

They turned and walked away.

I watched them as they reached the end of the aisle, turned, and disappeared from my sight.

And I tried to remember what I was looking for.

> *Blessed is he who has found his work;*
> *let him ask no other blessedness.*

THOMAS CARLYLE: *PAST AND PRESENT,* BOOK III

My Will Be Done

There's none so blind
as they that won't see.

JONATHAN SWIFT (1667-1745), "POLITE CONVERSATION"

Thursday, 2:15 p.m. The CBC report I had in my hand was the only thing that had come back on Andy Meadows. The rest of his labs would take another hour or so, but this would probably be enough. It confirmed my suspicions about what was going on here, and what I needed to do.

Andy was a fifty-three-year-old stockbroker. I had known him for more than fifteen years, and Barbara and I had occasionally run into him and his wife Joy on social occasions. He was a funny, friendly guy, and had the well-earned reputation of being a shrewd and capable broker and financial advisor. And he had always taken care of himself physically. He swam every day at the Y, and frequently played golf and tennis.

But something was changing with Andy. And that *something* was what brought him to the ER. Or maybe it was the insistence of his wife, Joy. She was sitting in the corner of room 5 when I pulled the curtain aside and stepped in.

Andy was sitting on the stretcher, watching his crossed ankles as they dangled below him. They both looked up as I entered.

"Okay, Doc, can I go home now?" he asked me impatiently.

"Soon, Andy," I answered. "Pretty soon."

I sat down on the other stool in the room and put his chart on my lap.

"Let's start at the beginning again," I said to both of them. "I want to be sure I understand what's going on."

I waited for one of them to say something, and it was Joy who spoke first.

"Robert, I've noticed lately that Andy has been stumbling some. He seems to be having trouble—"

"I told you I'm not doing any stumbling," he quickly interrupted her. "And I told you I don't know why I'm here. This is all your idea!"

His exasperation was apparent, and he sat there silently shaking his head. Then he said, "I bumped my shin on the coffee table the other night, and I've got some bruises on my arms from playing tennis the other day. That's all."

"Andy, you haven't played tennis in months," Joy said, almost pleading with him. "And you haven't been doing your swimming either. You've just been—"

"Don't tell me what I've been doing!" he snapped at her. "Stop putting words in my mouth and making stuff up!" This surprised Joy, and she shrank back into the corner of the room. And it surprised me.

"Andy, listen," I said, trying to calm him. "We're just trying to help you here, that's all. I'm just trying to figure out if anything serious is going on."

Something serious *was* going on. I had known it when they walked into the department. He hadn't seen me behind the nurses' station, and I had been able to watch him closely as the triage nurse led them over to room 5.

The first thing I noticed was that he looked much older than the last time I had seen him. It must have been only a few months, but he seemed stooped over and tired. And there was the way he walked. It was more of a shuffle than a walk, with his feet wide apart. "Broad-based" was the medical term. And then there were the bruises on his forearms. They were large and ugly, and multicolored, indicating this had been going on for several weeks. This was hardly the healthy and robust Andy Meadows that I knew.

When the triage nurse handed me his chart, the area for the chief complaint simply read "unsteady." That didn't narrow things down very much.

My initial exam and questioning had thrown up some red flags. But I needed to see some lab work, and we had gotten some things started. Now I was sitting in the room with them again, trying to figure out how best to handle what I was about to say.

I glanced down again at the CBC report lying on the top of his chart. It gave me a lot of information about the status of his white cells, red cells, and platelets. It was the detailed analysis of his red blood cells that caught my attention. His white cells were normal, and his platelets were borderline, but he had a mild anemia. And most significantly, his red cells were abnormally large, and they were pale. This was the kind of anemia we see with a chronic alcoholic. And it fit the picture I was seeing of Andy Meadows. As an alcoholic turns more and more to a "liquid" diet, his nutrition suffers, and he develops significant dietary deficiencies, especially of some critical vitamins. The lack of these, in combination with the toxic effects of the alcohol itself, would be causing his anemia. This combination will affect his brain, especially the cerebellum, which controls his coordination. The fact that he had these advanced findings was very troubling and needed to be addressed. Sometimes the damage to the brain could be reversed, but the longer it went on, the greater the chance the changes would be permanent.

I wasn't sure how Andy was going to handle this, but it needed to be done. This was one of the times I wished I was dealing with a complete stranger. It would be easier.

"Andy," I began, looking up at him. "How much are you drinking?"

The question must have surprised him, because he sat bolt upright. "How much am I...What are you trying to say, Robert?"

"Andy, I'm concerned about what I'm seeing here. You *are* having some trouble walking, and your initial lab work indicates that it could be from too much alcohol. I need to know how much you're drinking, and whether it's on a daily basis."

He glared at me, and I noticed for the first time the ruddiness of his cheeks. It was all coming together. Sometimes the obvious *does* escape us.

"I don't know what that has to do with anything…but…if you're going to ask me, well…I might have a glass of wine with my evening meal sometimes. But nothing excessive. Not every day, if that's what you're getting at."

"But Andy," Joy interrupted. "That's just not—"

"Just not what?" he snapped at her. "Listen, Joy, I'll answer Robert's questions. Don't you say another word!"

I glanced at her, embarrassed by this outburst. Something made me look down at her left arm, and I could clearly see the bruised imprint of a hand. It had been the grip of a strong individual, and nothing that would have happened by accident. She followed my eyes and looked down at her arm. Then she quickly folded her arms across her chest, hiding these bruises. She looked away and became silent.

This was an explosive situation, and it needed to be handled carefully.

"Andy, I know you're drinking more than that," I told him honestly. "And you know that too. The first thing here is to get an idea of where we are, and then get you some help. This is starting to take a toll on your health, and on…other things." I glanced over at Joy.

"Robert, I appreciate your trying to help," he said, suddenly becoming calm and uncomfortably solicitous. "And I know you have the best of intentions, but really, there's not a problem here. Maybe a glass of wine in the evenings, but nothing heavy. Believe me, I know about that. My father was an alcoholic, and I know what to watch out for."

Another red flag. "Andy, listen," I said, but he wasn't paying any attention.

"I think it's time that Joy and I head home, unless you're going to give me some medicine or something. And maybe you can just call us when the rest of the labs are back. Otherwise, I think that's about it."

He was firm in his resolve, and I realized he had closed this door and locked it.

"Andy, do you mind if I talk with Joy for a minute, just the two of us?" I asked him.

His eyes narrowed briefly, and he glanced over at his wife. Then he said, "Sure, I don't have anything to hide. But don't take too long. I know you're busy, and I really need to get home and check on a few things."

I stood up and motioned to Joy. "Why don't we step out in the hall and talk for a minute." She got up and followed me out into the hallway and then into an empty room 3. I pulled the curtain closed behind us, and pointed to the chair in the corner.

"Have a seat for a minute, Joy, and let's talk about this."

She sat down, and her hands dropped into her lap, once again revealing the bruises on her arms. And then she began telling me an all-too-familiar story.

Andy had always been a casual drinker, maybe a couple of beers on the weekend, or a glass of wine when they were out at a restaurant. But alcohol had never been a problem for him. Joy knew that his father had been an alcoholic, and that Andy seemed to always be afraid that he might follow that terrible path. But he hadn't, not until about a year ago.

Something had begun to change, and Joy couldn't remember what might have caused it. His work was going well and the kids were doing great. Their marriage was solid, and their passage into mid-life seemed to be going along smoothly. He was active in their church, and even taught Sunday school on a regular basis.

"Then one day, Robert, it was as if I didn't know him. At first, I would catch him drinking out on the porch, I guess trying to hide it from me. But when I found out and asked him about it, he just started drinking right in front of me. And when he told you he was having one glass of wine in the evening…"

"I know, Joy," I said. "It's obviously much more than that. This has been going on for a while, and his body is really taking a beating. This shuffling gait of his is something we see with people way down the road with this disease. I'm really worried about him. If he doesn't stop, this will kill him," I spoke as bluntly and as honestly as I could.

"I've tried, Robert, really I have," Joy sighed. "We all have. Even the boys have tried to talk with him, but he just denies that he has a problem. And then he gets mad."

She unconsciously began rubbing the bruises on her arm as she said this.

"I even asked our minister to speak with him," she continued, shaking her head. "You can imagine how that went. Andy almost physically threw him out of the house, and he hasn't been back in church since. Says they're a bunch of hypocrites and they need to get their houses in order before they go preaching to someone else."

She paused and slumped forward on the stool. "I just don't know what to do."

I didn't either. It was one thing to advise people to stop drinking, or stop doing anything that was self-destructive, and an entirely different thing to help them find some effective way to do it. Especially when they denied the problem in the first place.

But now I was worried about Joy, and I reached over and touched the bruises on her arm. "Tell me about this," I asked her.

She looked down at her arm and blushed. "He didn't mean to do this, Robert. It was just that…"

"Joy, I've seen a lot of this kind of thing," I said to her. "Too much. And I know this wasn't the first time. And I'm concerned it won't be the last. You don't have to live like this. Do you want me to confront Andy about it, or have the police get involved? This is serious business."

She thought for a moment, obviously concerned and a little afraid. Then she shook her head and said, "No, I don't want you to confront Andy. He likes and respects you, and he might be willing to talk with you at some point, so I don't want to jeopardize that. I've learned what not to say to him and when to just get out of the way. I think I'll be okay…And maybe…maybe he'll understand he has a problem, and we can get him some help. I'm just praying for that…"

There was no good answer at this point, and I said, "If you ever feel threatened, or if something else happens, call the police. Or call me. Do you hear me?" I stressed.

She sat up a little straighter. "Yes, I'll call…someone, if he…if some-thing happens."

Andy Meadows walked out into the hallway, impatient to get going. I wrote a couple of prescriptions for him and advised that he follow up with his family doctor in a few days. "In the meantime," I told him, "you shouldn't do any drinking at all, in light of your lab work. None, okay?"

"Sure, Robert, sure," he said, not very convincingly. Then, "Come on, Joy, let's get on home."

Joy didn't call me the next time something happened. And I found out about it in an unusual way. Barbara and I were driving back home from a restaurant in Charlotte, when out of the clear blue she said, "I ran into Joy Meadows the other day." I had been thinking about Joy earlier in the day, and Barbara's statement startled me. We didn't talk much about what went on in the ER, and never about specific individuals. I hadn't mentioned anything about my encounter several weeks earlier with the Meadowses.

"We were in the grocery store, and it was kind of strange," she continued. "Almost as if she didn't want to speak to me. She had on a pair of big sunglasses, and there was some bruising around her left cheek and eye. She said she had tripped and fallen going into her back door. And then she just sort of took off. Not really like her to do that."

"Hmm…" I muttered, and then quickly changed the subject.

Two months after that, Andy was back in the ER. This time he had pneumonia, and he was pretty sick. He was beginning to develop some ascites, free fluid floating around in his abdominal cavity. It can be caused by a lot of things, but in Andy's case, it was due to his drinking and his liver damage.

We checked some lab studies, and everything was getting worse.

I told him his chest X-ray revealed a significant pneumonia, and that he should be admitted to the hospital.

"Nope, can't do that, Robert," he emphatically answered. "Just get me tuned up here in the ER and send me back home. Don't have time to be in the hospital. I'll be alright with some antibiotics and maybe something for the cough."

Joy was standing in the corner of the room, head down and silent. I glanced in her direction, looking for support. She remained motionless and didn't say a word.

"Just get me tuned up a little," he repeated.

"Andy," I said, knowing I had to go here once again, but not looking forward to his reaction. "Tell me about your drinking. That's all a big part of this, you know."

His blotched and bloated face turned beet-red and he glowered at me.

"Robert, I've had just about enough!" he almost screamed. "That doesn't have anything to do with this, and you know it! You're just meddling here, and I don't need to hear any of it. Do you hear me? I don't want you to say anything more about any drinking. I don't have a problem! Never had, never will! I just don't know where you people—" he sputtered.

"Andy, I know better than that. And I'm not talking to you as a friend now, but as your doctor. Your drinking has put you in a dangerous place. It's what has led to your pneumonia. Your liver is failing, and your kidneys aren't functioning properly. Your belly is—"

"That's it!" he shouted, swinging his legs over the side of the stretcher. "Come on Joy, we're getting out of here. I don't have to listen to this bull, and I'm not going to. Do you understand me?" He made this last statement with his finger waving in my face.

I understood, and it took my best cajoling and begging to get him back on the stretcher. We treated him for his pneumonia, and though he should have been admitted to the hospital, we couldn't make him stay, and he went home.

It was the Friday after Thanksgiving, a month and a half after this encounter, when Andy Meadows came to the ER for the last time. EMS brought him to the department and to the cardiac room. Joy was walking right behind his stretcher.

There would be no asking him about his alcohol intake, or listening to his denials, or enduring his berating responses. Andy was in a deep coma, induced by the chemicals floating around in his bloodstream from his failing liver.

He was dying. Even a liver transplant wasn't going to save him at this point. We had several specialists look at him, and they all came to the same conclusion: Too many of his organ systems were failing all at once. Actually, they had been failing over a period of time. Now they were just shutting down.

It was a matter of time, and waiting. Joy seemed to accept this, and to understand where we were. Her children, most of them grown and married, were with her in the cardiac room. It only lasted a little more than two hours. And in that room, there was a deep and somber grief. But there was also a palpable but unspoken sense of anger and resentment. And hovering over all of these emotions was a dark and smothering sadness.

There are two kinds of people:
Those who say to God, "Thy will be done."
And those to whom God says,
"All right, then, have it your way."

C.S. LEWIS (1898–1963)

14

Gone

Things said or done long years ago,
Or things I did not do or say
But thought that I might say or do.
Weigh me down, and not a day
But something is recalled,
My conscience or my vanity appalled.

WILLIAM BUTLER YEATS (1865–1939), "VACILLATION"

3:05 a.m. I had heard the question, and I was just thinking about my answer. There was a lot to consider.

"Doc," Lori spoke again, making sure I had heard her. And then she repeated herself. "What's the one thing that's really bothered you in the ER, the one thing you have trouble forgetting?"

We were sitting at the nurses' station, enjoying the quiet of this middle of the night. We hadn't been talking about anything in particular, just relaxing and discussing whatever came to mind. Then this question.

She put her coffee cup down and I felt her eyes on me.

It seemed a simple enough question, and several things immediately came to my mind. I thought of different people and experiences, and searched for those that had bothered or provoked me the most. I was sifting through layers, and through years. There were those times when I had been shocked by the way we treated each other, the violent acts that forever changed or ended lives. Then I thought about the sudden and catastrophic things that had seemed

415

to destroy good people and good families. And then there were the children. No ER doctor or nurse can remain unaffected after taking care of tiny victims of abuse, or dealing with the unanswerable pain of SIDS, or facing the unexpected death of these little ones who aren't supposed to die.

But at the bottom of all those layers and all these years, there stood Willis Brown.

It was mid-January, and bitter cold. The clock on the wall seemed to have stalled at a little after four in the morning, a lonely but strangely peaceful time in the ER. Or at least tonight it was. The cold weather must have been keeping people at home and in bed. There were no patients in the department, and Jeff Ryan, Amy Connors, and I sat at the nursing station, talking and drinking coffee.

The conversation had turned to the topic of the desirability of growing pear trees, and Jeff was telling us why he had finally given up on peaches.

"Too many borers and diseases," he said with resolution. "Way too much trouble. Pears. That's the way to go. Asian pears."

Amy was obviously very interested in this, turning one page after another in her *People* magazine.

If this kept up, it would take more than strong coffee to keep me awake the rest of the shift.

"Rock Hill ER, this is Medic 2."

The EMS radio quickly shattered our peace and quiet. Jeff reached over to the receiver and pushed the hands-free button, allowing us all to hear.

"This is Rock Hill ER, Medic 2. Go ahead," he said, leaning close to the unit.

There was a slight pause, and then Gary James, the lead paramedic tonight on Medic 2, spoke again. "We're on the way in with a twenty-eight-year-old man, house fire. Burned pretty bad…" There was stress in his voice, something unusual for Gary. I leaned forward in my chair, listening carefully.

"Looks like mostly third-degree burns, total body…or nearly so," he continued.

In the background we could hear someone moaning, obviously in pain. He was saying something, but I couldn't make it out. We all looked at each other, and Amy shook her head.

"Is Dr. Lesslie nearby?" Gary asked.

"He's right here," Jeff answered. "Go ahead."

The radio crackled briefly with some kind of interference, then Gary said, "This guy's in a lot of pain, but…there's no place to start an IV. We've got morphine ready, but do you want me to give it IM? I might be able to find someplace to—"

"What's your ETA?" I asked, leaning closer to the radio receiver. Morphine given in the muscle would be slowly absorbed and difficult to titrate. I would much rather relieve his pain with something IV.

"We're four to five out," Gary answered. "What should I do?"

Jeff had gotten up from his chair and was heading to the trauma room.

"Hold off on the morphine," I told Gary. "We'll get a line going when you get here. What about his vital signs?"

"Heart rate's about a hundred," he told me. "His blood pressure… I…I can't find a place to put on the cuff. His burns…"

"That's okay, Gary," I told him. "Just bring him in as fast as you can."

"10-4, ER," he said, and in the background we heard the anguished cry of "Momma!"

I pushed the receiver's button to the off position and turned and looked at Amy.

"I bet it's a space heater," she said, shaking her head. "First really cold weather we've had, and I bet that's what happened. Caught fire while he was asleep."

She would turn out to be right about that. We later learned he had filled a space heater with kerosene and left it going too near his bed. The blankets caught fire first, and then he was trapped in an envelope of flame. A neighbor had happened to be awake, had seen the flames through a window, and called 9-1-1.

I stepped across the hallway to the trauma room, where Jeff was opening several emergency kits. We would need to get an IV going, probably a central line in his neck, from what Gary described. And we would need to be ready to manage his airway. It just depended on how bad these burns turned out to be.

Jeff opened one of the sterile trays, revealing its few simple contents. There were two stainless-steel cups, one for holding Betadine and one for holding sterile saline. There was a big stack of 4x4 cotton gauze, and on one end of the tray was an assortment of various scalpels. These blades were of different sizes and shapes and would be used only if absolutely necessary, and only in severe cases. This was our escarotomy tray, and the blades would be used to cut through burned tissue that surrounded an arm or a leg, or worse still, a chest. If a burn was third degree and completely encircled a body part, the burned tissue would quickly harden and tighten, blocking blood flow to that extremity. Or in the case of a chest wall, block the ability of a person to inflate and deflate his lungs. He would suffocate. The procedure was simple and gruesome. You just made a linear incision through the burned tissue, down to something that would bleed, and you made sure you had good pulses below the area. Or that your patient was able to breathe. Jeff was making sure we were ready for this, but it was nothing I wanted to have to do.

We both heard the ambulance doors open, and then the voice of Gary James.

"Trauma, right?" he asked Amy as he passed the nurses' station.

"That's right," Amy answered. "Jeff and Dr. Lesslie are in there now."

We both stepped to the head of the trauma room stretcher as Gary and his partner came through the door with their patient.

In twenty-five years I've seen a lot of burn victims, but this man before me was the worst. As gently as possible, we quickly transferred him from the EMS stretcher. Gary gave us what little information he had, confirming Amy's thoughts about a space heater and the suddenness of the blaze.

"Doc, I'm sorry about not being able to get a line started," he apologized.

As we moved this man to our stretcher, the extent of his burns became obvious. There were pieces of charred clothing stuck to his body, probably what remained of his pajamas. My search for any un-burned area of skin on his arms and legs was futile. Miraculously, most of his face and the right side of his neck were spared. He must have reflexively covered his face with his hands when he awoke and found he was on fire.

"Doc, I need something for the pain," he said in a voice just above a whisper.

It surprised me, and I stared down into his eyes. He was completely awake and clear, and was making a calm request. Somehow I couldn't put these eyes and this voice together with his destroyed body.

"Just something for the pain," he repeated, patiently pleading.

"Mr...." I looked in the direction of Gary James for a chart or note or anything that might have this man's name on it.

"Willis Brown," Gary told me. "His name is Willis Brown."

I looked down again and said, "Mr. Brown, we're going to get you something as fast as we can. We'll need to start an IV first, and it looks like the only place we'll be able to do that is here in your neck."

I was feeling the right side of his neck and the area just above his collarbone, locating the landmarks that I would use to place a cathe-ter in his jugular vein.

"Jeff, we'll need the central line kit, and a couple liters of saline ready."

He was already preparing this, and handed me some sterile gloves. As I put them on, it crossed my mind that I would probably only get one chance at this. There weren't many, if any other options.

"And get us some morphine," I added. "A couple of vials."

I soaked some of the gauze in the Betadine and began swabbing the side of his neck.

"Willis, this is some soap, and I'm just disinfecting the skin here," I told him. "It's going to be a little cold."

He nodded his head slightly but didn't say anything.

Then I wiped the area with saline, patting it dry with some more gauze. Next I located my landmarks and then picked up a syringe. It was armed with a 14-gauge needle, a really big one, and I was glad he couldn't see it.

"Willis, you're going to feel a stick here in your neck, and then some pressure. But it should only last a second."

I looked into his face. His eyes were closed, and he whispered, "Okay, Doc. I just need something for the pain."

"I know, Willis," I told him. "We're going as fast as we can."

He flinched a little as the needle pierced his skin, and then he was quiet. There was an immediate flow of blood into the syringe and an immediate sense of relief for me. I threaded seven or eight inches of a clear plastic catheter through the needle before sliding it out and tossing it on the nearby tray. Jeff handed me the end of the IV tubing and I quickly connected it to the hub of the catheter.

"Wide open on the fluids," I instructed him. "And let's start with ten of morphine. Another five every few minutes until we get his pain under control."

It wasn't long before Willis Brown was visibly more comfortable. He opened his eyes and looked up at me. "Thanks, Doc," he said to me. "It doesn't hurt so bad now."

The morphine was relieving his pain but was not going to knock him out. He was alert and speaking clearly.

Jeff had stepped out of the room and over to the nurses' station. Amy needed him on the phone. She had called the burn center in Augusta and they had asked for more information. I was alone in the room with Willis.

"How bad is it?" he asked me, looking up into my eyes.

What was I going to say? His question took me to a place I didn't want to be. Up to this point, I had been busy doing the necessary things to get him stabilized and as comfortable as I could. And now in a moment of calm, he asked this question.

I knew the answer, and I knew what was in store for him. But that was nothing I wanted to tell him. He was going to die. He couldn't survive these burns, and he was lucky to be awake and alive at this point. *Lucky*. Somehow that wasn't the right word.

"Willis," I said quietly, leaning close to his face. "You've been badly burned, over most of your body. We're going to be sending you to a burn center, the one in Augusta. They're experts in handling this kind of thing."

"How bad is it, Doc? Am I going to die?" He was calm, yet his eyes were pleading for a response, for the truth.

I took a deep breath. This man deserved an honest answer. I would be doing him no service by telling him otherwise. He needed to know.

"These are bad burns," I said quietly. "And…I don't think you can survive this."

He closed his eyes then, and his jaw clenched. And then I thought he nodded his head.

"Willis, do you have any family nearby? Anybody in town we can call?" I asked him.

He shook his head. "No, most of my people are in Charleston," he answered.

That would be at least three hours, and by then he would be in Augusta.

"No friends here? Nobody?" I asked again.

"No. There's no one." For the first time, I noticed some hoarseness in his voice.

And then, as if on cue, he started having trouble breathing. I knew it was coming, I just didn't know when. The burns on his chest were beginning to constrict his breathing, and he was having trouble moving air. It would only get worse.

Jeff had come back into the room and now stood beside me at the head of the stretcher.

"The helicopter is on the way," he told me. "Should be here in thirty to thirty-five minutes." Then he looked over at the monitor. "Pulse ox is 88 percent."

The oxygen in his blood was beginning to fall, and I needed to do something.

I heard the scraping of a metal stand being pulled up behind me and turned to see Jeff opening another sterile kit. It was our emergency intubation tray, the one we used for rapid sequence intubation. Willis Brown needed his airway controlled, and would need a tube placed in his windpipe. The process was simple. First he would be given some IV medication that would sedate him, and then more medication that would completely paralyze him. Then we would place the tube. If everything went well, it would only take a moment. He would be on a ventilator and would have to remain paralyzed, and completely sedated. And I knew Willis Brown would never again wake up.

"Pulse ox is 84," Jeff said, nodding in the direction of the monitor.

Willis was having more trouble breathing, and his pain was coming back.

"Doc, I think I need something more…for the pain." He was struggling now, and his voice was more raspy.

"Sure, Willis," I tried to reassure him. "Jeff, how about giving him another five of morphine. And we need to go ahead with rapid sequence," telling him what he had already anticipated.

Jeff had been organizing the escarotomy tray, and had opened three of the scalpels. He knew where we were headed.

"Okay," he answered, moving easily to the counter and drawing up the morphine. Once he had given it through the IV tubing, he turned to the intubation tray and began drawing up the necessary medications.

I glanced at the monitor. His oxygen saturation was still at 84 percent, but his color was getting worse. We didn't have much time.

"The chopper's twenty minutes out," Amy Connors said, standing in the doorway of trauma. "You need anything?"

Jeff looked up at me and then at Amy. "I think we're okay. Just tell us when they get here."

"Sure thing," she said, closing the door of trauma as she walked back to the nurses' station.

Willis seemed to be more comfortable now, and we were ready for the intubation. I caught Jeff's eyes and he looked away. Why was this so hard? I had performed dozens of these intubations and wasn't worried about that part of it. It was just…Maybe the people in Augusta would be able to do something miraculous. Maybe they would be able to save Willis Brown, and somehow keep him alive. Maybe...

But I knew better.

Once I gave him the sedative he would be gone. He would never again wake up. The people in Augusta would have to keep him on a ventilator, asleep and paralyzed, until he died. And that would probably be a matter of days, if not hours.

I stood there by his head, wondering what to say. Wondering if I should say anything.

Jeff silently picked up the first syringe and inserted the needle into the IV tubing. He looked up at me, waiting for my order to give the medication.

"Willis, this medicine is going to make you drowsy," I explained to him. "And then you're going to be asleep."

He opened his eyes and looked up at me. "Thanks, Doc," he whispered peacefully. And he seemed to understand what all of this meant.

Suddenly the magnitude of this moment was overpowering. Should I say something more?

I nodded at Jeff, and then it was done.

The trauma door opened and Amy stuck her head in. "They're almost here."

I shivered in the cold night air, watching the helicopter lights as they disappeared into the black sky. For a few moments I just stood there in the dark, cold and troubled. I was thinking about Willis and wondering if I had failed him. I should have said something more to him, I should have made sure that he understood what was happening, that his life was ending. I should have given him the chance to say something, or maybe...I'm not sure what.

Then I said a prayer for Willis as the beating of the chopper faded into silence.

15

Speechless

God, give me sympathy and common sense,
And help me home with courage high.
God, give me calm and confidence,
And please—a twinkle in my eye.

DOROTHY DAY

In the ER, we take what we do very seriously.

But in order to *survive* in the ER, you have to learn to never take yourself very seriously.

Wednesday, 3:45 p.m. Virginia Granger stepped out of her office and stopped, hands on her hips, and surveyed her department. She looked over in the direction of the nurses' station. I thought I detected a faint smile when she saw that Jack was again spending the day with us in the ER. He was sitting there with Jeff Ryan and me. Amy Connors had just rolled her chair over. A big thunderstorm was rolling through Rock Hill, and for the past half hour the ER had been really quiet. That would all change, once people got out on the roads and started skidding into each other.

But for the moment, we had a break and were just sitting and talking.

Jeff had just asked Amy to share some of her most interesting and peculiar experiences in the ER.

"You've seen some pretty crazy stuff over the years," he said. "Tell us some of your favorites."

Amy thought for a moment and was about to say something, when Virginia walked over.

She had heard this question, and after gathering what we were discussing, she pulled over one of the rolling chairs and sat down. In other places or other circumstances, this might have been the end of any light-hearted discussion. After all, Virginia Granger was the head nurse of the ER—and she was, well, she was Virginia Granger. But the nature of the ER, and of especially this ER, was one of family. We went through a lot together and we shared the same experiences—good, bad, or peculiar. And so it was only natural that Virginia should join in our conversation.

When she was comfortably settled, she looked over at Amy and said, "Yes, Amy. Tell us one of your favorite stories."

Amy grinned sheepishly and said, "Actually, Ms. Granger, it involves you and something you did a few years ago."

"Hmm…" Virginia mused. "Well, that makes it even better. Go ahead."

Relieved and encouraged, Amy began her story.

A Saturday in July, 6:32 p.m. Sheila Rice walked through the triage door and over to the nurses' station. She just stood there for a moment, shaking her head.

"What's the problem?" Amy Connors asked her.

"There's a woman out in the waiting room that's driving me crazy," Sheila answered her, obviously exasperated. "I don't know how to handle her."

Sheila was one of our more experienced nurses, and it was unusual for her to lose her patience or composure. It must have taken a lot to get under her skin.

But then again, everyone was a little on edge this evening. The ER had been busy all day. Every bed in the department was occupied. It was "standing room only" in the waiting room, and EMS was on the way in with three people from a wreck out on the interstate. There was no relief in sight.

"What's she doin' out there?" Amy questioned, her curiosity growing.

Virginia Granger walked up behind Amy as Sheila began to answer.

"Well, you can imagine what it's like in the waiting room." She glanced up at Virginia. "There are people everywhere. Most of them understand how busy we are and that we're trying to get to them as fast as we can. But this one woman, Bertha Wiggins, is really making a nuisance of herself. Every time I step out there, she gets right up in my face and demands to be brought back into the ER. She gets really loud and upsets the people around her. I keep telling her that we'll get to her as fast as we can, but—"

"What's her complaint?" Virginia asked matter-of-factly.

Sheila shook her head again. "That's just the thing. When she first came in, she complained about her wrist hurting. Then it was her back. And then it was her neck. I can't remember what it was last time, but her vital signs are completely normal and she looks fine. There are a lot sicker folks out there than Bertha Wiggins."

"Hmm…" Virginia murmured, pursing her lips. "I think I'll go out and have a chat with this Ms. Wiggins," she said, her voice low and ominous.

Amy glanced up at Sheila and their eyes met. Both of them knew the fate of those who landed in Virginia's crosshairs.

A few minutes later, Virginia walked back in from the waiting room. She didn't say anything, but nodded at Amy and then walked over to her office in the back of the department.

Half an hour went by, and Sheila brought several people back through triage. After she had led an elderly man into room 5, she stopped at the nurses' station and said to Amy, "Apparently Bertha Wiggins doesn't know who she's dealing with. She didn't pay any attention to Ms. Granger and just got in my face again. This time she told me she had a rash, and that it was probably contagious. That cleared out a few chairs around her. But as I turned to come back here, a woman sitting close to her got up and followed me to the door. She stopped me and said that Bertha had told her that the real reason she was in the ER was to get a note to be off from work tonight. She's supposed to work third shift at one of the nursing homes in town and doesn't want to go in because some of her friends are having a big party. I guess some people will do just about anything to—"

"She said what?" Virginia Granger interrupted. She had just stepped out of the cardiac room and heard most of what Sheila had just said.

Surprised, Sheila turned around and repeated Bertha's shenanigans.

"Well, we'll soon put a stop to this," Virginia huffed. Then she strode off toward the triage entrance.

A few minutes later she walked back up to the nurses' station with a look of satisfaction on her face.

"I guess that takes care of that," she announced.

"What happened?" Amy asked her. "What did you say to her?" This was going to be good.

"I didn't say anything," Virginia stated. "Ms. Wiggins was nowhere to be found. Some of the other people in the waiting room said she just got up and walked out. Didn't say a word. I expect she finally got the message."

Amy looked over at Sheila and shook her head, feeling just a little disappointed.

"We need some help in cardiac!" one of the doctors called out. Virginia immediately headed in that direction, Sheila walked back out to triage, and Amy resumed her work at the desk. Bertha Wiggins's unruly and inappropriate behavior was quickly forgotten.

Twenty minutes later the ambulance doors burst open, and the two paramedics of EMS 3 came rushing into the department, transporting a young woman on their stretcher. She was screaming and moaning, rolling from side to side. It was all that Bill, one of the paramedics, could do to keep her from falling off onto the floor.

Lori Davidson hurried over to the stretcher. "What's going on? What's the problem?"

Within a minute there was a crowd of ER staff surrounding the patient.

Bill, flushed from exertion, began to explain. "We got a call from dispatch that there was a woman down in the parking lot of the hospital. No other information, but we were just down the street so we responded. Found her out on the pavement by the ER," he continued, nodding at the writhing and wailing woman before him. "Didn't take the time to call in or anything. We just loaded her on the stretcher and came in." He paused, catching his breath. "Hope that's okay," he added.

"Sure, that's fine," Lori quietly assured him. "But what's she complaining of?" she asked him, stepping closer to the stretcher and picking up the woman's wrist. Her pulse was 80 and regular. Normal.

"Well, I don't know the answer to that one," Bill responded, scratching his head. "She won't say anything. Just keeps rolling around and carryin' on like this."

Sheila Rice walked through the triage entrance, bringing in a young mother with two children. Her attention was drawn to the commotion at the ambulance entrance and she glanced over in that direction. A puzzled look crept over her face. The woman on the stretcher somehow looked familiar…

Just then, Virginia Granger walked over from around the nurses' station. It was as if Moses were parting the Red Sea. Only Virginia didn't need a wooden staff or a booming voice. Without saying a word she simply approached the EMS stretcher, and the surrounding crowd of people parted, making way for this imposing figure.

The area quickly fell quiet, except for the persistent moans of the young woman. She still squirmed from side to side, her eyes tightly closed.

Virginia reached the side of the stretcher and just stood there, feet apart, fists clenched and on her hips. She stared down at the woman and didn't say a word.

Bill looked at the head nurse, then down at his patient, and then back up. Something was going on here, but he didn't have a clue what it might be.

Then Virginia spoke. It was but a single word and was uttered quietly, but with an unmistakable firmness.

"Bertha."

The name pierced the air at the ambulance entrance, and now even the young woman on the stretcher fell silent.

Her thrashing stopped and she lay quietly on her back, her head facing up. Then ever so slowly, her right eyelid began to open. Without moving her head, Bertha began looking around, searching for the source of this word that still seemed to hang in the air above her.

Her eye came to rest on the resolute face of Virginia Granger. Then there was a drawn-out, pitiful sigh, and she seemed to be trying to disappear into the thin mattress of the EMS stretcher.

Virginia just stood there, looking down at Bertha Wiggins.

Finally, Bertha opened both eyes and slowly sat up. Without saying a word, she slid to the end of the stretcher, jumped down, and stood dejectedly in the hallway, a child caught in the middle of some forbidden act.

Bill looked on in amazement, wondering at the sudden healing of his previously distressed patient. Sheila Rice quietly shook her head and then led her new patients down the hallway. And Amy Connors stood at her vantage point behind the nurses' station and chuckled.

Bertha was silent, speechless, as she followed Virginia out through the triage entrance, back to the waiting room, and to the end of the line.

Amy leaned back in her chair and glanced over at Virginia, who just shook her head and muttered, "Humph...the nerve of some people."

We were quiet for a moment, and then Amy said, "Now, Ms. Granger, it's your turn. Why don't *you* tell us about some of the things you've seen that really stick out in your memory? Some of the crazy stuff."

We all turned to her, anticipating something good. She was silent for a moment, and then she pursed her lips and began to stroke her chin.

"There've been a lot," she began. "But the ones that really stick out are the times when I've been taken completely by surprise. Didn't know how to respond or what to do. In fact, I didn't even know what to say."

At this, Jeff cleared his throat and looked off into the distance. The thought of Virginia Granger being speechless was an unimaginable event in itself.

This didn't go unnoticed, and Virginia stopped, adjusted her bifocals with her right hand, and peered over them at the now squirming Jeff Ryan.

"As I was saying," she continued with exaggerated gravity, "those are the times I remember."

Then we waited. Amy rolled her chair a little closer, and out of the corner of my eye, I saw Jack edge forward in his seat.

"Before I came to Rock Hill," she began, "I worked in a big hospital upstate. I was the head nurse in the ER there as well, and we were really busy. There were several residency programs in the hospital. The orthopedic program was especially good. We always had some of their residents in the ER, and they were always busy.

"Now we were set up a little differently there than we are here. We had two 'ortho rooms' in the back of the ER, connected by a sort of closet. That's where we kept our casting supplies and crutches and whatnot. And that's how we were able to go from room to room without going out into the hallway.

"Because of our volume, we had several ER techs. That's a luxury we don't have here. Their job was to sort of float around the department and help where needed. Usually, that was back in the ortho rooms. The residents would need help putting on a cast or splinting someone, and they would need an extra pair of hands. Two of our techs, James and Willis, were really good at this. The ortho residents had come to depend on them. They were both in their fifties and had a lot of experience. And it was my job to ride herd on them. You see, they were both…well…they always got their work done, yet they always seemed to have a good time. I guess that's why everyone liked them. Sometimes they weren't always as serious as I would have liked."

Virginia paused here, and for some reason, glanced in my direction.

"Anyway," she continued, "we couldn't have managed without them. Then one afternoon…hmm-hmm." She stopped and shook her head. "We had called the ortho resident down to see a middle-aged woman with a badly fractured ankle. She was a vice president in one of the local banks and had tripped on the curb as she was getting into her car. As she fell, she twisted the ankle. It looked awful. She was going to need surgery, and the resident was putting a plaster splint on it to get it stabilized until that could be arranged.

"She was back in one of the ortho rooms, sitting in a chair and facing away from the door. I just happened to walk by, and I stopped in the doorway to check on what was happening. The resident was sitting in a chair beside her, wrapping the plaster around her foot, ankle, and lower leg. Willis was standing in front of her, carefully holding her foot in the air. It isn't easy, holding a foot and leg in the air by just the toes. But Willis could do it, and without so much as a tiny twitch. And that was important for the resident. He wanted a good splint, and he didn't want that leg to move one little bit.

"Willis looked up as I stepped into the doorway and gave me just the tiniest of smiles. And maybe a slight nod of his head. He was intent on what he was doing. Nothing was going to interfere with his holding that leg still.

"I was about to move on down the hallway when I caught sight of James coming out of the closet in the back of the room. Something made me stop at the edge of the door. Apparently he hadn't seen me standing there. If he had, I can assure you things would have turned out differently.

"He nonchalantly walked into the room and politely nodded to our patient. Now, we had all of our techs wear surgical scrubs, since it could be messy work and they frequently got plaster on themselves, and other stuff. Willis and James had on their scrubs that afternoon, just like always.

"James seemed to glide across the room. Then he stopped right behind Willis. I saw him reach into his pocket for something, but I couldn't make out what it was. Not at first. Then I caught a glimpse of something bright and shiny, and all of a sudden, I knew what he was going to do. But it was too late.

"His hands were out of sight of that patient, and of course Willis had no idea that James had taken out his cast knife and snapped it open. James was quick as a flash with that blade. Before anybody knew it, he had grabbed the drawstring of Willis's scrubs and cut it clean in two. Then he just turned and walked back toward the closet just as calm as could be, and he was gone. Then it was like…all slow motion. Willis knew what had happened and his eyes got real big. But he couldn't move. He had to hold on to that woman's foot, and he didn't dare budge. The resident didn't have any idea what was going on—at least not until Willis's scrubs started heading toward the floor.

"And then there it was. Willis was standing in the middle of the room, holding this woman's foot in the air, his pants bunched on the floor at his feet. That's when I noticed his underwear, or 'drawers,' as we used to call them. He was wearing these extra-long boxers made of black silk, and they were covered with little red hearts. The resident glanced over at him and then at the patient, and then he just kept putting on that plaster. Never said a word. And the patient never said anything either. Not then, not even later.

"I was speechless, and just turned away and started looking for James. But I knew he was going to have much more than me to be worrying about."

We were all laughing, and Virginia added, "And you know, from that afternoon on, anytime someone mentioned those black drawers with little red hearts, Willis would just get real quiet and leave the room."

She shook her head, smiling.

"But," she went on, "that really doesn't compare to what your father did one night in the orthopedics room. A Halloween night, I believe it was." She looked over in my direction and waited. I knew what she was talking about, but I just sat quietly and shrugged innocently.

"Why don't you share that one with us, Dr. Lesslie?" she goaded. "I'm sure your son would find it quite interesting."

They were all looking at me. There was no obvious avenue of escape. But in reality, I didn't mind telling this story. I considered it one of my finer moments.

Halloween night, 10:15. J.D. Howell was sitting back comfortably on one of the beds in the ortho room. The curtain between the two beds was drawn, and the other bed was occupied by a patient with a fractured wrist. We had contacted the orthopedist on call, and he would be coming in to take care of that patient.

J.D. was all mine, and he was proving to be somewhat of a challenge. He was forty years old, looked twice that, and his blood alcohol was probably four times the legal limit. He had swayed into the ER listing from side to side, complaining of right knee pain. He couldn't recall any specific injury. But he knew it hurt and he wanted something for the pain.

He had no limp, at least when he thought no one was watching, and his examination was completely benign. Just to be sure, I had ordered some X-rays of that knee. They were normal, as expected. I had given him all of this good news and advised that he get home, put some ice on it, and try some Tylenol or ibuprofen. I had been writing up his chart at the nurses' station when Lori walked up and said, "Your friend back in ortho wants to talk with you again. He's determined to get something for pain before he leaves, and if he doesn't, he's planning on spending the night." She smiled as she said this, but then walked off, clearly leaving me to deal with this problem.

That bugged me a little, and as I walked down the hallway toward the ortho room, I planned to make quick work of this.

I was halfway there when someone behind me called my name.

"Robert. Hey, Robert!"

I turned around and glanced back at the nurses' station. And I couldn't help but laugh out loud. Standing across the counter from Amy Connors was one of my partners, Andy Rogers, and his wife, Joanna. It turned out they had just left a Halloween party, having won the "best costume" award for a couple. This was a number of years ago, and they were dressed as "Ghostbusters," replete with silvery outfits, boots, backpacks, and "ray guns." Now these were no little toy pistols, but big multicolored complex-looking contraptions. As I walked toward them, they both raised their ghost-fighting weapons and blasted away. The noise was hilarious, and several people peeked out from behind their curtains to see what was going on. It was a combination of a siren, some kind of whistle, and maybe a hoot owl. And all the time the ray guns were making these noises, they were flashing all kinds of different colored lights. It was great.

And that's when it came to me.

"Andy, I need to borrow that ray gun for just a minute. Would you mind?"

He glanced at me dubiously. "Okay, but what do you have in mind?"

"Just an idea," I answered. "An inspiration."

I took the gun in my hand and test-fired it a couple of times.

"This is perfect," I told him, then turned and walked quickly down the hall. As I passed one of the supply carts, I grabbed a towel and wrapped it around the gun, completely hiding it.

When I walked into ortho, J.D. was still lying back on the stretcher, singing some strange and unrecognizable tune. He looked over at me and said, "Listen, Doc. I really need something for the pain. This knee is killin' me. How about helpin' me out?"

Then I heard the voice of Doc Wiggins from behind the curtain. He was on for ortho tonight and was talking to his patient.

"We'll just inject this wrist with something to help with the discomfort, and then we'll put it back in place. It's gonna smart a little, but then we'll be done."

I'm sure Doc had a first name, but I never heard anybody call him by it. I never did. He was always "Doc Wiggins" from the first moment I met him until the day he died. He was probably the first orthopedist in the area, and even though he was in his early 70s, he was still active and took calls on a regular basis. I think he had treated everyone in York County at some time or another. Everyone liked and respected him. He was always straightforward and a man of few words. Just like tonight.

I walked over to J.D., holding the covered ray gun carefully in one hand, and gently patting his "injured" knee with the other.

"J.D.," I said to him, mustering as much seriousness and professionalism as I could. "We're going to get you something for the pain, and I think you're going to feel a lot better in just a few minutes. In fact, we're going to try a brand-new, experimental treatment."

"A what? Now, just a minute—" he protested, waving his hands in front of me.

"No, no, don't worry," I reassured him. "This is all very safe and approved by the ABC people."

"ABC? Ain't those the people who run the red-dot stores?" he asked, obviously not totally inebriated.

"No, the ABC is the, uh, the…Anyway, it's approved and everything," I stammered, caught off guard.

It was then that Doc Wiggins stuck his head around the curtain, curious as to what was happening. J.D. couldn't see him, and Doc just stood there, staring. I nodded slightly at Doc, and then refocused my attention on J.D.'s knee.

"Now, as I was saying," I resumed. "This is really going to help you. And all I need for you to do is just lie real still and straighten out your leg."

Through the fog of cheap bourbon, J.D. was still skeptical.

"Are you sure about this, Doc? I mean, wouldn't it be easier just to—"

At this point, I dramatically removed the towel from the ray gun, and with a flourish, tossed the towel onto a nearby counter. J.D. stared at the gun in amazement and, for a moment, was silent. Then his eyes began to grow bigger, almost popping out of his head. I glanced over at Doc Wiggins. He was just shaking his head.

"What in the world is that thing?" J. D. asked, reflexively grabbing both knees with his hands.

"Don't worry, J.D.," I reassured him. "This is not going to hurt at all."

I stepped closer to the stretcher and gently patted his knee again. Reluctantly, he straightened it out. Then he tightly gripped the rails of the stretcher.

Very professionally, I examined the ray gun, making sure all of the settings were correct. "Don't want it on full blast," I told him. "Maybe about half strength."

I heard Doc Wiggins clear his throat at that, and I struggled to keep a straight face.

"Okay, J.D., here goes." I placed the tip of the gun on his knee and waited for just a few seconds, just for effect. Then I squeezed the trigger.

J.D. jumped a little at the noise and the flashing lights. Then, when he realized it wasn't going to hurt, he seemed to relax and watch curiously.

I moved the tip of the gun all over his knee for at least a minute, making sure to not miss a spot. Finally I stopped, and pointed it at the ceiling.

"How is that?" I asked him. "Better?"

J.D. felt his knee with both hands and then moved it around, flexing and extending it.

"Nope, feels the same," he said, shaking his head. "Still hurts."

I stroked my chin and then said, "Well, according to the directions, this might take two treatments. Especially with a bad injury."

He nodded his head. I again made some adjustments to the ray gun, twisting anything that looked technical.

"This time, I'm going to turn on all the juice," I told him. "Full power."

His eyes got even bigger as I again approached him with the gun. But he didn't say anything, and he didn't move.

I fired the weapon and began moving it all over his knee, just like before. This time I did it a little longer, maybe a minute and a half. When I finished, I touched the side of the gun, then quickly snatched away my fingers as if it had overheated.

"Be careful there, Doc," J.D. advised.

"How does that knee feel now?" I asked.

He did the same thing again, palpating his knee with both hands, and then stretching it out fully.

"You know, it *does* feel better! Yes sir, Doc, it doesn't hurt nearly like it did! I think that thing really helped. What did you say it was?"

Without hesitating I said, "It's a joint techno-atomizer." Where that came from, I don't know. But it sure sounded good.

"Well, whatever it is, it really works. Just wait till I tell the boys."

I grabbed the towel from the counter and wrapped up the "techno-atomizer" once again. Then I stepped over to the doorway.

"J.D., the nurse will be back with your papers in just a minute, and you can be on your way."

He was still rubbing his knee and didn't look up as he said, "Okay, Doc—and thanks."

As I turned to leave, I happened to glance in the direction of Doc Wiggins. He was still standing at the edge of the curtain, looking at me. He was smiling and shaking his head. And he didn't say a word.

...And a time to laugh.

ECCLESIASTES 3:4

16

Another Word for Love

We try to define love in a lot of different ways—ways that are most often superficial, "feel-good," and transient.

Real love requires work, sacrifice, and understanding. Mainly it involves being willing to live beyond ourselves. Once we are able to do that, we can learn how to truly forgive—and accept forgiveness.

4:45 p.m. Edna Strait was rolled into the ER on the stretcher of EMS 2.

"Go ahead and take her back to the family room," Lori Davidson told the two paramedics with her. "I'll be back there in just a minute." Then she added, "And be sure to stay with her."

The family room doubled as our "psychiatric room," providing privacy and security for those patients who needed to be watched closely but didn't have a significant medical problem.

Edna fit in that category. She was 62 years old, and we had been witnessing a gradual decline in her mental status over the past few years. That decline had accelerated over the past three or four months, after she finally received the official diagnosis of Alzheimer's disease.

Her husband Charlie had been faithfully taking care of her all this time, in spite of her growing dependency. They had no children and no relatives in town. Some of their church friends had tried to help out when they could, but the disease is grinding, and after a year or so, Charlie was mainly on his own.

We saw Edna on a regular basis, with minor bruises from falls, an occasional urinary tract infection, and once with a bad case of pneumonia. It was during the pneumonia episode that we approached Charlie with the idea of some kind of care facility for Edna. He was a slender man, probably ten years older than Edna, and was becoming feeble himself. None of us thought he could continue with this for very long. But he would have nothing to do with a nursing home, telling us without hesitation that he was going to care for his wife as long as he was alive. He was determined, and we understood that. But we couldn't have known that those words would soon come back to haunt him.

Lori grabbed the clipboard for the family room and headed down the hallway. Then she stopped and turned to me. "When is Charlie getting here?" she asked.

I looked up at the clock on the wall. EMS 1 had called in with their ETA about five minutes ago. "Should be in just a few minutes," I told her. "No more than five."

"I guess we need to keep them apart," she thought aloud. "Edna won't know where she is, but Charlie will be looking for her. I'll make sure they're separated."

"Good idea," I agreed.

Lori walked down the hall and I waited for our next ambulance.

It wasn't long before EMS 1 brought their stretcher through the ambulance room doors.

"Take Charlie back to the trauma room," I directed Denton Roberts. "Everything still stable?"

They brought their stretcher up beside me and I looked down at Charlie Strait. He had an IV going in his right forearm, and a sheet was drawn up to his chin. A bloody bandage covered his face. There was only a small hole for his mouth and nose, and I could see nothing else.

"Dr. Lesslie, is that you?" a small voice asked from beneath the pile of gauze.

"Yes, it's me, Charlie," I answered him. "You're in the ER now, and we're going to take care of you."

"Where is Edna?" he asked, anxiety in his voice. "Is she here yet? How is she? I need to see her."

"Just relax, Charlie," I told him. "Edna's going to be fine. Right now though, we need to take care of you."

His hand came up from the stretcher, the IV tubing preventing free movement. He was searching for me, and I grasped his hand in mine.

"Dr. Lesslie, she needs me," he pleaded. "You know how she gets…"

I did know. And Lori would be taking the necessary precautions to be sure Edna remained calm and didn't do anything to hurt herself. Over the past few weeks, she had shown us an unpredictable and violent side of what remained of her personality, especially when Charlie was not with her.

"We're going to take care of Edna. Try not to worry about that," I assured him.

Then I nodded to Denton in the direction of the trauma room and he began pushing the stretcher down the hallway. It was with some difficulty that I was able to release myself from Charlie's grasp.

When we had received the call forty-five minutes earlier, it had been unusual. There were two EMS units on the scene and a couple of police officers. Some neighbors had called 9-1-1, reporting they had heard some gunshots coming from the Strait house. When the first policemen had arrived, they knocked on the front door and were greeted by Charlie Strait. He was standing in the doorway, blindly groping for the screen-door latch, trying to let the officers in. Blood was streaming down his face and onto his shirt. His eyelids were swollen shut and his face had a strange peppered appearance. In the background, walking from side to side in the living room, was Edna Strait. She was carrying a rifle in her hands and mumbling incoherently.

She didn't resist as they slowly approached and unarmed her. She had no idea where she was nor what was happening.

Charlie grabbed the shoulders of the first person he came in contact with, still groping blindly. "Don't hurt her!" he begged them. "She doesn't know what she's doing!"

Denton arrived on the scene shortly after that, and then he had called us.

I walked across the hall and into the trauma room. Jeff Ryan was carefully removing the blood-soaked bandages from Charlie's face.

"His blood pressure and pulse are fine," he told me. "No evidence of any other bullet wounds, just his face. Chest and belly are clear. Nothing on his back."

Hearing this, Charlie spoke up. "Dr. Lesslie, she only shot me one time, just in the face. No place else. And I'm going to be fine. Just…"

I stepped over to the stretcher and patted his shoulder, waiting for Jeff to finish his work.

"Just relax, Charlie, and let me take a look," I said.

Jeff peeled off the last piece of gauze, and I couldn't help exclaiming, "What in the…"

"Rat shot, doctor," Charlie said matter-of-factly. "Edna shot me with rat shot."

That explained what I was seeing. Charlie's face was a peppered, swollen mess. She must have shot him at close range, because the pattern of the tiny pellets was very tight.

"How far away was she when she did this?" I asked him.

"Well, she was in the living room," he began. "And I was getting her something to drink from the kitchen. We keep a .22 rifle in the closet, 'cause we've got bats in the attic, and when she hears them, she kind of goes crazy. Anyway, when I turned the corner into the living room, there she was, maybe eight or nine feet away, and she had the rifle in her hands. Then she drew down on me and fired. I really didn't think she would. She's pointed that gun at me before, and I thought I had it pretty well hidden. But…I guess not."

He was reaching up to touch his face, but Jeff grabbed his hand.

"Better not do that," he told Charlie. "We need to get it cleaned up."

"Oh, sorry," Charlie muttered, putting his hand back on the stretcher and tucking it under the small of his back for good measure. "I understand."

I picked up some sterile gauze and soaked it with saline. Gently, I began to clear away the clotted blood from around his eyes.

"How is Edna?" he asked me again.

"She'll be fine," I told him. "Now, tell me what you can see."

I had cleared the blood from around his right eye. The lids were swollen, and there were a few pellet holes just above his upper eyelashes. I gently pried the lids open, trying to get a look at his eyeball. I didn't see any obvious wounds of the eye itself, and his pupil was round and it reacted to the light of the overhead lamp.

"I can see your face, Doctor," he told me.

"Good," I said, relieved. "Now, how many fingers do you see?"

I held up two, then four, then one, and he identified them all correctly.

"That's good Charlie. I think this eye is going to be okay. We'll need to get some X-rays, since there are a bunch of pellets here."

I had been relieved to learn that rat shot had caused his wounds. These were tiny pellets, a bunch of them, and they were designed to be fired in an attic without blowing a hole in the roof. There wouldn't be any deep bony penetration, but we had to worry about an injury to his eyes.

I began to clean the blood from around his left eye. This one looked different. There were about ten pellet wounds of the upper lid, and when I pulled the eyelid up, it was obvious they had penetrated the globe. His pupil was dilated and irregular in shape, and I could easily see blood within his eye.

"Doctor, I don't see anything yet. Am I supposed to?" Charlie asked me.

Jeff just shook his head, and I heard a faint grunt as he turned away.

"Charlie, this eye looks pretty bad. I think there are some pellets lodged within the eyeball itself, and...well, we're going to need to get the eye specialist involved here. You're probably going to need surgery."

"Am I going to lose that eye?" he asked, more calmly than I would have.

"I'm afraid there's a good chance of that," I told him honestly. "We'll just have to wait and see what the specialist finds, and what he thinks."

"Wouldn't surprise me," Charlie said. "She was standing right in front of me, and Lord knows I ought to be dead."

Jeff placed clean dressings on his face and then started an IV. We would be giving him antibiotics and something for pain.

"How long do you think this will take?" Charlie asked me. "I mean, how long do you think I'll be in the hospital? There's nobody to take care of Edna, except me."

Jeff looked at me and shook his head, amazed, as I was, by this man's dedication to his wife.

"Charlie, Edna might be in some trouble with the law here. After all, she shot you in the face, and you might lose—"

"No, no, no!" he stated emphatically. "If it's up to me, of course I won't press charges. She didn't mean to do this. I know that for sure. She's not in her right mind, you know that. And my Edna would never try to hurt me. I can't let the police do anything to her. She'll just…just…I need to get her back home, and we'll…everything will be alright."

He tried to get up from the stretcher, but Jeff gently yet firmly made sure this didn't happen.

"Charlie, you need to sit still and relax, okay?" I told him. "I'll go and check on Edna. And I'll talk with the police and tell them your concerns."

"Thanks, Dr. Lesslie. She's not in her right mind, you know. And she'd never want to hurt me."

He was right about the first part. And yet she *had* hurt him. He was going to lose an eye and his face would be disfigured for the rest of his life. And yet his main concern was for her.

I glanced back at him as I opened the door. Charlie Strait was a pitiful sight, sitting alone on that stretcher, his face completely bandaged, and his bloodstained shirt clinging to his slender chest and arms.

"She didn't mean to..."

Saturday, 9:45 p.m., in August. "10-4, Medic 1," Jeff spoke into the ambulance radio. "Major trauma on arrival."

He hung up the phone and turned to Amy Connors. "Better get X-ray on the way, and lab. Sounds like a bad one."

I had heard the tail end of this and asked him, "What's coming in?"

"Head-on accident on highway 21, near where the four-lane becomes two. The driver of a pickup truck crossed the median doin' about 90 and ran into a Toyota sedan. They're bringin' in the driver of the pickup. Head injury, it sounds like. Vitals are okay, and no other evidence of any injury. But he's unconscious, and smells of alcohol."

I slid the chart of the patient I had just seen in ortho over to Amy. "How about getting some films of this guy's hand? Got in a fight with his girlfriend and punched his car door. Pretty smart—but then, it *is* Saturday night."

Turning back to Jeff, I asked, "What about the people in the Toyota?"

"Just one," he answered. "Twenty-one-year-old girl. She's dead at the scene."

He shook his head and added, "Medic 2 is bringing her in, and taking her straight back to the morgue. The coroner is on his way now."

"Drunk drivers..." Amy muttered angrily. "Why can't we keep them off the road? How many people will they kill before something is finally done about it?"

It was a valid question. Most of us read about fatal auto accidents in the newspaper, and the subtle mention that "alcohol may have been a factor." And then we forget about it and turn the page. But in the ER, we see the devastation intoxicated drivers wreak on our highways. We see the aftermath, and we're the ones trying to put the pieces back together. All too often, that can't be done. And then we deal with the family and friends whose lives have been forever changed.

"You know, Dr. Lesslie," Amy said, looking up at me. "This is a little unusual. The drunk is usually the one who walks away with barely a scratch."

She was right about that, or at least so it seems. I knew she would never wish anyone harm, but I also knew these accidents were hard on all of us.

"I'll get X-ray on the way," she said with businesslike resolution. She would do her job.

Ten minutes later, Medic 1 came through the ambulance doors with their patient and headed for major trauma.

"Vital signs stable," Denton Roberts told me as they passed the nurses' station. "But he's still unresponsive."

Jeff and I followed them down the hallway and into trauma.

"What's this guy's name?" Jeff asked.

"Clayton Andrews," Denton answered. He was sweating profusely, as was his partner. "Took us a while to get him out of the truck. He's just nineteen years old. And his parents are coming in right behind us. They don't live far from where this happened, and they were on the scene. In fact, they got there just after we did."

Jeff helped them move Clayton onto the trauma stretcher. I began to examine him, trying to elicit some response, some sign that his brain was working. There was nothing, not even a reaction to forceful rubbing over his sternum.

The paramedics had placed him in full spinal immobilization as a cautionary exercise. After we cleared his neck of any injury, we freed him from his collar and splints. He had good muscle tone, and no evidence of an abdominal or chest injury. The only physical evidence I could find was some bruising over his left eyebrow and some blood at the edge of his nostril.

And he *did* smell of alcohol.

"The girl didn't stand a chance," Denton said, referring to the driver of the Toyota. "She probably never knew what hit her. His tire marks just suddenly veered across the median and he struck her head-on. No sign of brake marks anywhere. She was wearing her seat belt, but nothing was going to save her. Head, chest…She was pretty messed up."

"Hmm…" Jeff muttered, rechecking Clayton's oxygen saturation.

"And you know her parents, Dr. Lesslie," Denton added. "Or at least her mother."

"Who is she?" I asked him, bothered by this new information.

"The girl's name is Jill Mackenzie. And her mother is Annie," he told me. "Annie Mackenzie, who used to work in the lab."

Oh, no. I knew Annie well. We had worked together for more than ten years, when she had been in charge of the second shift in the hospital's lab. I didn't know her husband or her daughter. But I knew that Annie was a wonderful woman. She was dependable, professional, and she was always smiling when she came to the ER.

"Do they know what happened?" I asked him. "Do they know their daughter's dead?"

"Yeah, they do," Denton said quietly. "They have to meet the coroner in the morgue and identify Jill. I just can't imagine…"

He didn't have to finish his thought. None of us could imagine that long walk down the dimly lit back hallway of the hospital.

Clayton turned out to have a terrible brain injury. His CT scan demonstrated a massive and inoperable shearing and separation of his brain matter. The impact of the accident had caused his head to whip back and forth. He must have struck his forehead on the dash or steering wheel. He wouldn't survive this injury.

His blood alcohol came back at four times the legal limit.

I sat down with his parents in the family room and gave them this awful news. They had been at the accident scene and had seen their son being loaded onto the EMS stretcher. And though they were expecting the worst, you can never really be prepared.

I gave them some time to be alone. After they collected themselves, they of course wanted to see their boy. Jeff led them up the hallway to major trauma, and I met them there. They were silent as they came into the room, and then the first words came from Mr. Andrews.

"What about the girl?" he asked me. "What about the driver of the other car? Will she be alright?"

They didn't know, and I told them what had happened. They looked at each other. Then he took his wife in his arms.

I was about to leave the room when Mrs. Andrews said, "Dr. Lesslie, do you think he will hear me if I speak to him? Will he understand me? There are so many things I want to say, and…and…Is there any way he can hear me?"

Her voice trailed off as she looked down at her son. I had seen his CT scan and knew the extent of the injury to his brain. The doctor in me would tell her no, he was completely unconscious and completely unaware of what was going on around him. But how did we really know? How could we know for sure?

"Mrs. Andrews," I quietly said to her. "There's a chance. Talk to your son."

She was leaning down over her boy as I left the room.

A few minutes later, the door of major trauma opened, and the Andrewses stepped out. I was standing at the nurses' station, and they started in my direction.

But something stopped them.

Something caused Mrs. Andrews to pause and look behind her.

Walking up the hallway, walking directly toward them, were the Mackenzies, Tom and Annie.

"Oh Lord," Amy whispered from behind the desk.

Annie Mackenzie's reddened eyes caught mine, and then she looked away and focused on the couple in front of her.

They didn't know each other, but somehow they knew. The coroner had told the Mackenzies about the condition of the Andrews boy, and that he was in bad shape. And Annie had wanted to come to the department to speak to me.

I didn't know what to expect. This could be a volatile encounter. Several thoughts flashed through my mind, none of them good.

But things were beyond my control, and the two couples were now facing each other in the hallway, only inches apart. They just looked at each other, motionless, in what seemed like an eternity. One couple's boy had just killed the daughter of the other couple. I waited, ready to intervene.

Then Annie Mackenzie stepped closer to Clayton Andrews's mother and put her arms around her. She didn't say anything, neither of them did. And they began to cry. Tom Mackenzie was standing beside his wife, and he reached out his hand and laid it on Mr. Andrews's shoulder.

And they stood there.

Tuesday, 8:15 a.m. It was about eight months ago that Henry Bartlett had started coughing. It was only a little a first, every now and then. But then there had been a little blood when he coughed. He had hidden this from his wife and hoped it would just go away. But it hadn't. Finally, when he could no longer ignore it, he went to see his family doctor.

Twenty-five years of cigarette smoking had given him lung cancer, and at fifty-three years of age, it had given him less than a year to live.

It wasn't long after the initial diagnosis that we began seeing Henry in the ER. Once he had pneumonia and needed to be admitted to the hospital for IV fluids and antibiotics. As the weeks passed, he began losing weight and strength. Then he would come in with vomiting or shortness of breath. And there was the time last month when he had fallen and broken his wrist. He was having a hard time with this, at least physically.

His spirit remained amazingly positive. Even at the very end, he was never depressed or anxious. And he was always patient with the ER staff. He just rolled with whatever came his way and let us do what we needed to do.

A big source of strength for Henry was his wife, Jean. She had no misunderstanding of where all this was headed, and she was always there with him, always encouraging him.

His positive spirit was sorely tested that last morning in the ER. Henry had had a rough couple of days and had tried not to come to the ER. He knew the end was fast approaching, and he wanted to be at home when it came. But he had developed a high fever and his shortness of breath was worse. Jean insisted that he come to the hospital, even if only to be made more comfortable. Somehow she knew this would be the last time.

Lori was with them in room 2. She and Jean had gotten to know each other over the past months, and had become friends.

By now, Jean knew the routine. She helped get Henry situated on the stretcher. She rolled up his bathrobe sleeve in anticipation of Lori starting an IV, and then she covered him with a blanket. He was having bad chills along with his fever.

I had seen Henry a week earlier. I was shocked by the change in him in such a short time. He seemed to have lost even more weight and was now little more than a skeleton. His temperature was 103, and his respirations were rapid and labored.

"Pulse ox is 88," Lori told me, reaching for the oxygen tubing hanging on the wall. This was a low reading, indicating that he wasn't getting much oxygen through his lungs and into his blood. But what could we do, other than provide him with some temporary relief? Lori secured the tubing's nasal prongs and then turned the valve on. "Three liters okay?" she asked.

"That's fine," I told her, and then turned to Henry. "How are you feeling, Mr. Bartlett? Do you need anything for pain?"

"No, no. I'm fine, Dr. Lesslie," he understated. "Well, maybe something for the fever. That might help with these chills."

"Coming right up," Lori said, handing him a medicine cup containing two white tablets. In her other hand she had a glass of water. Jean took this from her, and stepped over to Henry's side to help him.

A portable chest X-ray showed that Henry's left lung was completely full of fluid. His right side, where the cancer had started, was barely functioning. It was the worst X-ray I had ever seen, at least in someone who was still alive. His cancer doctors had advised us there was nothing to be done, other than trying to keep him as comfortable as possible.

After I had looked at the X-ray, I motioned for Jean to follow me out into the hallway. I wanted to tell her where I thought we were.

In a quiet voice, I told her. "Jean, this is the worst I've ever seen Henry."

She looked down at the floor and nodded her head. "He seems to be getting weaker and weaker by the minute."

Then she looked up and asked, "How much longer do you...I know you can't be sure...but..."

"You're right, Jean," I said to her. "There's no way of knowing, but he is wearing out fast, even since he got here. I think we need to anticipate that...well, it could be this morning."

There was a painful silence. Then she nodded her head and smiled. "Okay. I need to get back there with him."

"Jean," I said, gently taking her elbow. "Is there someone we can call? Some family member? I've heard the two of you mention Eric in the past. Isn't that your son?"

She stopped, completely still now, and stared at the door in front of her.

"Yes, Eric is our son, Dr. Lesslie. But it won't do any good to call him."

I thought she was referring to where he lived, and that the distance would be too great for him to get here soon enough. "Where is he?" I asked her.

She turned and faced me. "He lives in Charlotte."

That was a surprise. Charlotte was only twenty or thirty minutes away. Surely he would come to Rock Hill if he knew his father was dying.

"But it's no use calling him," she said with a sad resoluteness. "He won't come."

She saw the confusion on my face and then explained, "Eric and Henry had a falling out several years ago. Actually, Eric had the falling out. It was about money, or something like that. Henry was only doing what he thought was best, and he tried to explain that to Eric. But he only got mad and said he'd never speak to Henry again. And he hasn't. Henry has called him and written him, and when we finally figured out the computer, he even e-mailed him. But Eric has never responded. It's broken my heart, and I know it's broken Henry's."

She paused, and I said, "What if I called him? What if I explained what's happening, and that it...it might be the last chance he has of seeing his father alive."

"It won't do any good, Dr. Lesslie, but thank you. I know my son, and he's just too headstrong."

You don't become an ER doc by being timid. I was sure that if I could only talk with this man, I would be able to convince him to make the short trip to Rock Hill.

"Jean, if you don't mind, please give me his number," I asked her. "It can't do any harm."

Reluctantly, she opened her purse, took out her organizer, and read the number to me. I wrote it on a scrap of paper and walked over to the nurses' station. Jean returned to her husband's bedside.

"This is Eric Bartlett," the voice said. I was calling him at his work number. Maybe that was why he sounded all business.

"Eric, this is Dr. Lesslie, and I'm calling from the ER in Rock Hill."

I proceeded to explain the condition of his father, and that he didn't have much longer to live. I minced no words, making it as plain as possible.

When I finished, there was only silence. And then, "So?"

It was a simple word, but utterly cold and heartless. I wasn't sure how to respond.

"Eric, your father is dying, and—"

"There's nothing I can do about that, is there?" he coldly stated.

Wow. This was going to be difficult.

"I thought you would want to be here with him," I said. "And I want to be sure you understand he's not going to live much longer."

"Listen, Dr....whatever your name is. I'm not coming to Rock Hill. Do you understand that? And you can just call me when it's over."

I didn't say anything. I just kept searching for some word, *something* that would change his mind.

"You get that?" he added tersely.

"I got it."

There was a click on the other end. And I hung up the receiver.

I took a deep breath and walked over to room 2. As I entered the room, Jean and Henry looked up at me. There was expectation in their faces, and I had trouble meeting their eyes.

It was Henry who spoke. Jean must have told him what I had been doing.

"Did you talk with my son?" he asked, gasping between each word.

I looked at Henry and silently nodded my head. And I just stood there, not knowing what to say, and not wanting to say anything.

A sadness seemed to pass over him, and then it was gone.

Henry took his wife's hand in his, looked up at her, and smiled.

Then he turned to me, nodded his head, and with that same smile on his face, he said, "Tell him…tell him I forgive him."

Forgiveness is another word for love.

GEORGE FIELDS, JULY 8, 2009, CAMP JOY

Dancin' in Heaven

*Earth has no sorrow
that heaven cannot heal.*

THOMAS MOORE (1779–1852)

Monday, 10:15 a.m. Danny Miller. It had been awhile since we had last seen him in the ER. A few years ago, it had seemed we were seeing him once or twice a week, but something must have changed.

He was twenty-one or twenty-two now. Could it be that many years since we'd first seen him? He'd been four years old then and had celebrated his birthday earlier that afternoon. His parents had brought him to the ER after he had fallen out of his wheelchair.

Danny had suffered some unrecognized problem during his birth, and sustained brain damage due to a lack of oxygen. Cerebral palsy was the technical name for his condition, though that isn't a very specific term. It covers a wide range of problems and conditions. In Danny's case, it affected his motor system but not his ability to think.

During the first few months of his life, it had become apparent that something was wrong. He was alert and responsive, but he had difficulty moving his arms and legs, and his development was way behind other children his age.

When his parents received the news of his diagnosis, they didn't believe it at first. They had two older children at home who were perfectly normal, and this kind of thing just didn't happen, not to them. They weren't prepared for all that lay ahead.

The next couple of years were difficult, but they seemed to be adjusting to the challenges of taking care of a child with special needs. Danny couldn't walk or even crawl, and was placed in a special stroller at about the age of two. As he grew, his arms and legs became more contracted. His head, always too heavy for his weakened neck, began to tilt to one side. They had tried physical therapy and constant stretching exercises, but the changes in his body were inevitable. When he was a little more than three, they had a special wheelchair made for him. It allowed him to be moved from place to place, but he wasn't able to propel himself, and needed almost constant attention.

He couldn't speak, due to the lack of development of his facial muscles. But he tried. There was nothing wrong with his brain, and he didn't miss a thing. He just couldn't express himself.

I had been in the ER the afternoon of his fourth birthday. Somehow his wheelchair had slipped over the edge of their driveway, and he had tumbled onto the pavement. They were worried about possible fractures and had brought him straight to the hospital.

He had some bad bruises and abrasions of his right elbow and leg, and some on his face. But nothing was broken.

I can remember him looking up at me, and seeing the smile in his eyes. He was trying to say something, but I couldn't make it out. His parents were unable to decipher what he was mumbling and just told me not to worry. Danny continued to look at me, and I felt helpless. Finally I turned away and talked to his parents.

It was obvious then they weren't doing well. They were becoming more frustrated with his condition and the constant demands on their time and energy.

They motioned for me to step out of Danny's room. His father said, "Dr. Lesslie, we're getting to the end of our rope with Danny. We love him, of course…but you can imagine how hard this is on us. And on his brother and sister. He needs so much attention, and it somehow doesn't seem fair to them."

He was right about his first statement. I couldn't imagine how hard their daily life must be. The part about this not being fair, though— that bothered me. But I wasn't the one whose life had been totally redirected by the birth of this young boy.

Then Danny's mother said, "We're looking into a special home for him. Some place where they know how to care for him, where there are…others just like him."

They seemed a little embarrassed sharing this with me, yet they were determined. A few months later, Danny came back to the ER with a fever and bad cough. He was in his same wheelchair, but this time he was accompanied by two people I didn't recognize. It turned out they were staff members of a group home in Rock Hill, one that served the needs of children like Danny.

He was his usual bright and engaging self, still unable to speak. He had pneumonia on that visit, but didn't require hospitalization. We were able to get his treatment started and get him on his way back to the group home.

I asked Danny's attendants about his parents. Did they know he was in the ER?

"Well, I don't think they know," one of them told me. "They moved… Where did they move to, Frances? Wasn't it somewhere in Tennessee?"

Her co-worker answered, "Yes, somewhere near Memphis," Frances answered. "And we have directions not to notify them unless something is really bad. Do you think we should call them, Doctor?"

I told them that his condition was not that serious, and they needed to follow the request of his parents. Maybe their supervisor could make that decision when they got back to the home.

After that visit, we saw Danny on a regular basis. It seems he was in the ER every few weeks with an assortment of problems. Nothing ever really bad, just bumps and bruises and sometimes another fever. These were straightforward things that could be diagnosed and treated without his being able to talk with us.

And we watched him grow up. He had to get another wheelchair, something bigger and sturdier. And his useless limbs became more contorted. Still, he maintained a bright and cheerful spirit every time we saw him, speaking his happiness to see us through his eyes.

Then, when he was about sixteen years old, he sort of disappeared. He just kind of stopped coming to the ER. After a few months someone mentioned this, and we realized it was true. He hadn't been in the ER for quite a while.

One evening, when I was taking care of a young girl from Danny's group home, I decided to ask the woman with her about Danny. I glanced down at her nametag. Apparently she noticed my hesitancy in trying to pronounce her name.

"I know, Doctor," she said smiling. "Nobody can pronounce my name. I'm from the bayou country in Louisiana. Just call me 'Miss B.' That's what all the children do."

Having been rescued I said, "Thanks, Miss B. Do you have any idea where Danny Miller is? We haven't seen him here in quite a while."

"Oh, his family moved him to another facility, somewhere in the lower part of the state. He's been gone quite a while now. And you know, we really miss that boy. He was something special."

I told her we all agreed. I was turning to leave when she added, "I just don't know, though. I've been working at the home for over five years, and I've never once seen his parents. That's just never made any sense to me. To none of us. Like I said, he is such a special young man. He has 'the light,' you might say. Every Sunday afternoon, we would gather all the children together and read Bible stories to them. Not all of them understood what was going on, mind you, but Danny certainly did. He always wanted to be up front, and he listened closely to every word. And though he couldn't tell us, we knew he understood. The Lord had touched that young man, that was for sure. And it's that light of his, that spirit that touches everyone around him."

She paused and patted the arm of the little girl on the stretcher in front of us.

"Yes sir, we all miss him."

And now here Danny was in the ER again. He hadn't changed much during the years he had been gone. Maybe some more facial hair, and a little more weight. And though still in a wheelchair, imprisoned by his misshapen body, his eyes hadn't changed. His gaze was still bright and engaging, and there was still that "light" that Miss B had talked about. He had clearly become more animated as he was rolled into the department through triage and he seemed happy to be back in our ER.

I was glad to see that Miss B was once again with Danny. When I asked her where Danny had been living, she told me that he had been moved back to Rock Hill several weeks ago and had been placed in the same group home. They had brought him to the ER because he had a low-grade fever and seemed to be uncomfortable.

"You know, Doctor, it's difficult trying to figure out if anything is hurting Danny," Miss B told me. "He's been gone for a while and I haven't had a chance to work with him. I just can't understand what he's trying to say. But something's different today, and I somehow thought we should bring him in to the hospital."

I assured her we would take care of him, and directed the triage nurse to take Danny to room 4. Brandy Phillips was covering that room, and she walked over to help them get Danny settled.

Brandy was young, twenty-four at the most, and had been in the ER for only a few months. She came to us with some critical-care experience in another hospital and was still "learning the ropes" in our department.

Miss B and her co-worker walked out of Danny's room and over to where I was standing at the nurses' station.

"We'll be going back to the home now," Miss B said to me. "Just give us a call when he's ready to come back, and we'll be right here."

They turned and left the department. I resumed writing up the record in front of me.

Ten minutes later, Brandy Phillips came walking out of room 4, shaking her head. She walked up to me and said, "Dr. Lesslie, I have no idea what is going on with the patient in room 4. I can't understand anything he is trying to say, not one word."

She was obviously frustrated, and I gave her a second to collect herself.

"His temp is 100.1, but I can't be sure about his blood pressure," she continued. "The cuff is too big, and his arms are…well, they're just so small and hard to get to. What should I do? I guess I could try a pediatric cuff."

She had put Danny's chart on the countertop. I picked it up.

"Let me go and see if I can figure out what's going on," I told her. "And don't worry about not being able to understand Danny. None of us have ever been able to, and we've had a bunch of years to try."

Lori Davidson had been sitting behind the nurses' station, and she stood up when I said this.

"Let me go with you, Dr. Lesslie," she said. "I'd like to see Danny again. It's been a while, and maybe I can help."

"Sure," I told her. "Come on."

We walked into room 4, where we found Danny curled up on the stretcher. The rails had been pulled up, and he was leaning against one of them. He was unable to move and was in an obviously uncomfortable position.

Lori quickly stepped over and helped him to be more comfortable.

He looked up at her and then at me, and his expression was one of recognition and then relief.

Then he seemed to become more serious. He tried to say something. He was working hard, and when he saw our lack of comprehension, he seemed to become frustrated. That was unusual for Danny. I had never known him to lose his patience. He had always seemed to accept our shortcomings.

Lori leaned over and spoke quietly and slowly to him. "Danny, can you tell or show us what's the matter? Do you hurt anywhere?"

He tried again, mouthing his words with great effort and obvious difficulty. But we couldn't understand what he was trying to get across to us. I examined him the best I could. But couldn't find any obvious problems. It was a difficult exam, and I knew it was only of limited value.

"Lori, I'm going to the desk to get Amy to order some labs and a urine. And we'll get a chest X-ray." I looked down again at Danny and added, "We probably need to send him around in his wheelchair for that. The stretcher will be too clumsy."

Lori looked over at me and said, "I'll stay with him for a few minutes, and see if I can make any progress."

I went out to the nurses' station and ordered the labs and X-ray. Then I just stood there and wondered what I was going to do with Danny. A few minutes later, Lori walked over and shook her head.

"I'm sorry," she said. "I just can't understand him. I tried, but I just can't."

Forty-five minutes later, he was being wheeled back to the department from X-ray. The tech with him stopped in front of Amy and asked which room Danny was in. As she rolled him toward room 4, Amy slid the results of his lab work across the top of the counter.

His urine was completely clear, but his CBC was abnormal. His white count was 15,500, an elevated level that probably indicated an infection somewhere. When I put his chest X-ray up on the view box, I had to step back and get my bearings. His thorax was contorted, just like the rest of his body, and it was difficult to make out the important physical landmarks. After a few minutes, I was satisfied that there was no pneumonia present. His lungs were clear.

That was when Jack walked up and quietly stood at my shoulder.

"That's an unusual X-ray, isn't it?" he asked, startling me a little. I had almost forgotten he had come to work with me this morning. One of the radiologists had come through the ER earlier and asked Jack if he wanted to sit in on a few MRIs. There were a few heads scheduled, and at least one lumbar spine. I thought it would be a good experience for him, and he had gladly followed the radiologist down the hallway.

I turned and faced him.

"Yeah," I answered. "There's not much normal on this chest X-ray. This is a tough case. It's the young man in room 4 with a fever and elevated white count. He's probably got an infection going on somewhere, but he can't communicate with us. And it's going to be difficult to find out where it's coming from."

"What do you mean he can't communicate?" Jack asked me, glancing over in the direction of room 4. The curtain was still open, and the X-ray tech had left Danny sitting in his wheelchair, alone in the room.

I explained Danny's problem and the impossibility of getting any kind of complaint or history from him.

Jack nodded his head and said, "Mind if I try?"

That might be a good idea. I guess I had been too busy to remember Jack's years of experience at Camp Joy.

This was a summer camp that the Associate Reformed Presbyterian Church had been operating for the past thirty years. Three sessions each summer, a group of fifty or sixty individuals with special needs would spend a week at Bonclarken, the denomination's retreat located just outside of Hendersonville. Each one of them would be paired with a counselor, a "special friend" who would spend the entire time with them, 24-7. Some of these campers were pretty self-sufficient and high-functioning, while others required a lot of help with everything, including eating and bathing and using the restroom.

It was an intense week for everyone there. For the campers, their week at Camp Joy was the highlight of their year. And for the counselors, the week spent in selfless and sometimes difficult service was life-changing. Not everyone could do this, but for those who dedicated themselves to their camper, the experience taught them a lot about these "special needs" individuals, or as they soon came to understand, these "special people" with needs. It also taught them about love, and what "unconditional love" was all about. These campers placed no conditions on their affection and loved freely. There really is no place on this earth quite like it.

Jack and his two sisters and brother had all been counselors at Camp Joy, and it had impacted each of their lives. In fact, Jack would be heading up to Bonclarken in a few weeks for his sixth session as a counselor. During those summers, some of his "special friends" had been high-functioning and mainly required a lot of emotional support and encouragement. Later, as he became more experienced, he was given the assignments of more complex campers, those who required a lot of physical help, and those who had great difficulty in communicating with others.

I hadn't thought of that.

"Sure, Jack, see what you can do with him," I told him. "His name is Danny. But don't be surprised if you can't understand anything he's saying. We've all tried."

I quickly told him about Danny's level of mental functioning and that it was a matter of communication, nothing else.

He walked over to room 4, and I watched as he stepped over beside Danny's wheelchair. He knelt down and put his arm around Danny, then leaned his head close to Danny's. I watched as Danny's eyes lit up and I saw his mouth began to move excitedly. I couldn't hear what they were saying and walked back over to the nurses' station.

Ten minutes later, Jack walked up and stood beside me. He had picked Danny up from his wheelchair and placed him on the stretcher. Then he covered him with a hospital blanket before leaving his room.

Lori was standing on the other side of the counter beside Amy, helping her log in some orders for one of our patients.

"Well, what did you learn?" I asked, hoping that he had discovered something, but not really expecting him to have anything to offer.

"Wow!" Jack exclaimed. "Danny is really a special spirit. But I guess you guys know that, though."

Lori looked up as he said this, and tilted her head, waiting.

"He kept apologizing for causing so much trouble. He knows how difficult it is to understand him."

That was an understatement, but I was surprised and anxious to hear what else Jack had learned.

"Well," he said to me, "Danny thinks he has appendicitis."

"He what?" I responded. "Appendicitis? Did he tell you that?"

It suddenly made sense, with his low-grade fever and elevated white count. It was almost impossible to examine his abdomen since his rib-cage almost touched his pelvis, so that could certainly be the source of his problem.

"He's not sure," Jack explained. "But he thinks that's what it might be. He has pain in the right lower part of his belly, and he's nauseated. Doesn't that sort of fit the picture of appendicitis?"

Lori chuckled and smiled at Jack.

"It does fit the picture," I told him. "But we'll need a CT scan of his abdomen to be sure."

Then I looked down at Amy and said, "Can you get that scheduled as quickly as possible? We need it done right away."

It turned out that Danny Miller in fact did have appendicitis. He was taken to the OR later that afternoon and had his appendix successfully removed, with no complications. A few days later, he would be going home.

That evening, as we drove out of the hospital parking lot, I asked Jack how he had been able to understand Danny. "A lot of us tried, you know," I told him again. "But it just wasn't any use."

He looked over at me and matter-of-factly said, "You know, Dad, you just have to take your time and listen. That's all. If you listen closely enough, you can begin to understand. And then suddenly, it becomes clear."

He was being completely serious, and fully expected me to understand. I just shook my head. I realized this was a gift that not all of us possessed. Or maybe we do. Maybe we just don't work hard enough at having "ears that hear." One thing was for certain, though. It was because of Jack and this gift that we had been able to help Danny.

We were silent, and then Jack said, "I overheard Miss B, from the group home, say something that really makes a lot of sense. She said that though Danny is trapped in that body and in his wheelchair, someday he will be dancing. 'Dancing with the Lord' is the way she put it. I know that's true. And it will be a great day."

He paused, reflecting. "There will be a lot of people dancing."

I looked over at my son, and marveled.

Behold, I make all things new.

REVELATION 21:5 RSV

New Beginnings

There is a time for everything,
and a season
for every activity under heaven:
a time to be born and a time to die.

ECCLESIASTES 3:1-2

Thursday, 7:15 a.m. Jack and I had just sat down at the nurses' station. We were talking with Amy about her husband's big dirt-track race the following night, and she had asked Jack if he wanted to come.

Before he could say anything, the ambulance doors burst open and someone began screaming.

"Help me! Somebody come quick!"

We all turned in the direction of this outburst. Standing in the entrance, holding the doors open with both hands, was an obviously distraught young man. He was barefooted, dressed in blue jeans, and his shirttail was flapping in the slight vacuum created by the automatic doors.

He was frantically searching the department and when his eyes caught mine, he repeated, "Help me! My wife's havin' a baby in the car!"

I immediately turned to Amy. "Who's out in triage?"

"Lori," she told me, reaching out and pressing the triage intercom button. "I'll give her a call."

She leaned down over the speaker and said, "Lori, we got a woman havin' a baby in the parking lot. Might need some help."

The atmosphere of the department was suddenly changed. Lori barreled out of triage and headed straight for the open ambulance doors. She paused only long enough to grab the emergency OB kit that we kept on a shelf in the hallway.

"Help me, please!" the young man said again, this time turning and starting out into the parking lot. Lori was right behind him.

Jack looked at me and said, "Shouldn't we get out there? I mean, if she's…"

I had stood up and was making my way from behind the nurses' station. Apparently I was not moving quickly enough for Jack.

"Don't you think we need to…to run or something? What if—"

We were moving through the ambulance doors and I turned to him and said, "Lori is out there, and she'll holler if there's a problem."

I understood his excitement and his anxiety. But my response was tempered by a few decades of hearing many of these same emergent cries for help. Usually there was no cause for alarm and certainly not for running. Nonetheless we took each one seriously, and I could see that Lori had reached the back door of a late model maroon station wagon, parked at an awkward angle near the ambulance entrance. The young man had opened the door and Lori was bending over, peering inside the interior.

We were ten yards from the car when Lori straightened up, turned around toward me, and beckoned with a wave of her hand. She was calm as always, yet I sensed an urgency in her unspoken request. This was confirmed when she set the OB kit on the pavement at her feet and began to open it.

Immediately my pulse quickened, as did my step. Racing through my mind were the steps I needed to perform. It had been a while since we had done this. Usually we were greeted by a young woman in active labor, but who had not progressed beyond the point of no return. We were able to get her on a stretcher and up to Labor and Delivery before any precipitous activity. It was always a little disappointing, tempered with a significant measure of relief.

Hearing the rattling wheels behind me, I turned to see Amy Connors pushing a stretcher across the parking lot. She was having a little trouble navigating the cracked and uneven pavement, but had almost reached us.

Lori looked up at her and with a slight shake of her head said, "Not yet."

It was then that I noticed Jack. He was standing just behind me, wide-eyed, and trying to get a glimpse of what was going on in the backseat of the car.

"What've we got?" I asked Lori, reaching the door and leaning in.

"She's crowning and pushing," she calmly reported. "And this is her third baby."

That was cause for more concern. This was going to happen and it was going to happen quickly.

"Ohhhh, doctor, make sure my baby is okay," the young woman moaned between pants.

I caught a quick glimpse of her face. She was frightened and obviously in pain. Her damp hair hung limply across her forward and into her eyes. She tried without success to brush it aside.

"Everything's going to be alright," I said, trying to calm her. "But it looks like we're going to have a baby here in the car. Try to relax as much as you can and just let us help you."

She looked at me with wide-opened eyes and just nodded.

She was reclining in the backseat, her left leg draped over the back of the front seat. It must have been an uncomfortable posture, but that was the least of her concerns. Looking down, I could see the black-thatched top of the baby's head pressing through the birth canal. I felt something at my left shoulder and turned as Lori handed me sterile gloves. I quickly put them on and noted that she stood ready with a suction bulb, prepared to clear the child's airway as soon as it was accessible.

Then she did something that barely registered on my consciousness, but which I was able to recall later in a calmer moment. She turned to my son and quietly said, "Jack," nodding her head and shifting slightly to make room for him. I *sensed* more than saw his presence behind me.

I delivered the baby's head and then its shoulders. In a split and slithery second, I had a baby girl in my hands. She was screaming and objecting to the syringe that Lori was inserting into her nostrils and mouth. And it sounded good. She was healthy. Her color was good, she had all of her arms and legs and fingers and toes.

"Can I see him?" her mother asked, lying flat on her back, exhausted.

"It's 'her'," I said. "And yes you can, in just a second. Let us get her cleaned up first."

"It's a girl?" the voice came from somewhere behind me. It was her father, the young man who had just burst into the ER, and he was clearly excited.

"Yes," I heard Lori tell him. "It's a girl and she's doing great."

"A girl? Are you sure?" he asked again. "We have two boys at home and we've been hopin' for a girl and…Are you sure?"

"Yes, it's a girl," Lori told him. "We're sure. And she's perfect."

She reached down to the OB kit and handed me the umbilical cord clamp. And as I snapped it into place, she gave me the scissors. I was almost ready to sever the white, rubbery cord when I thought of Jack. He was at my elbow, and I handed him the scissors, motioning for him to step a little closer. I held the cord taut, one finger directing where he should cut.

He stared at me but didn't say anything. An insistent nod of my head made my intentions clear. Lori prodded him with an elbow.

His hands were shaking as he reached out and opened the scissors, placing them where I pointed.

"Here?" he mumbled nervously.

"Right there," I answered, waiting.

His first attempt was a little timid, barely nicking the cord. Then without any further prompting on our part, he gathered himself and made a clean cut.

"Good," Lori approved. Then, wrapping the little girl in the warming blanket, she handed her carefully to her mother, laying the baby on her chest.

"Here, Mama," she said to her. "Here's your baby girl."

Jack and I backed away from the car and the young father moved to the door.

Then he turned and grabbed Lori, giving her a big hug. And then he grabbed Jack, hugging him and lifting him off the pavement. Jack looked at me over the man's shoulder, with his eyes big and a sheepish grin spreading across his face. He didn't know what to say.

Then, just as suddenly, he put Jack on the ground and turned to his wife.

"Honey, are you okay?" he asked her, gently patting her knee.

Amy pushed the stretcher next to the station wagon and within a few minutes mother, father, and newborn little girl were all on their way to Labor and Delivery.

Jack and I stood beside each other as Lori finished cleaning up the remains of the OB kit. She then walked off toward the ER, leaving the two of us in the parking lot.

"Well, what'd you think?" I asked him.

"Wow, Dad, that was…that was something else! And it all happened so fast. I mean, one minute there was nothing, and then…then there was a baby. Just like that."

"Uh-huh," I agreed.

"And thanks for letting me cut the cord. I mean, that was really…I wasn't expecting that."

"You did great, Jack. But don't tell your mama. I promised her you'd only be 'observing.'"

I knew that wasn't going to happen.

Later that morning, during a quiet moment between patients, Jack and I had walked back to the lounge for some coffee. As we stepped out into the hallway, he stopped and asked me, "Dad, how often do you do that?"

I knew he was talking about the parking lot delivery, and I said, "Not very often, maybe once or twice a year. But it's always fun. Pretty exciting, wasn't it?"

"Yeah, it was," he agreed. "But do things ever go bad? I mean does it sometimes turn out differently?"

I thought for a moment before I answered. Prior to my residency training in emergency medicine, I had spent a year and a half in pediatrics. As peds residents, we responded to all C-sections and all difficult deliveries in a large community hospital. And sometimes things did go bad. There had been too many terrible tragedies, most of which had been anticipated. But there had been some that came out of nowhere and were devastating for all of us. Looking at Jack's eager and still excited face, I knew I shouldn't go there. Not right now.

"The good thing about delivering babies in the ER—"

"Or in the parking lot," Jack interrupted.

"Or in the parking lot," I agreed, smiling at him, "is that these expectant women are usually healthy and are multips."

"What's a 'multip'?" he asked, puzzled by the term.

"It just means that they've had multiple babies. This might be their second, third, or fourth child. Labor for them is usually much shorter, sometimes less than an hour. That's why they frequently don't make it to the hospital in time, like this morning."

"Hmm," he mused, nodding his understanding. "I guess Mama was a 'multip' when she had me."

Jack was our third child, and he was right.

"Yeah, she was. And you introduced yourself to us pretty quickly," I told him, remembering that spring evening twenty-two years ago.

He looked me square in the face and said, "You know, Dad, I've always known that you delivered me then, but until today, I never really thought about what that meant. I don't remember too much about it myself," he quipped. "But what was it like for you? I mean… what were you thinking?"

I leaned against the hallway wall and looked at him. What had I been thinking?

It had all happened so fast. One minute I was standing by Barbara in the labor room, talking with Eddie Blanchard, our obstetrician. He had just completed his exam and determined her status.

"Barbara, looks like we're ready to go," he had said to her.

And the next minute we were headed down the hall toward the delivery room. Eddie was on one side of the rolling bed and I was on the other.

"Robert, you want to deliver this one?" he had asked me.

It was a bolt out of the blue. He hadn't even looked in my direction and the question had been nonchalant, as if this was some everyday occurrence and just routine.

A thousand thoughts had sped through my mind. I had delivered a reasonable number of babies and I knew what to do. And I knew Eddie wouldn't have considered this had he not been confident in my ability to handle it. Then again, I knew he would be standing right behind me.

But what would Barbara think? Would she be comfortable with this?

I looked down at her. She was white-knuckling the bedrails, experiencing another painful contraction. Her eyes were opened wide and she looked straight at me, nodding and somehow finding a smile.

"Sure, Eddie," I answered, wondering if it was really me saying that. "That would be great."

"Good," he responded, still not looking in my direction. "Then let's get going. Go get scrubbed up."

And then we were in the delivery room. Barbara had been moved to the delivery table and I was putting on a gown and gloves and mask. Eddie was standing behind me, his arms folded casually across his chest, not bothering to put on gloves or gown himself. That was when I knew this was going to be me.

"What was I thinking?" I repeated Jack's question.

He had leaned a little closer, expectantly awaiting my reply.

"Well, just like this morning, it all happened pretty quickly," I began. "And it was pretty amazing. You were easy, once things got started. Your mama pushed a couple of times and there was your head and then your shoulder. And I can remember thinking, *Don't drop this one!* I wasn't about to do that, and I grabbed you for dear life. The doctor in me took over and I made sure you were breathing and that we cleared your airway. You were perfect. Well-shaped head, everything where it was supposed to be. And then the father in me took over. We hadn't known whether you would be a boy or a girl, but now I knew. I was standing there holding my firstborn son. Your mama asked, 'Is everything okay?' But I couldn't answer her. I couldn't speak. I just stood there, holding you, and trying to get myself under control."

Suddenly I remembered those feelings, that awesome sense of something…almost holy. I felt my face flushing and tears beginning to form in my eyes. Then I looked over to see Jack staring at me intently with those same big, dark eyes that had first looked into mine twenty-two years ago.

"It was Eddie who told your mother we had a healthy son," I continued. "And he took you in his big hands and placed you in her arms. And then she was crying and I was crying and you were crying. It was a wonderful moment. And it was a rare and wonderful gift."

We were silent for a moment, and then he said, "Thanks for that, Dad."

I put my arm around his shoulders and we turned and walked up the hallway.

It was five 'til seven, and Tom Anders, my relief, was walking into the department. He was carrying a grocery bag of supplies for the night ahead. A bag of chips was precariously perched on its top.

"Ready to go home, Robert?" he asked cheerfully. Tom didn't mind working nights, and in fact signed up for more than his share of them. "No hospital politics at 3 a.m.," he frequently said.

"Yes, we're ready to go," I answered, glancing in Jack's direction. "Nothing to turn over to you. Everything's been taken care of."

"Great. Thanks," Tom said to me. Then turning to Jack, "Do any brain surgery today?"

"Not today, Dr. Anders. Maybe tomorrow," Jack answered, smiling.

"Good. Well, I guess I'll see you in the morning." He turned and walked down the hall toward our office.

We were standing in front of the counter at the nurses' station and I turned to my son.

"Jack, if you have just a little more time, there's someone I want you to meet."

"Sure," he said. "I don't have anything planned for this evening. Actually, I'm kind of tired, and I'll probably just stay home tonight."

"This won't take long. And I'm not sure how many opportunities you'll have to meet this man."

We walked to the back of the department and then to the staff elevators. The doors closed behind us and I pushed the button for the fourth floor.

We stood in silence as we smoothly ascended, stopping at the highest level of the hospital. The doors silently glided open and we stepped out.

"This way," I instructed him, pointing to our left. "We need to go to 4-B. It's a general medical floor."

We walked into a deserted waiting area and I stopped.

"Jack, let me tell you something about the man you're going to meet," I began.

He looked up at me, his expression open and waiting.

"His name is Duncan MacKinnon, and he's quite an interesting fellow."

I then told him how I had first met Duncan. It had been a cold December morning, about a year and a half ago. He had come into the ER complaining of nausea and some difficulty swallowing. And though he was able to swallow and to drink liquids, he had gotten to the point where he couldn't get anything solid down. This had been going on for a week or so and he finally had enough and came to the ER to get it checked out.

"He was almost eighty, but looked like he might have been sixty," I told Jack. "He was lean, strong, and his mind was as sharp as a tack. And he had a great sense of humor," I remembered.

Duncan MacKinnon had no family in the area and he lived alone. His story was bothersome, and when he told me he had lost ten pounds over the past two weeks, I became more concerned.

A suspicious chest X-ray had led to other imaging procedures and within a short period of time, I had to inform him of his diagnosis. He had esophageal cancer, and from the looks of his studies, it was inoperable. A surgical consult confirmed our worst fears, offering little if any hope.

"Maybe some radiation," the surgeon had told Duncan. "That might slow things down. But I'm afraid there's nothing else we can offer."

He had stoically accepted the news, seemingly expecting this death sentence. I think he had known when he first came to the ER. And yet, there was a peace about him, something different that we didn't often see in this circumstance.

I hadn't seen Duncan for several months after that. Then, about a year after we had made this diagnosis, he had come back to the ER. He had become dehydrated, now finding it difficult to even keep fluids down. Prior to that time, he had worked hard at maintaining his weight and energy levels, drinking a lot of liquid supplements. But that was no longer working.

We began to see him on a regular basis after that. He didn't want to be admitted to the hospital, but just wanted to be given some IV fluids and then be sent home. Amazingly, he was blessed with little to no pain.

A week ago, he had come to the ER in pretty bad shape. We had started an IV and had given him a couple of liters of saline. But I knew what I needed to do.

"Duncan," I told him. "I can't send you home this time. You need to stay in the hospital."

"I know, I know," he had said softly, nodding at me. "I locked up the house and gave the key to my neighbor."

And that was it. He had been in the hospital ever since that day.

I paused and gazed down at the floor. Then I looked up at Jack.

"This is a good man," I told him. "And he has an interesting outlook on life. You'll see."

I tapped on the door of room 417 and pushed it open. There was no response, and I assumed Duncan had not heard us. We stepped quietly into the room and I closed the door behind us.

He was lying on his back in the hospital bed, his failing body barely forming any contours under the thin hospital blanket.

His eyes were closed, and he was humming a familiar and haunting melody. Then, somehow sensing our presence, he stopped his humming, opened his eyes, and turned his head in our direction.

"Dr. Lesslie," he greeted me, still with surprising strength in his voice. "Glad you could come by this evening. And who is this young man with you? This must be one of the young Lesslies."

Jack stepped toward the bed and held out his hand to Mr. Mackinnon.

"I'm Jack Lesslie," he said, but now he was hesitating. Duncan was struggling to free his right hand from the hospital sheets. It was fettered with the IV line, taped securely in place on the back of his wrist. His arm and hand were covered with bruises and his skin was paper-thin. He looked down and shook his head in frustration.

"Doggone it…" he muttered, still struggling to free himself.

Jack reached down and patted the back of his wasted hand, and then grasped it gently. It was something his mother would have done.

"Yes, I'm Dr. Lesslie's son, and I'm glad to meet you."

Duncan relaxed at this, and his arm settled back on the sheets.

If possible, he had lost even more weight since I had last seen him, just two days earlier. He was disappearing, melting away. Yet his spirit remained strong and his eyes were bright and engaging. For a moment I wondered if bringing Jack up here had been a mistake. But when he looked at Jack and smiled, my initial thoughts were confirmed. This would be a good thing.

"So," Duncan said, "I understand you're not sure what you want to do with yourself. Not sure about going into medicine, or architecture, or…Well, you're just not sure."

Jack was about to respond when Duncan continued.

"Well, that's okay. In fact, that's good. You need to be sure about how you want to spend the rest of your life. At least, as far as work is concerned. But you know, that can always change. You can change direction most times, though it becomes more difficult as we get older."

He told Jack about some of the things he had done during his life, careers he had pursued, jobs he had worked. And then abruptly he said, "Let me tell you about something your father did for me. He might not even remember this, but I do. Always will."

He looked at me knowingly, but I had no clue where this was headed.

"Last fall," he continued, "I was having some problems and needed to come to the ER for some fluids. It was a Saturday afternoon and I tried to put it off as long as I could, but...Well, I had to come in. The problem was, it was the Clemson–South Carolina football game and I was going to miss it. My nephew had gone to Clemson, and Lord forgive me, I had become a Tiger fan. Didn't want to miss that game, but I had no choice.

"When I got to the hospital, your father was on duty, and he got an IV going and all that, and I just happened to mention something about the ballgame. Well, the next thing I know, the nurses are putting me in a wheelchair and rolling me somewhere down the hall. They took me into your father's office and into the call room. Then they propped me up in the bed and turned on the TV. Never missed a minute of the game. Got to watch the whole thing."

He smiled and looked in my direction. "Yep, Dr. Lesslie came back to peek in on me a few times, said he was just checking on the score of the game, but I knew better."

I remembered that visit, and asking the nurses to take him back to our call room. It was a small thing, and certainly no sacrifice to me. I was a little embarrassed.

"Yes, I won't forget that," Duncan repeated. "Can't remember who won that game, but I'll never forget what your father did for me."

We were silent for a moment, and then he said, "You know what I really regret? I really wish we had had a chance to play some cribbage."

He looked over at Jack and winked. Then he continued. "Your father was talkin' about how he could whip me and all. Sounds like he needs a little lesson in humility, and this old navy hand could probably give him one. We used to play a lot of cribbage, me and…me and the boys." These last words trailed off, and there was an awkward silence. I sensed it was time for us to leave, and I stretched and made a tentative move toward the door.

"One more thing, Dr. Lesslie, Jack," Duncan said, his voice once again strong and clear. "The hospital chaplain came by yesterday. Good fellow, well-intentioned and all. I suppose he just wanted to make me feel better, share some warm and fuzzy thoughts. Well, he got to talking about the 'circle of life,' about how we are born, then we live our lives, and then we die. About how that comes full circle somehow. I guess he thought that would make me feel better about where I am, close to the end and all."

He glanced at me briefly, but then looked directly in Jack's eyes. "But you know, son, I don't think that's the case at all. Life is not circular, with us somehow coming back to where we started. No, I think it's more linear. We're on a path, and that path starts the day we're born. And whether we understand it or know it or even believe it, we are all on that same path. And that path leads us all to one place. We are all marching to God's throne. And standing at the side of God's throne is Jesus. And you know, it's all about Him, isn't it? The problem is we don't all understand that. If we did, we would live our lives differently. We would pay more attention to the journey, and to the people who are on that journey with us. But it still remains, we're all on the same path. And when we reach the throne, well, that will be the best beginning of all."

He stopped, and I could tell he was tired. This time we needed to leave and allow him to rest.

We told him goodbye, made sure that everything he needed was within reach, and then we stepped out into the corridor.

As we walked down the hallway, Jack said, "Thanks for bringing me up here."

"He made me promise to bring you with me the next time I visited," I responded. "That was good for him. It was good for all of us."

We reached the waiting area, still deserted, and I stopped once more.

"Did you hear him humming when we first went into his room?" I asked Jack.

"I did, but...I couldn't quite make it out. It sounded like something I had heard before."

"He was humming 'It Is Well with My Soul,'" I told him. "It's a great old hymn, but one you've probably not sung in our church. Do you know the words?"

"No, I don't think I do," he answered.

"There's some interesting history behind the writer of the lyrics, and the words are very powerful. The first verse is the only one I can remember, and it goes like this,

> When peace, like a river, attendeth my way,
> When sorrows like sea billows roll;
> Whatever my lot, Thou hast taught me to say,
> It is well, it is well with my soul.

The next day, Jack and I took our lunch break and went around to the cafeteria. After we had eaten, we were walking back to the department and passed the staff elevators.

"Dad, why don't you go on back to the ER? I think I'll go upstairs and check on Mr. MacKinnon. You think that would be okay?" he asked me.

"I think he'd like that," I said. "And take your time."

I walked on to the ER and Jack got on the elevator.

At the nurses' station, I had picked up the chart of a child in room 3. "Fever and cough." I was turning to go to that cubicle when I noticed Jack walking up the hallway toward me. He had his hands in his pockets, and there was a troubled look on his face. He stood before me, looking down at the chart in my hands, not saying anything.

Then he looked up at me and quietly said, "I went up to room 417... and it's empty."

Later that night, after I had taken a shower, I walked back into our bedroom and over to the bed. There, on top of my pillow, was a piece of paper. Jack had sat down at our computer and searched the web. He had found the lyrics to Duncan MacKinnon's hymn and printed a copy. As I glanced at the sheet of paper, I noticed he had circled the fourth verse.

> *And Lord, haste the day when faith shall be sight,*
> *The clouds be rolled back as a scroll;*
> *The trump shall resound, and the Lord shall descend,*
> *"Even so"—it is well with my soul.*

Bonus content from

ANGELS
and
HEROES

*To the men and women
who put their lives
on the line every day—
for each one of us.*

Contents

O reader!
Had you in your mind
Such stories as silent thought can bring,
O gentle reader!
You would find
A tale in every thing.

WILLIAM WORDSWORTH (1770–1850)

Introduction for *Angels* and *Heroes*

When I was asked to consider writing a book about the experiences of firemen, police officers, and paramedics, my first response was one of reluctance and trepidation. My first two books were stories drawn from my own experiences and I was writing about how the people in them had affected me. This would be something different, and something I needed to think about.

I told them I would talk to some of my friends in those fields, and see where that would lead. I had no idea what the Lord had in store for me over the next few weeks and months.

As I began to sit down with these men and women, it quickly became clear they had a lot to say, and powerful stories to share. They weren't only interested in telling me about dramatic saves and incredible encounters, though some of them will be found in these pages. What they *really* wanted to tell me about were the people who had touched their hearts and changed their lives. That was what was important to them.

And almost to a person, they would call me after that first or second meeting and say, "Robert, I've got something else I want to share with you." These would be the experiences they had filed away somewhere, deep in their hearts, and had only shared with a few people, if anyone. These were the most powerful and moving stories, and the stories that needed to be told. They were true accounts about life and death, about the preciousness of our time on this earth, and about a faith that upholds and sustains us.

I realized then that Harvest House had given me a great opportunity and a significant responsibility. It's not everyday that we can tell the stories of real heroes, or of angels in our midst.

Fire Station No. 1

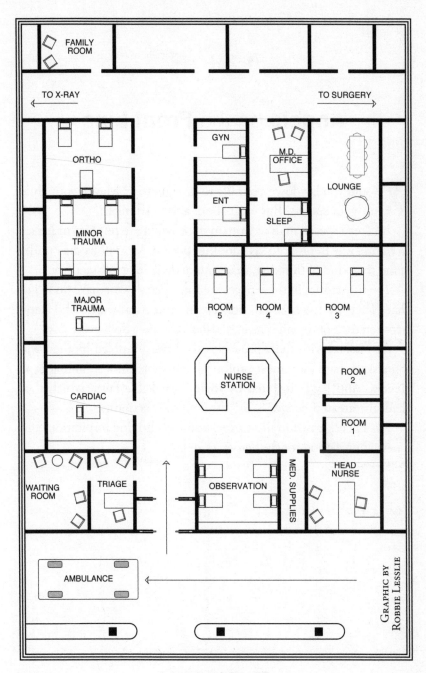

Layout of the ER

Angels on the Front Line

Would you lay down your life to save another? Maybe your child, or your spouse. But what about a total stranger?

It takes a special man or woman to be willing to put him or herself in harm's way in order to save another person. Most of us can't understand that kind of thinking, that kind of deliberate self-sacrifice.

The true stories in these pages are from people who have done just that. They are the firemen, policemen, and paramedics who stand between each of us and certain disaster. And they do it every day.

As I talked with these professionals, I was humbled by their willingness to share their most profound and sometimes troubling experiences. And I was inspired by their unshakable faith, which they demonstrate in their words and through their actions.

It is my hope that in these pages you will also find inspiration, and a new appreciation for the heroes among us.

1

Salt Lick Road

This is my Father's world.
O let me ne'er forget
That though the wrong seems oft so strong,
God is the ruler yet.

"This Is My Father's World"
Maltbie D. Babcock (1858–1901)

Friday, 2:15 p.m. Sharon and Mike Brothers were putting the final touches on EMS Unit 5. The Hickory Grove Christmas parade was scheduled to start in less than two hours, and they had waxed and polished the ambulance until it sparkled. They were to be the lead vehicle, and if the parade was anything like last year's, they would be followed by a vintage Plymouth, two fire trucks, and a tractor pulling Santa on a hay wagon. It wasn't going to be a very long parade, and they wanted to be sure their ambulance made the right impression.

Mike was standing behind the vehicle, trying to attach a large wreath to the back doors. So far, he wasn't having much success.

Sharon opened the front door and slid into the driver's seat. As she was hanging some brightly colored balls from the rearview mirror, the dash radio crackled to life.

"Good grief!" she exclaimed, dropping and breaking one of the ornaments.

Then she heard one of her friends from dispatch say, "We've got an accidental shooting on the west side of the county. No other report yet, but it doesn't sound too bad."

There was silence as Sharon began picking up the broken decoration. She was off duty, and she waited for someone to respond to the call.

"Sharon, are you there?" the dispatcher asked.

"Doggone it," Sharon muttered to herself.

She picked up the radio receiver and answered. "This is Sharon. I'm not workin', and I'm out at the house with Mike. We're getting ready for the Hickory Grove parade."

Sharon suspected what was coming next, and she was right.

"We've got every unit out on a call," the dispatcher informed her. "You guys are pretty close, maybe a mile and a half away. Is there any way..."

Sharon sighed and looked at her watch. If it was a simple call, they could probably get to the scene, pick up the patient, get to the hospital in Rock Hill and then back to Hickory Grove just in time to make the parade.

"Sure, we can do it," she answered. "But you know it's me and Mike," she added.

It was contrary to EMS policy for a husband and wife to work on the same unit. They both had different partners when they were working, but today they had scheduled themselves to be off for the parade.

"That's fine," the dispatcher responded. "The shift supervisor is aware and says it's okay. This should be a routine run."

Sharon wrote down the address of the call, tossed the radio receiver into the passenger seat, and jumped out of the ambulance.

"Mike, come on! We gotta go!" she called out to her husband.

"What's going on?" he asked. His wreath was dangling from one of the door handles, and when he stepped away to find Sharon, it fell to the ground. He mumbled something incoherent, shook his head, and then kicked the greenery over into the yard.

Sharon walked around to where he stood and quickly told him about the call.

"Let's get going!" he said to her, quickly moving to the driver's door and jumping in. She hurried around to the passenger side, shaking her head as she saw the disheveled wreath lying in the grass.

"Oh, well," she sighed.

As Mike turned the ambulance around in their driveway, she glanced at the notes she had made and told him where they were headed.

"Salt Lick Road."

"Isn't that a dirt road off Highway 5?" he asked her. "Some ol' loggin' trail?"

"I think you're right," Sharon answered, pulling a county map out of the glove compartment. "Let me be sure."

She knew just about every road and cow path on this side of the county, but she wasn't familiar with Salt Lick Road. She traced Highway 5 with her finger, searching for this obscure location.

"There it is," she exclaimed. "About a mile past Shiloh Church."

They were now on Highway 5, and Mike switched on the lights and siren.

"What did they say was the problem?" he asked Sharon.

"A shooting accident of some kind," she answered. "Didn't sound serious, but Cheryl was dispatchin', and she didn't have much information."

Mike slowed as they sped past Shiloh Church, and Sharon peered ahead on their left for the road sign.

"Look, there it is!" she called out to him, pointing to a neglected wooden sign haphazardly nailed to a pine tree. "Salt Lick Road," she read.

They turned onto the dirt track and had to slow to a crawl to battle the ruts and twists of the old lumber trail.

"You think anybody lives out here?" Mike asked her. "I mean, this place is the middle of nowhere."

Sharon glanced down at her note. "That's what Cheryl told me," she answered, shaking her head. "Salt Lick Road. There must be a house out here somewhere."

The road seemed to be getting narrower, and they had to drive across fallen branches and dodge an old truck tire. Mike was about to stop and turn around when just up ahead, they saw an old clapboard house standing in the middle of a small, grassless field. The yard around it was littered with trash. Sharon noticed a small child's bike, its front wheel bent and useless.

On the right side of the house was an old Chevy truck, its axles propped up on cinder blocks, wheels and tires missing.

There was no driveway or gravel, just the bare dirt. Mike got as close to the house as he could.

Odd. Nobody came to the door or peered out from any of the windows. Their siren was still on, and somebody should have heard them approaching.

For the first time she could remember, Sharon felt uneasy. There was something wrong about this place.

"Let's go," Mike said, jumping out of the ambulance and heading to the rear of the vehicle. He was opening the doors and taking down the collapsible stretcher as Sharon stepped down and turned toward the house. She scanned the door and windows again for any movement. Nothing.

Mike had turned off the engine and the siren. As Sharon stood in front of the house, she became aware of the eerie silence. Nothing seemed to be moving or alive. Suddenly she felt an uncomfortable chill. It was a mild December day, but something made her shiver.

The loud cackle of a crow startled her. She looked away from the house. There, behind the beat-up truck and near the edge of the clearing, stood a dying black walnut tree. Its once proud and strong limbs were now reduced to a few spindly, twisted branches, dark black and silhouetted against the winter sky. Two crows were perched on the topmost branch and peered down at these recent intruders. With another cackle directed at Sharon, they took off from their limb and disappeared over the tops of the surrounding pine trees.

Silence again.

Mike walked around from behind the ambulance, pushing the unit's stretcher before him.

"Did Cheryl say the county had been notified?" he asked, wanting to be sure that law enforcement was on the way.

"I thought she did," Sharon replied hesitantly, not completely sure of her answer.

Mike glanced up at the gloomy and depressing house. He wasn't satisfied with Sharon's response. "Let's hold on before we go in there. I'll call dispatch and make sure an officer is on his way."

He let go of the stretcher and turned back to the ambulance and its dashboard radio.

Sharon was only twenty feet from the front door and for the first time noticed it was cracked open, but only an inch or so. Its rusted and torn screen door was closed, but the door itself was ajar and obviously not latched. She stepped toward the house and onto the small concrete slab that served as the front stoop.

As she opened the screen door, the screeching of its rusted hinges caused her to shiver again, and she thought about waiting for Mike. But something was pulling her into the house. She reached out and tapped lightly on the wooden front door and then pushed it in a little ways.

"Anybody here?" she called out into the silence. "This is the EMS. Is anybody hurt?"

She strained to hear any response, but there was only the sound of the breeze in the pines behind her, stirring as the evening was coming on.

"Anybody here?" she called again, pushing the door wide open and stepping into the house.

Am I crazy? she thought. *What if...*

And then the smell overwhelmed her. It was a combination of decomposing garbage, urine, and some musty odor she couldn't recognize. But it was awful. Although she had been in a lot of places, including a lot of rundown and neglected houses and apartments, this was the worst.

As her eyes grew accustomed to the darkness, she was shocked by what she saw. The room she was standing in was large and square, with a few dirty windows on two sides covered with old and yellowed sheets. The wooden floor was littered with debris and scattered pieces of what seemed to be clothing. A door to her left led to the kitchen, where most of the foul odor seemed to be coming from. She could see stacks of dirty dishes on the small table, all containing unrecognizable remnants of food. On one of the two kitchen chairs, there was a pizza box. It was open, and Sharon could see a few moldy pieces of discarded crust in the bottom of it. A milk carton was overturned on the worn green linoleum floor, with a small puddle spreading out in front of it. It was starting to dry, and must have been there for a while.

This must be a mistake, Sharon thought. She wondered if she had written down the wrong address, or if someone had phoned in a bogus call. No one had been living in this place for a while.

"Hello! Is anybody here?" she called out once more.

She glanced around the room again, listening for any sign that someone else was in the house. It was completely quiet.

She looked over to her right, to a doorway that probably led to the bedrooms. Against the wall beside that door was a sleeper sofa. Its mattress was pulled out, and Sharon could see that it was filthy and partially covered with an old army blanket.

She wondered if hoboes had been living in this house, or druggies, or…maybe worse. Then she felt that chill again. She turned to the front door, ready to get Mike and get out of this place.

Sharon took two steps and heard the floor creak beneath her. It startled her, and she chuckled nervously at her own silliness. Then she heard the clatter of stretcher wheels as Mike approached the front door. His presence brought a welcome sense of relief.

She was reaching for the front doorknob when she heard it. She froze where she stood and then spun around, searching for the source of the noise.

It was coming from the direction of the doorway to the bedrooms, but somehow it had seemed closer. And then she heard it again. It was a whimper. The kind made by a small child.

Mike stepped through the door. "What ya got, Sharon? Cheryl said a county deputy should be here in—"

"Shh!" she quieted him, pointing to the right side of the room. Her finger jabbed the air, and she whispered, "Listen!"

"Wha—" he started to say.

"Shh!" Sharon repeated, pointing now to the sofa.

And then they both heard it. It *was* the whimper of a small child. Then it was joined by another.

Mike and Sharon bolted toward the sofa, each grabbing one side to move it. It didn't weigh much and was threatening to fall apart, so they had no trouble pulling it out from the wall.

Sharon gasped, unable to speak.

"Good Lord!" Mike sighed heavily.

Sitting on the floor with their backs to the wall were three little blond-headed girls. The oldest couldn't have been more than four. They were filthy—each wore only soiled and tattered panties. They looked up at Mike and Sharon with wide, sad eyes, not moving at all. The youngest started to whimper again, and then they all began to. The lower lip of the oldest girl began to tremble, and large tears streaked down her dirt-covered face.

Sharon sprang into action, quickly getting to the girls while taking off her jacket.

"Come here, sweethearts," she whispered to them soothingly, drawing them to her and covering them with her jacket. They didn't resist, and they pressed themselves against the warmth of her body.

Sharon looked up at Mike, a mother hen protecting her brood. He just shook his head and began to glance around the room.

"I think the bedrooms are that way," Sharon told him, motioning with her head to the nearby doorway.

They both heard the siren of the county patrol car as it approached through the woods.

"Good," Mike said with relief. "I'm going to see if anyone else is in the house. It looks like somebody abandoned these kids—just left them here."

"But what about the gunshot?" Sharon asked him. "Somebody called in an accidental shooting. Maybe they got tired of waiting and just took off without the children."

"Could be," he replied, moving toward the doorway. That didn't make much sense, though. Something else was going on here.

"Be careful," Sharon said to him, clutching the little girls even tighter. They were quieter now, and had stopped their whimpering.

Mike disappeared toward the bedroom as the county car came to a stop in the front yard. Sharon heard a door slam as the deputy got out and approached the house.

"Oh no!"

It was Mike. Sharon could hear the shock and disbelief in his voice. John Pendergrass, the county deputy, was coming through the front door just as Mike uttered this exclamation. He heard it too, and immediately drew his revolver.

She motioned to the door but didn't say a word.

"Sharon!" Mike called out. There was a tone of desperation in his voice she had never heard before.

"It's John Pendergrass," the deputy called out, heading quickly to the doorway. "Where are you, Mike?" he asked. Then he disappeared as well.

Mike was easy to find. He was standing on the far side of the only bedroom in the house. It was small, and just as filthy as the living room and kitchen.

"Mike…" John called out. Mike's back was to the deputy, and he was standing in the bathroom doorway, steadying himself with one hand tightly gripping the door jamb. He didn't turn around when John spoke his name, but just kept staring into the small room.

"Mike," John repeated, stepping over to where he stood and standing behind him. He looked over the medic's shoulder into the bathroom and gasped as if all the air had been knocked out of him.

Against the far wall was the bathtub. And in the bathtub was the body of a young woman. She was fully clothed. There was no water in the tub—it looked as if she had just climbed in to relax for a while. She was leaning comfortably back against the end of the tub, with her head resting on the edge. Most of her brains and the back of her head were missing, splattered against the tiled wall. Her mouth was partially open, where she had inserted the business end of a handgun.

Her left arm was draped over the side of the tub, and on the floor, just out of reach of her lifeless fingers, was a cordless phone.

Mike and John were silent for a moment, staring in horror and disbelief. Then John spoke. "We ran down this address and the names of the people who live here. The husband works over in York, and we got in touch with him. He should be here any minute."

Mike just nodded his head without saying a word.

Another deputy sheriff pulled into the yard, and after the two officers had talked, they made a sweep of the rest of the house and the surrounding yard and woods. Nothing else turned up, just the bleak realization of the desolate and distorted world of these little girls.

Sharon had bundled them up as best she could and was sitting with them in the back of one of the deputies' cars. They would be taken to Rock Hill General to be examined. And then there would be the decision of finding a safe place for them to stay.

"Billy and Samantha Myers," the second deputy had told John and Mike. "That's Samantha in there," he added, motioning toward the house. "Billy should be here any minute. But I don't think the kids need to be here. We need to move them on to the hospital."

Mike agreed and said he would follow the deputy to the ER in his ambulance. He had completely forgotten about the Hickory Grove parade. It would be starting in about five minutes without them.

"I'm not sure I want to be here either," he added, his initial shock now giving way to anger. "What kind of a father would allow his children to live like this? How could *he* live like this?"

"You guys go on," John replied. "I'll wait here on Billy Myers. I have a couple of questions for him myself."

Sharon shepherded the three girls through the back entrance of the ER and led them into the empty ortho room. They needed some privacy— and to be out from under the curious eyes of strangers. Word was starting to filter through the community about the tragedy somewhere off Highway 5. The girls hadn't said a word during the thirty-minute trip to the hospital, and when Sharon tried to lift them up onto one of the stretchers, they clung desperately to her legs. She grabbed a blanket from a nearby counter and sat down on the floor, wrapping it around herself and the girls, and cradling them once more.

Later that evening Sharon and Mike learned that Billy Myers was in jail, with multiple charges pending. The three girls had been examined by the ER doctor and were okay. They were undernourished, but there was no evidence of physical abuse. Their emotional health was a different matter. They were now in the emergency custody of an aunt who lived on the northern side of Rock Hill. The girls had recognized their Aunt Ruth but had only hesitantly left the protective embrace of Sharon when their aunt and uncle had arrived in the ER. Sharon had been reluctant to let them go, but the agent from the Department of Social Services had assured her they would be safe.

Samantha Myers had shot herself shortly after Billy had left the house for work. She had been struggling for several years with depression and, according to another sheriff's deputy, because of the physical and emotional abuse of her husband. Something had snapped this morning. She had found Billy's handgun, gone into the bathroom, and left her three daughters forever motherless.

As they drove home in the winter darkness, Sharon and Mike were silent, each uneasy from their own troubled thoughts.

As a mother, Sharon couldn't begin to understand what had happened in that lonely house today. She couldn't understand how that family had so utterly disintegrated into the waste and depravity they had witnessed. And what was to become of those girls? Their father obviously wasn't capable of or interested in taking care of them. And how long would their aunt and uncle be willing to provide for them?

They were turning into their driveway when she realized what she needed to do.

"Mike, I've got a thought, and I need to make sure it's okay with you," she began. "If it's not—well, that's fine."

Mike pulled the ambulance to a stop and cut off the motor. Then he took the key out of the ignition, sat back in his seat, and turned to his wife.

"What's on your mind?" he asked her.

She hesitated for a moment, still wrestling with her decision. But only for a moment.

"I know how much you've been wanting that new Beretta over-and-under 20-gauge shotgun," she began. "And I've been puttin' some money back each month and next paycheck should just about give me enough. I was goin' to surprise you with it at Christmas, but I...I think we need to spend that money on those little girls. They need some clothes, and I didn't see a single toy in that house, and I..."

Mike started laughing, and Sharon stopped mid-sentence.

"What's so funny?" she asked him. "What are you laughin' at?"

He shook his head and just smiled at her.

"Let me tell you what *I've* been thinkin'," he told her.

He proceeded to tell her of his plans to surprise her with a Caribbean cruise in January. They had never been on one, and Sharon had wistfully expressed her hopes that someday they would be able to do just that. They both knew how expensive it would be, yet Mike had somehow been able to put the money aside without his wife's knowing about it.

"I was really excited about surprising you with that at Christmas," he told her. "But on the way home, I was thinkin' about those little girls and how we should best use that money. If it's okay with you, let's put our money together and see what we can come up with."

"A cruise!" Sharon exclaimed. "Why you ol'...How did you keep your mouth shut about that? A shotgun...I mean, that's just a...well, a shotgun. But a cruise!"

She leaned over and hugged him around his neck. Then she kissed him on his cheek and mussed his hair.

"A cruise!" she cried out again. "Why, of course we'll give that money to the girls."

After a few days of shopping, they loaded up their SUV and headed to the home of Ruth and Fred Biggers, the girls' aunt and uncle.

Sharon had called and talked at length with Ruth about how they were doing and what they needed most. They pulled into the driveway, parked, and walked up the steps to the front door. They were empty-handed, having decided to bring the gifts in later. They just wanted to see the girls. This would be the first time since that terrible afternoon less than a week ago.

Sharon looked over at Mike. He nodded at her, smiled, and rang the doorbell.

From within, they could hear the scamper of little feet, and a deep voice calling out, "Not so fast, girls! Take your time."

The door opened, and there stood Karlie, Sue Ellen, and Jasmine. Jasmine was the youngest, and she bolted through the door and grabbed Sharon around her knees, burying her face in her cotton slacks. The other two were jumping up and down and calling out Sharon's name. Then Karlie, the oldest girl, reached out and took Mike's hand in hers, looking up at him with those same large, brown eyes. This time, unlike their first meeting, she was smiling.

Fifteen years had gone by. Sharon and Mike were driving down Highway 5 on their way to the mountains for a weekend getaway. They had just left the Biggers's house, having dropped off Christmas gifts for the three girls, something they had been doing for a decade and a half.

Karlie had been away at Clemson, where she was in nursing school. She was doing well with her class work, and during her clinical rotations she demonstrated a rare gift of empathy, something she attributed to "Aunt Sharon." She planned on becoming a nurse practitioner and wanted to specialize in pediatrics.

Sue Ellen was a senior in high school, and was struggling. She found books "boring," and Ruth and Fred were having problems with her behavior. The last time Mike and Sharon had visited, he had made it a point to have a talk with her. They had discussed a lot of things, and she had opened up with Mike, telling him what was troubling her. On the way home that night, he had told Sharon, "Sue Ellen is going to be okay. It may take a while, but she's going to be okay."

And Jasmine. She was a junior in high school and was wide open. She played volleyball, sang in the chorus, was president of her class, and was a favorite of her teachers. She didn't remember anything of Salt Lick Road, and none of them ever talked about it. They did know about their father, Billy, and that he had spent time in prison. When he got out, he had disappeared. The last anyone had heard of him, he was somewhere in Tennessee.

"The girls seem to be doing fine," Mike said as they drove down the highway.

"Yeah—they do, don't they?" Sharon agreed.

As they slowed to negotiate one of the many sharp turns, they both glanced over to their left, toward the entrance to a well-worn logging road. The rutted dirt track disappeared forlornly into a large stretch of pine forest. Still nailed to one of the first trees was a wooden sign, now barely hanging on by one remaining nail and pointing to the ground. Most of the letters were now faded, but you could still just make out "Salt Lick Road."

Sharon glanced up at Mike as they passed, and she saw the smile forming on his face. She gently patted his leg, and turned again to the road ahead.

2

A Line in the Sand

Everything was going wrong.

Michael Greenfield had stuck to his routine this morning, just like he always did. He had been up and showered and out the door at 6:30. Now he was sitting in his patrol car, checking out his equipment, just like always. He had unloaded his firearm and placed the clip on the seat behind him, inspecting the barrel, making sure it was clean. Just like always. And then he realized he hadn't packed his lunch. For a moment he thought about going back inside and quickly making a sandwich. But he glanced at his watch and realized he didn't have enough time. This was his first day riding solo, and though he knew he was ready, he was still more than a little nervous. And he didn't want to be late.

After all, Michael was a rookie, and the fact that he had finished number one at the police academy would mean there would be a lot of eyes on him. He would just have to pick up lunch somewhere.

He was satisfied with the condition of his duty weapon and was reaching toward the seat beside him when his radio suddenly demanded his attention. He tossed the handgun down and picked up the receiver. The loaded clip of bullets bounced to the back of the seat and underneath several loose pages of yesterday's reports.

"Any units in the vicinity of Mt. Gallant and Celanese, report to the scene of a 10-50. No PI's" (personal injuries), the dispatcher reported.

Michael was all the way across town and not officially on duty yet. Besides, this sounded like a routine fender-bender, with no one really hurt. He listened as two units near the accident responded. They were en route. That should handle it. He put the receiver back into its holder on the dash. Then he put his gun back into its holster and backed out of his driveway.

His assignment today was patrolling a quiet area of town. Shouldn't be too demanding. Yet it was his first time riding alone, and there was still that uneasy, nervous feeling in the pit of his stomach. Excitement, he supposed. And that was okay. His chief had told him that if you weren't at least a little nervous, you were in danger of becoming overconfident. And when you were overconfident you made mistakes. He wasn't going to tell his chief that he forgot to pack his lunch on his first day solo.

Michael chuckled, laughing at himself. He reached for his left breast pocket and for the pen he kept there.

"Doggone it!" he exclaimed, feeling his face flush. As he brushed his hand against his chest, he quickly realized he hadn't put on his Kevlar vest. It wasn't mandatory, at least not yet with the police department. His wife—well, that was a different matter. She had insisted from the very beginning that he wear the protective vest anytime he was on duty.

"If you don't worry about yourself," she had said, "You should worry about me and about Jenny. We want you to come home at night, you know."

Jenny was only a year old and wasn't yet aware of what her father was wearing, or even that he was a policeman. But Michael had promised his wife he would wear the vest, and so far, he had done that.

But today he had left it hanging over the back of the chair in their bedroom. He thought about turning around and heading back home, but decided against it. It was now a quarter of seven, and he was officially on duty. And anyway, his assignment was pretty cushy. Busting a few jaywalkers would probably be the extent of his excitement. No, he would head over to his patrol area and wait until he got home this afternoon to apologize to Becca.

Then he thought about his lunch again and decided to stop at Sam's Market and pick up something there. It was on the way to his patrol area, and it would only take a minute.

Michael picked up his radio and reported his location.

"10-4," the dispatcher responded. "Keep your radio open."

Everything was going wrong.

Roddy Anderson stood in the middle of the convenience store and wondered how things had suddenly gotten so complicated.

It was a simple plan, and foolproof. Or so he had thought. Roddy had been released from the "big house" in Columbia a week ago and had met with his parole officer yesterday. Clean as a whistle, he had convinced the officer that he was about to get a job and get his life in order.

"Just stay out of trouble, Roddy," the man had told him, even patting him on the back. "And I'll see you in a week."

The problem was that Roddy didn't have a job yet and he needed some money. Not a lot, just enough to get him by for a few days. Something would come along for him, it always did. But he was a multiple offender, and one more conviction would put him away for life. He had to be careful.

That's why this job had seemed perfect. It was going to be simple, with no fuss and no trouble. Just walk into the store, show his gun to the attendant, grab the money, and be gone. At this hour of the morning, there shouldn't be many, if any, customers in the place, and it all should take a minute or two at the most. He would wear a mask and gloves, and be gone without a trace.

But it had all turned south in a hurry.

When he got to the store, he had seen the old man behind the counter reading his newspaper. Roddy quickly put on his gloves and slipped the ski mask over his head, adjusting the eyeholes as best he could. They weren't quite big enough, and he had trouble seeing very much peripherally. But it would have to do.

He had stepped into the store and toward the checkout counter. The old man had looked up at him and then over to his right somewhere. Roddy had followed his glance and had seen the middle-aged couple standing in front of the milk and juice refrigerator. They were studying the label of a container of orange juice and hadn't looked in his direction.

Roddy pulled out his .38 and silently pointed it at the man behind the counter. He held his other hand palm up, nervously gesturing for the old man, now pale and shaking, to get whatever money he had out of the cash drawer.

That's when things went haywire. He heard the woman behind him scream loudly, and then something dropped on the floor. It was the container of orange juice. It burst and went everywhere. Roddy looked back at the couple just as they ducked out of view behind the refrigerator. Something made him step back from the counter, and it was a good thing. The baseball bat missed his head by only an inch or two, and he could feel and hear the whoosh as it swept by him. He turned and faced the old man, now wide-eyed and ready to swing at him again. Roddy thought about shooting him but was worried about the noise it would make. He swung the revolver, backhanding the man, striking the right side of his face and splitting the top of his ear.

The blow stunned the old man, and he slumped to the countertop, dropping the bat and grabbing the side of his bleeding face.

During all of this, the ski mask had shifted on Roddy's head, and he could only see out of one eyehole. Without thinking, he pulled it off and stuffed it into his pants. The old man raised his head and stared at Roddy, noting every detail of his face, recording it forever in his mind. Roddy knew what he was doing, and he swore.

He held the gun on the man and said, "Listen, it's nothin' for me to shoot you, you hear me? I don't care if I do or don't. It's up to you."

The man nodded silently, his blood dripping onto the newspaper.

Roddy had called out to the two in the back of the store, threatening to shoot the man in front of him if they didn't come up to the front. It had worked, and now here they were. Roddy was holding his gun on the old man. The couple was sitting on the floor a few feet away where Roddy could keep an eye on them, and he was.

The woman was sobbing, and tightly holding on to her husband. She looked up at the bleeding man behind the counter and sobbed, "Sam…"

A new understanding spread across Roddy's face and he said, "So, you the owner of this place?"

Sam didn't say anything, but just kept holding his wounded ear.

"Well, that makes things a little easier," Roddy went on. "Just hand me the money in that drawer, and make it quick."

He motioned toward the cash register with his gun, and then glanced down at the couple sitting on the floor. The man was starting to have a cramp in his leg and was trying to straighten it out.

"Sit still!" Roddy yelled at him. "I don't want either of you moving."

The man grabbed the back of his thigh and winced, rocking a little back and forth in obvious pain.

"What's the matter with you?" his wife blurted. "Can't you see he's hurting!"

Roddy looked at the man and said, "You need to keep her quiet. And if you can't, I will."

"Here's the money," Sam said from behind him, trying to draw his attention from the couple.

Roddy spun around and looked down at the counter. He could see three twenty-dollar bills, a five, and some loose change.

He swore again and then stepped closer to Sam. "Are you sure that's all you have?" he asked him, the barrel of his gun now pressed between Sam's eyes.

Sam didn't blink, but just looked calmly at him and said, "This is a small store, son, and this is all I have."

"I'm not your son!" Roddy snapped. "And I can't believe this is all I get for my trouble." He reached down, grabbed the loose bills and change, and stuffed it all in his pants pocket.

"Now, old man, I'm sure you have a storage room somewhere in the back here," he said, glancing to the rear of the small store. "I think it's time we all take a little walk."

Sam could see Roddy's mind working, and he didn't like the look on his face.

"Listen, mister," he spoke quietly to him. "Just let these two people go, and you can do whatever you want with me. They haven't done anything to you, and I'm sure—"

"Shut up!" Roddy yelled at him. "We're way past that. I'm not about to go back to Columbia for a pitiful sixty-five dollars! Come on, you two, get up on your feet."

"But—" Sam began to plead.

"I said shut up!" Roddy yelled, drawing his gun back as if to strike him again. "Come on out from behind that counter."

Once again Sam's eyes betrayed him. It had been a fleeting glance, but Roddy had noticed it, and he turned in the direction of the front door.

He swore once more, this time barely under his breath. A police car had pulled up in front of the store and an officer was getting out. Roddy stepped back, out of sight of the front door, and pointed his gun again at Sam's forehead.

"Don't make a sound," he told him menacingly.

Michael Greenfield's father had been good friends with Sam Keeches, and Michael had grown up coming to this small store for candy and occasionally lunch. He wished he had some time to talk with Sam this morning, but that would have to wait. He was in a hurry.

Reflexively, he patted the butt of his handgun and slipped his radio into its holder on his belt. Then he got out of the patrol car and walked toward the store.

Through the glass of the front door, he could see Sam standing behind the counter on the right side of the store. He was staring straight in front of him, probably talking with an early morning customer. Michael pushed the door open, and the faint tinkle of a bell announced his arrival.

"Hey, Sam—it's Michael!" he called out, stepping quickly over toward the counter.

Sam was slow to turn to his young friend, and when he did, Michael could see the blood dripping down the right side of his face. He stopped dead in his tracks and reached down for his weapon.

"I wouldn't do that," Roddy said quietly, stepping out from behind a rack of chips and crackers, his .38 now pointed directly at the policeman's head. "Just stop where you are and don't move."

He glanced over Michael's shoulder and asked, "Anybody with you? You got a partner?"

"No, just me," Michael answered, wishing this wasn't his first day solo.

"Good," Roddy said. "We've already got a crowd here."

For the first time, Michael noticed the couple cowering on the floor. He quickly put things together and said, "Listen, whatever your name is. Just let these people leave the store and you and I can work things out. I know you don't want anyone getting hurt."

"Well, buddy," Roddy said with a smirk, "I'd say it's a little too late for that." He glanced over at Sam's bleeding face.

"It can stop here," Michael persisted gently. "We can all walk away from this without anyone else getting hurt."

"And where am I going to walk to?" the ex-con asked. "Like I said, it's a little late for that."

He glanced around the store, quickly formulating a plan.

"Take your gun out and drop it on the floor," he told Michael. "And do it real slow. I've shot a man before, and a police officer might be sort of fun."

Sam looked at his young friend and slowly nodded his head, confirming his fears about this desperate man.

Michael reached down and unsnapped the strap of his holster, then slowly began to remove the gun with his thumb and index finger.

"Real slow," Roddy reminded him.

Sam shuffled the newspaper on the countertop, causing Roddy to glance over at him. It was only a split second, but it was enough time for Michael to draw his handgun and level it at Roddy's head.

"Don't do anything crazy," Michael said to the startled man in front of him. Roddy's eyes had widened when he saw the barrel pointed at him, but then a snarl spread across his face.

"Looks like we got ourselves a real Mexican standoff," he quipped. "Let's just see who blinks first."

The butt of Michael's firearm was resting in his left palm, and something just didn't feel right. Then with a sinking feeling, he knew. There was no clip in the gun. It was empty. The clip was lying uselessly somewhere in the front seat of his patrol car. And he knew there was no bullet in the chamber.

Michael stared at Roddy Anderson and watched as beads of sweat began to appear on the man's forehead. Anderson's gun trembled for a moment, but he noticed it and struggled to hold it steady.

"Do you want me to call 9-1-1?" Sam asked Michael.

"You do, and I'll kill him!" Roddy called to the store owner with no hesitation, not looking away.

"Just hold steady, Sam," Michael told him. "I'm sure we're going to come to some understanding here."

He stared at a small freckle between Roddy's eyes and was surprised to realize how calm he was. He should have been scared to death, trying to face down a criminal with an empty pistol in his hand. Yet somehow he remained cool and was able to think clearly. At one point, his mind began to drift to thoughts of his wife and little girl, and what they would be doing right now. But he quickly put that aside and stared harder at that freckle.

Michael Greenfield knew the situation here, and he knew what he had to do. If he put the gun down, this man would kill him and everyone else in the store. He was that desperate. Sam knew it, and now so did Michael. Somehow he had to get the man to give himself up and lay down his weapon. It was the only chance these people had of staying alive, even if it meant giving up his own life.

That's when it struck him that he had to be willing to die so the other people in the store could live. Two were complete strangers and one was a friend, an old man. Then, with a calm certainty, he realized he could do that, and that he *would* do it. And with that certainty came an unexpected but overwhelming peace.

He continued to stare at the freckle. Then out of nowhere, he chuckled aloud. This whole thing was really absurd. Didn't a Mexican stand-off require that both participants have loaded guns?

"What are you laughin' at?" Roddy demanded, blowing the sweat from his upper lip.

"Nothing." Michael answered, quickly removing the grin from his face. He didn't need to provoke this man more than he already was.

The radio at his side suddenly crackled to life.

"Officer Greenfield, this is dispatch. What's your location?"

No one in the store moved.

"Officer Greenfield—what's your location?" the voice repeated itself, this time with an edge of impatience.

"Tell her you're somewhere downtown," Roddy told Michael. "And that you're headed toward Cherry Park."

Both locations were far from Sam's Market and would distract anyone searching for him for at least fifteen or twenty minutes.

"Go ahead, tell her!" Roddy insisted.

Michael reached with his left hand for the radio, careful not to let this man see the empty butt of his weapon. He took the radio out and held it to his face, pushing the send button.

"Dispatch, this is Officer Greenfield," he calmly spoke into the receiver. "I'm at Sam's Market and I need backup."

"You sorry—!" Roddy began, stepping toward the policeman.

Michael straightened his arm out, pressing the barrel of his gun firmly against the ex-con's forehead.

"Repeat, dispatch. I need backup right now."

He turned the radio off and dropped it on the floor, once again cradling the pistol in both hands.

Roddy Anderson was speechless with rage and a sudden helplessness. He had lost control of this situation, and he stood there staring at Michael, his eyes wide and his lips now trembling. He was struggling for an idea, some way of knowing what he should do next.

Michael knew that anything could happen and that this man was at his most dangerous. Yet he still remained calm and steady.

That bothered Roddy more than anything, and it made him mad. His finger began to twitch on the trigger, and for the first time Michael thought he might die in this store, on this morning, at any minute.

But he knew time was on his side. Backup was on its way, probably only a matter of minutes. And then…then, anything could still happen. He needed to try one more time.

"Listen, you can still end this, you know," he spoke quietly to the man standing right in front of him. "No one needs to die here. But that's up to you. This place will be crawling with police in about five minutes, and I see only a couple of choices. You and I can kill each other…I'm not going to miss from this distance. But should you somehow make it out of the store, you'll just die in the street. Or, and this is the best choice, you can put your gun down on the floor and walk out of here with me. No one else gets hurt. There's no more blood on your hands."

He paused and then added, "It's up to you now."

In the distance, they heard the wail of fast-approaching police sirens. Sam glanced at the door and then back at Michael. The couple on the floor slid even closer to each other.

Roddy was really sweating now, the perspiration dripping into his eyes. He desperately wanted to wipe them with his shirt sleeve.

He glanced at the door and then back to Michael. His trigger finger continued to twitch, as if it had a mind of its own and would be making this decision.

"It's the only choice," Michael repeated softly.

With that, Roddy let out a sigh and dropped the gun to the floor. Michael quickly kicked it away as the man slumped down on his knees, exhausted.

Four police officers burst into the store, weapons drawn, quickly spreading out in all directions. Two officers brusquely pulled Roddy's arms behind his back and cuffed him.

One of the officers walked up and said, "Well, well. If it isn't Roddy Anderson." He looked over at Michael and said, "I need to hear about this one, Greenfield. This is one bad dude you've arrested."

They were hustling Anderson out of the store as Sam Keeches came from behind the counter and put his arm around Michael.

"Thanks, son," he said to him. "You saved my life." Sam looked over to the couple, now standing by the counter, holding each other, and sobbing. "You saved all of us today. Your dad would be proud of you."

Sam didn't understand, and he never asked his young friend about it. But at that moment, he felt Michael Greenfield slump against him, and he had to brace himself to hold the two of them up. And then Michael stood up straight and took a deep breath.

"I'm just glad I happened along when I did," he said. "I'm glad I could help."

He didn't tell Sam about the empty handgun. He never told anyone, not even his wife.

"Now," he said with more animation. "What about one of your chicken salad sandwiches to go?"

If the **Shoe Fits...**

*The most wasted of all days
is one without laughter.*

E.E. CUMMINGS

A ndy Wilson was at his breaking point.

He had been a good sport through it all—the short-sheeting, the jalapeno-laced scrambled eggs, even having the legs of his brand-new uniform sewn together. But when was this "rookie orientation" going to end?

He had been assigned to Station 6, one of the busiest fire stations in the city, and had quickly meshed with the group of veterans working there. He liked the chief, Rick Stevens, and everyone on his crew. He even liked the "Big Swede," Eric Larson, even though Larson was clearly the ringleader when it came to practical jokes. But what were you going to do? Andy was just a rookie, three weeks out of training, and Eric Larson was…well, he was six-foot-five and weighed a trim 260 pounds. Andy was just going to have to wait him out. But it was getting old.

"Good job today, kid," Stevens said, slapping Andy on the back. "That attic was a little tricky, and you handled it well."

Their crew had responded to a house fire, a small wooden structure only a quarter of a mile from the station. They had had to go through the roof, and Andy had been assigned the lead. He had quickly cut a hole through the shingles and rafters, then made his way through the narrow attic, carrying the heavy hose by balancing precariously on the rickety rafters. They were able to save most of the house, and no one had been hurt.

"Thanks, Chief," Andy responded shyly. "Just trying to do my job, and learn from you guys."

Eric Larson walked by just then, carrying his jacket in one hand and his hat in the other. "Yeah," he muttered as he passed them. "Not too bad for a newbie."

Andy's eyes followed Larson as he walked through the engine bay and toward his locker. He shook his head, just a little, but Rick Stevens noticed it.

"Put your stuff up and then come to my office," he told Andy. Then he turned and walked away.

Andy wondered if he was in trouble. He quickly stowed his gear and headed to the chief's small office in the front of the station.

"Close that door, Andy," Stevens told him. Then motioning to the chair in front of his desk, he said, "Have a seat."

Nervously, Andy sat down. This had never happened before. Had he forgotten to do something? Missed some important protocol? Failed to properly use some equipment?

He leaned forward in the chair, his hands gripping the armrests.

"Listen, I know things haven't been exactly easy for you around here," the chief began, drumming his fingers on the top of his desk. "Especially with Swede."

Andy stiffened a little in the chair.

"Chief Stevens," he muttered in a confused response. "I—"

"How would you like to get even with Larson?" Stevens interrupted, looking directly at his rookie fireman and smiling mischievously.

"'Get even'? What do you mean?" Andy asked him, his mind racing.

"Look, we all know that Larson is the instigator of the practical jokes around here," the chief continued, leaning back comfortably in his chair and folding his hands behind his head. "He's the real mastermind. Has been for years. Just ask the guys. By the way, have those bald patches on your head started filling in?" He moved his own head from side to side, pretending to examine Andy's hair. "Who do you think put that super glue inside your helmet?"

Without thinking, Andy reached up and patted the irregular areas on the back of his scalp, remembering that embarrassing moment and the clipped clumps of glued hair left on the locker-room floor.

"I thought it might be him..." he mumbled.

"Of course it was him!" Stevens laughed. "He takes great pride in being the master joker around here. Now it's time to turn the tables."

He paused, watching the young rookie in front of him. Andy was obviously deep in thought, and the chief gave him a moment to chew on the idea.

The young fireman continued to study the back of his head with his fingers. Then he looked up at the chief and with determined resolve asked, "What do we do?"

Stevens leaned forward, slapped his hands on the desk, and said, "Attaboy! I knew you'd be up to this!"

He leaned even closer to Andy, glanced with mock caution at the office door, then motioned the rookie to come nearer.

"I've got an idea," he whispered. "And it can't fail."

Now becoming excited at the prospect of teaching the Big Swede a lesson and giving him a dose of his own medicine, Andy nodded expectantly and waited.

"Okay," the chief began, still whispering. "Here's what I'm thinking."

He proceeded to give Andy a brief history of Swede's favorite pranks. It would be hard to catch him in one of his own traps, so they would need to expose one of Larson's weaknesses and exploit it.

"And I know just what that is," Stevens proclaimed confidently.

Since his earliest days with the unit, Eric Larson had always been a creature of habit, to the point of obsessiveness. He had become entirely predictable in his daily routine. He got up at the same time each morning, he went to bed at the same time, he set his clothes out the same way every night. It was all like clockwork.

Stevens explained these quirks to Andy Wilson and then leaned back in his chair, quietly studying the rookie's response.

There was a confused look on Andy's face, and he finally said, "I don't understand, Chief. How are we supposed to use that? I mean, what are we going to do with the fact that he's so predictable?"

"You'll see, Andy," Stevens answered, smiling knowingly. "Tonight, you'll see."

At 10 p.m., right on cue, the Big Swede stood up in the dayroom and said, "All right, that's it for me. I'm heading to bed. You guys handle any emergency," he quipped, patting Andy on his shoulder as he walked by him and out of the room.

Chief Stevens glanced over at his fellow conspirator and silently nodded, smiling.

Forty-five minutes later, they could hear Larson's quiet snoring just down the hallway. Stevens stood up and motioned for Andy and the two other firemen in the room to follow him into the kitchen. He quietly closed the door behind them and with a finger to his lips, signaled them to be silent.

Whispering, he told the group his plan.

"Here's what we're going to do," he began, with a twinkle in his eye. "Anytime there's an alarm, Swede jumps out of bed, always to the left and just beside his boots. Then he pulls his pants on and steps into the boots while he's pulling the suspenders over his shoulders."

"You got it, Chief!" one of the firemen excitedly whispered. "I've watched him do it a hundred times. Sometimes even in his sleep, without waking up!"

Andy and the others chuckled at this, a little too loudly for Stevens.

"Shh!" he quieted them. "Don't wake him up."

"I don't think you *can* wake him very easily," one of them said. "He sleeps pretty hard, and sometimes the alarm doesn't even do it."

"I know," the chief agreed. "And that's going to help us. We're going to go into his room in a minute and a couple of us are going to pick up his bed and move it around, reversing it."

There was a puzzled look on Andy's face, and Stevens went on to explain.

"Swede always jumps out of bed on the *left* side, landing right beside his boots."

He waited for the men to show some sign of understanding. After a moment one of the firemen said, "I get it! This time, when he tries to get out of bed, the left side will be up against the wall. He won't be able to find the floor!"

"The only thing he'll find is that big Pittsburgh Steelers flag he hung up there a couple of years ago," one of the men threw in. "It's as big as a barn."

"One other thing..." the chief added, stepping over to the refrigerator and opening the cabinet above it. He retrieved a pair of old, beat-up boots and quietly put them down on the table.

Andy reached over and picked up one of the black lace-up boots.

"These things are tiny!" he whispered. "They can't be more than size 8."

"7," Stevens informed him. "And Swede wears a size 15. We're going to swap them."

This time there was no puzzled look on Andy's face. "And then we pull the alarm!" he said excitedly, imagining what was soon to transpire. "This is perfect, Chief!" he told him. "What a great idea!"

"Can't fail," Stevens agreed knowingly. "Let's get at it."

The group of grown-up kids quietly made their way down the hallway and toward Eric Larson's bedroom. When they reached the doorway, Stevens resorted to hand signals to direct his men. The room was dark, but there was enough light to easily see the huge outline of Swede under his blanket.

Two of the firemen grasped the foot of his bed while Stevens and Andy took hold of the head. Silently mouthing the words "one... two...three," Stevens signaled them to pick it up. They raised it off the floor smoothly and began to circle clockwise. This was the critical moment. If they could do this without waking him up, they were home free.

Swede was a bigger load than they had imagined. But they were able to swing the bed around without jostling him, and he snored the entire time.

They set the bed down carefully, and then Stevens swapped Swede's size 15 boots for the tiny pair they had brought with them.

He motioned to the neatly folded pants on the floor beside the boots, ready to be pulled on at a moment's notice. Then he raised his right index finger in the air, raised his eyebrows, and pulled a half-dozen huge safety pins out of his pocket. He leaned down and began to pass them through the lower part of each pants leg, securely pinning them together.

One of the firemen began to snicker, but a quick glance from the chief silenced him.

Stevens stood up, examined their handiwork, and then motioned everyone to move toward the doorway. Once again, he put his finger to his lips, commanding their silence. When he was satisfied that everything was ready, he reached down to a transmitter on his belt and pushed its button.

There were three deafening blasts from the overhead speakers, followed by the almost painfully loud wailing of a siren.

How could anyone sleep through this?

Larson sat straight up in his bed with his eyes still closed. He shook his head, trying to clear it.

"What the…!" he muttered, still not completely awake.

Bam!

There was a loud noise as something crashed into the wall.

Chief Stevens reached behind him and switched on the lights in the room.

Andy could barely contain himself. The scene playing out in front of the group of firemen was beyond anything they could have hoped for.

The comatose Swede had recognized the wail of the alarm and instinctively swung around to his left—and into the wall. It hadn't been there when he had gone to bed, but there it was now. He groped with both hands, trying to find the open space in his room. His eyes were still closed, and he floundered in the bed, both legs seeming to climb up the wall in front of him.

Then he grabbed the Steelers flag and yanked it down on top of himself.

"What the...!" he repeated, this time louder and more animated.

The flag landed on top of him, and his flailing arms quickly caused it to wrap around his head and torso. Now he was locked in mortal combat with this unyielding cloth that had attacked him, and the impenetrable object in front of him.

He was finally waking up a bit, and though he was unable to see because of the flag, his movements became more purposeful. He began to feel along the sides of the bed, and he quickly discovered the open area off to his right. He swung his legs around, planting them squarely on the floor just to the side of the waiting boots.

All the while the alarm continued to howl, causing his movements to become even more energetic.

Swede somehow found his pants and shoved his feet into them. He gripped his trousers with one hand and continued to battle the flag with the other.

But something was wrong. His feet quickly came to the obstruction in his pants legs caused by the safety pins, and would go no further down.

He started yelling angrily. None of the other men in the room could understand Swedish, but the meaning was very clear.

The big fireman let go of the flag and grabbed his pants with both hands. Then, with a herculean effort, he jammed his feet into the legs, determined to get the trousers on. There was a loud ripping sound, and his feet suddenly poked through the sides. The safety pins had held, but the inside seams of the legs had given way, splitting all the way down.

He leaned back on the bed and held his stockinged feet up in the air, feeling them and making sure they were now free. The tattered ends of his pants flapped helplessly.

By this time, his audience was red-faced. Each man was trying desperately to contain himself.

Swede then searched beside him for his boots, located them, and began to put them on. He had a peculiar way of doing this, as the chief had pointed out earlier. He would get one foot started into one boot, and then the other. Once this was done, he would stand up and stomp around a little bit, driving his feet into his boots. A quick lacing up and tying of knots and he was done.

Not tonight.

Chief Stevens reached over and tapped Andy on the shoulder.

"This is gonna be good!" he whispered in his ear, nodding at Swede and grinning.

Andy was grinning too. This was all going better than any of them had hoped.

Not for Swede, though. He was trying to jam his enormous feet into the size 7 boots, and it wasn't happening. He was up on his tiptoes, since that was about the only part of his feet he could get in, and for a moment, he almost looked like some overgrown and amazingly clumsy ballerina.

That's probably what did it. The sight of him perched awkwardly in the tops of those boots, his ripped pants flapping haphazardly, and the yellow-and-black Steelers flag still wrapped around his head and shoulders, was all that one of the firemen behind Andy could take. He lost control and burst out laughing, and the others joined in. The chief immediately tried to shush them.

It was too late. Swede had heard the laughter, and he froze where he stood, precariously perched on the tiny boots. His knees were bent, and he was groping around, trying to find where the laughing came from. He was beginning to understand.

"Wait'll I get my hands on you…" he growled, now violently trying to grab whoever it was standing in front of him.

"Who's there?" he bellowed. He reached out again, trying to grab the source of this laughter. The effort did him in. His arms began to flail wildly as he lost what little balance he had, and he fell straight down toward the floor. He was able to break the fall with his arms and hands, barely saving his face from an unwanted impact.

The big fireman was an even more absurd vision now, lying sprawled on the floor, and everyone in the room broke out in uncontrollable laughter. Everyone except the Swede. He was reaching out helplessly, trying to locate the people who had done this to him.

Somehow, his fall had partially disentangled the flag draped around his head and upper body, and he reached up to it, grabbing an edge and beginning to pull it down.

"Uh-oh," Stevens whispered with alarm, the laughter in the room suddenly coming to a stop.

Andy stood motionless, staring down at their handiwork. This was something Swede wouldn't forget for a long time. None of them would.

He turned to the door and took a step, then stopped abruptly. It was closed, and he was the only one in the room. He and Eric Larson.

He glanced back over his shoulder and was shocked to see that Swede had almost freed himself from the flag. His eyes were still covered, thankfully, and Andy just had time to—

The door was locked! He twisted the handle again just to be sure. But it wouldn't budge. On the other side of the door, he could hear muffled laughter.

Andy Wilson stood up straight, took a deep breath, and turned around.

Swede had just unwrapped the flag from around his head and was now struggling to get his eyes used to the light. He shook his head, trying to clear it. Andy remembered thinking it was what an angry bull might do.

And then his eyes locked on those of the younger fireman.

Wilson's knees almost buckled.

But after a few agonizing moments, Larson's scowl began to relax, and a slight smile began to tug at his face. There was even a tiny twinkle in his eye as Swede uttered a drawn-out, almost sympathetic, "Sooo..."

Humor is the shock absorber of life;
it helps us take the blows.

PEGGY NOONAN (1950–)

About the Author

D r. Robert Lesslie, author of the bestselling *Angels in the ER*, is a physician who lives and actively practices medicine in Rock Hill, South Carolina. Board-certified in both emergency medicine and occupational medicine, he is the co-owner of two busy urgent care/occupational clinics.

For more than 25 years, Dr. Lesslie worked in and directed several of the busiest ERs in the Charlotte, North Carolina, area. He also served as medical director of the emergency department at Rock Hill General Hospital for almost 15 years. During his tenure as medical director, he received the American Medical Association's Continuing Education Award. He also traveled around the country, giving lively, innovative lectures to the Emergency Nurses Association at their annual meetings in major cities.

For seven years, Dr. Lesslie wrote a weekly medical column for *The Charlotte Observer* presenting a wide variety of topics, both medical and editorial. He also pens a regular column on medical, philosophical, and personal topics for the YC, a monthly publication in York County, South Carolina.

Dr. Lesslie enjoys the fast-paced environment of the ER and the need to make rapid and accurate diagnoses. He views his medical career as an opportunity to go beyond simply diagnosing and treating individual patients. For him, it is a way to fulfill a higher calling by meeting the real physical and emotional needs of his patients.

An active member of his home church in Rock Hill, Dr. Lesslie serves as an elder, and he and his wife, Barbara, teach Sunday school and sing in the church choir. They are also involved with an outreach program for disabled/handicapped individuals, Camp Joy, where Dr. Lesslie serves as the camp physician for a week each summer. He also enjoys mentoring high school and college students considering a career in medicine.

Dr. Lesslie and his wife, Barbara, have been married for more than 35 years. Together they raised four children—Lori, Amy, Robbie, and Jeffrey—and are now enjoying five grandchildren. In his spare time, Dr. Lesslie enjoys gardening, golf, hunting, reading, and bagpiping.

A Note from the Editors

We hope you enjoy this exclusive two-in-one book, *Angels in the ER* and *Angels on Call* by Robert D. Lesslie, MD, specially selected by the editors of the Books and Inspirational Media Division of Guideposts, a nonprofit organization that touches millions of lives every day through products and services that inspire, encourage, help you grow in your faith, and celebrate God's love in every aspect of your daily life.

Thank you for making a difference with your purchase of this book, which helps fund our many outreach programs to military personnel, prisons, hospitals, nursing homes, and educational institutions. To learn more, visit GuidepostsFoundation.org.

We also maintain many useful and uplifting online resources. Visit Guideposts.org to read true stories of hope and inspiration, access OurPrayer network, sign up for free newsletters, download free e-books, join our Facebook community, and follow our stimulating blogs.

To learn about other Guideposts publications, including the best-selling devotional *Daily Guideposts*, go to ShopGuideposts.org, call (800) 932-2145, or write to Guideposts, PO Box 5815, Harlan, Iowa 51593.